ELECTRONICS SERVICING
VOL. 4
(Television and Radio Technology)

ELECTRONICS SERVICING VOL. 4 (Television and Radio Technology)

K. J. Bohlman
I.Eng., F.I.E.I.E.

Dickson Price Publishers Ltd
Hawthorn House
Bowdell Lane
Brookland
Romney Marsh
Kent TN29 9RW

Dickson Price Publishers Ltd
Hawthorn House
Bowdell Lane
Brookland
Romney Marsh
Kent TN29 9RW

First published 1994
© K. J. Bohlman 1994

British Library Cataloguing in Publication Data
A catalogue record for this book is
available from the British Library

ISBN 0-85380-187-8

Photoset by
R. H. Services, Hertford, Hertfordshire
Printed and bound in Great Britain by
The Bath Press, Avon.

CONTENTS

Other Books of Interest

Part 1
Electronics Servicing Vol 1 (Electronic Systems & Science Background)

Part 2
Electronics Servicing Vol 2 (Core Studies)
Electronics Servicing Vol 3 (Control Systems Technology)
Electronics Servicing Vol 4 (Television & Radio Technology)

Part 3
Digital Techniques
Colour and Mono Television Vol 2
Colour and Mono Television Vol 3
Principles of Domestic Video Recording and Playback Systems

Revision
Electronics Servicing 500 Multiple Choice Questions and Answers for Part 1
Electronics Servicing 500 Questions and Answers for Part 2
Video Recording and Playback Systems 500 Q & A

Practical
Fault Location in Electronic Equipment

Inspection Copies

Lecturers wishing to examine any of these books should write to the publishers requesting an inspection copy.

Complete Catalogue available on request.

PREFACE

THIS NEW VOLUME, based on the author's popular *Colour & Mono Television* series is **designed to fully cover the Part 2 syllabus in Television & Radio Reception Technology for the City & Guilds 224 Course in Electronics Servicing**.

The basic concepts of recent circuit techniques have been included and covered at a level appropriate to the Part 2 course. However, in some chapters extra information has been given to cater for the needs of students proceeding to the Part 3 course in Television Reception, and others who require the information in the pursuit of their technical duties.

The modern advanced television receiver is a complex electronic system with integrated circuits performing nearly all of the circuit functions. In dealing with examples from circuit practice, discrete circuit versions have been used solely as an introduction to show how signals are processed and generated. This method of learning, in the author's view, consolidates the principles met with in Core Studies and provides the student with a stimulus for the understanding and acceptance of the ideas behind integrated circuit versions which are also covered in this book.

A companion volume entitled *Television Reception* will deal with the television topics of the Part 3 Course.

K. J. Bohlman
Lincoln, 1993

CHAPTER ONE

RADIO RECEIVERS

Objectives

1 Explain the principles of 'superhet' receiver and how r.f. selectivity reduces 'image' channel interference.
2 Explain how i.f. response eliminates adjacent channel interference.
3 Identify pre-selector, mixer, i.f., demodulator and a.g.c. circuits in a.m. receivers.
4 State the need for r.f. amplification. Identify f.m. tuner circuits with manual and electronic tuning, f.m. demodulators, a.f.c. and a.g.c. circuits.
5 Explain the principle of frequency synthesis tuning and sweep search.

EARLY RADIO RECEIVER designs using the **tuned radio frequency** principle suffered from inadequate selectivity, were prone to instability and lacking in gain. These basic limitations led to the development of the **superheterodyne receiver**.

In a 'superhet' receiver the frequency of all incoming signals is converted to a fixed and fairly low frequency at which most of the receiver gain and selectivity is obtained. Because this fixed frequency is lower than the signal frequency but above the audio frequen-

cy range it became known as the **intermediate frequency** (i.f.). Since the i.f. amplifiers operate below the signal frequency, they are capable of providing high gain with good stability and after initial tuning need no further adjustment.

A.M. SUPERHETRODYNE RECEIVER

An a.m. 'superhet' receiver deals with amplitude modulated waves and a basic block diagram is given in Fig. 1.1. In order to

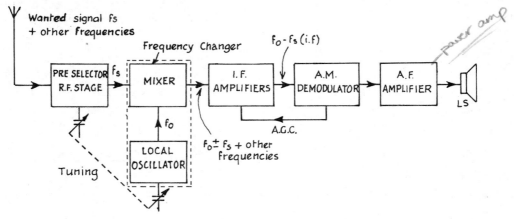

Fig. 1.1 Basic A.M. receiver block schematic.

Waveband	Frequency band	Wavelength
Long wave (l.f.)	150 – 300 kHz	2000 – 1000 M
Medium wave (m.f.)	525 – 1600 kHz	571 – 187.5 M
Short wave (h.f.)	6 – 18 MHz	50 – 16.7 M

convert the wanted signal frequency into the intermediate frequency a 'frequency changer' stage is required. Here the signal frequency is 'mixed' with the output of a local oscillator, the frequency of which is varied by the receiver tuning.

A large number of signal frequency voltages are induced into the aerial, *e.g.* a.m. radio transmissions cover the frequency bands as listed above.

Note that wavelength (λ) is given by:

$$\lambda = \frac{3 \times 10^8}{\text{Frequency (Hz)}} \, .$$

The pre-selector stage is used to select the desired signal f_s together with its sidebands from all the unwanted signal frequencies and this ability arises out of the 'selectivity' of the stage. The pre-selector is a variable tuned stage so that any desired signal within the band may be selected, see Fig. 1.2, which shows for example, selection within the M.W. band.

The wanted signal f_s from the pre-selector is passed to the mixer stage where it is mixed with a sine wave output f_o from the local oscillator. Among the newly generated frequencies are the sum and difference frequencies $f_o + f_s$ and $f_o - f_s$. The difference frequency $f_o - f_s$ is the intermediate frequency and this is selected by the i.f. amplifier which provides most of the gain and selectivity of the receiver.

The i.f. is a fixed frequency and this means that when the pre-selector stage is tuned to select a new wanted signal f_s, the local oscillator tuning is also adjusted by 'ganging' the tuning capacitors so that a constant difference frequency is obtained, see Fig. 1.3.

After amplification in the i.f. stages, the down-converted signal and its sidebands are fed to an a.m. demodulator stage where the audio signal is extracted from the modulated i.f. carrier. The audio signal is then raised to the required power level in the audio stages to drive the loudspeaker.

Large changes in volume may occur when tuning from one station to another due to differences in received signal strength. To overcome this all a.m. receivers incorporate some form of automatic gain control (a.g.c.). This works by measuring the average value of the i.f. carrier and producing a d.c. control voltage from it. The d.c. control voltage is fed to one or more i.f. amplifier stages to automatically vary the gain of those stages. In this way the volume of sound is kept fairly constant with changes in signal strength.

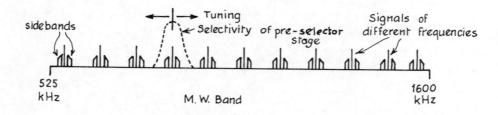

Fig. 1.2 Selecting the wanted signal and its side bands.

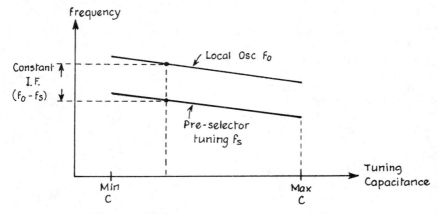

Fig. 1.3 Maintaining a constant intermediate frequency.

A.M. Receiver Formats

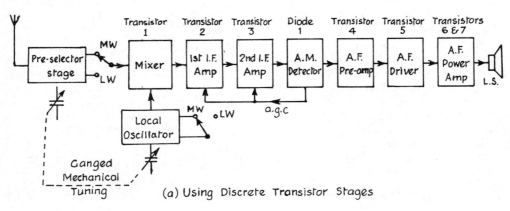

(a) Using Discrete Transistor Stages

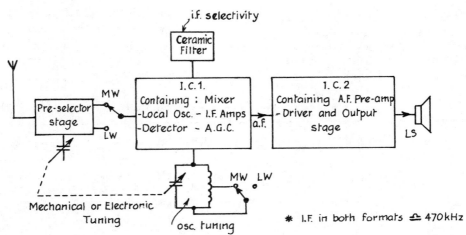

(b) Using Integrated Circuits

Fig. 1.4 A.M. Radio receiver formats.

Frequency Changer Stage

The mixer and the local oscillator sections form the 'frequency changer' stage. The mixer is presented with two inputs; the signal frequency voltage (f_s) and the local oscillator voltage (f_o). In a.m. and some f.m. receivers the 'additive mixing' principle is used.

In additive mixing the signal and oscillator voltages are added together in a non-linear (square-law) device such as a transistor with suitable biassing applied, see Fig. 1.5. When operated in the region exhibiting a square-law relationship, the collector current I_c will contain the following frequency components:

f_s . . .   the signal frequency
f_o . . .   the oscillator frequency
$f_o + f_s$ . . .   the sum frequency
$f_o - f_s$ . . .   the difference frequency
                    (wanted i.f.) plus harmonics
                    of f_o and f_s.

Only the difference frequency $f_o - f_s$ is required as this constitutes the intermediate frequency and is picked out by the tuned circuit $L1$, $C1$ connected in the collector circuit. It should be noted that merely adding f_o and f_s together will not produce the i.f., a non-linear device must be used.

The difference frequency that is chosen is not critical and in most a.m. radio receivers lies within the range of 455–475 kHz.

If therefore $f_o - f_s = 470$ kHz
$f_o = f_s + 470$ kHz,

i.e. the local oscillator is tuned **above** the signal frequency. Table 1.1 lists some oscillator frequencies for selected signal frequencies in the M.W. and L.W. bands where an i.f. of 470 kHz has been assumed.

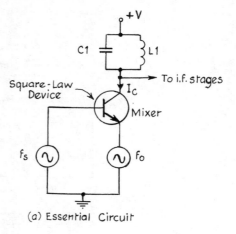

(a) Essential Circuit

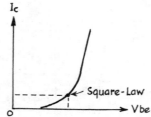

(b) Square-Law relationship

Fig. 1.5 Additive mixing.

When a receiver is correctly tuned in to a broadcast, it is not tuned to a single frequency but to a band of frequencies representing the carrier and its side-frequencies. Consider a carrier of 200 kHz amplitude modulated with a single tone of 3 kHz – the frequencies present in the transmission are:

200 kHz (f_c)
203 kHz ($f_c + f_m$)
197 kHz ($f_c - f_m$)

Table 1.1 Calculation of local oscillator frequency.

	Signal frequency	Local oscillator frequency
M.W.	525 kHz	525 kHz + 470 kHz = 995 kHz
	1.0 MHz	1 MHz + 470 kHz = 1.47 MHz
	1.5 MHz	1.5 MHz + 470 kHz = 1.97 MHz
L.W.	160 kHz	160 kHz + 470 kHZ = 630 kHZ
	201 kHz	201 kHz + 470 kHZ = 671 kHZ
	276 kHz	276 kHz + 470 kHZ = 746 kHZ

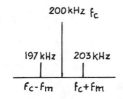

(a) Transmitted signal frequencies

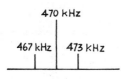

(b) Translated frequencies

Fig. 1.6 Frequency translation to the I.F. Band.

These frequency components are shown in the amplitude-frequency diagram of Fig. 1.6(a).

When tuned in to this transmission with the receiver local oscillator set to 670 kHz, the mixer output will contain:

$$f_o - f_s \begin{cases} 670 - 200 \text{ kHz} = 470 \text{ kHz} \\ 670 - 203 \text{ kHz} = 467 \text{ kHz} \\ 670 - 197 \text{ kHz} = 473 \text{ kHz} \end{cases}$$

Thus the side-frequencies of the received carrier now become side-frequencies centred on the i.f. of 470 kHz, as in Fig. 1.6(b). In other words, the original carrier and its side-frequencies have been **frequency translated**, *i.e.* moved to the frequency band of the i.f.

Choice of I.F.

The choice of the frequency of the i.f. is mainly settled by the need to prevent interference. The chosen i.f. must not be a frequency used for transmission. It will be noted that 470 kHz lies between the L.W. and M.W. bands. If a transmission was present on the i.f., it would break-through the i.f. stages (**i.f. break-through**) regardless of the receiver tuning. In some receivers an **i.f. trap** is fitted in the r.f. stage to remove this kind of interference.

The local oscillator may be tuned above or

below the signal frequency by the intermediate frequency. However, it should be noted that with an i.f. of 470 kHz it is not possible to tune the local oscillator below the signal frequency by the i.f. on L.W. Thus with a.m. receivers operating on the L.W. and M.W. the local oscillator is tuned **above** the signal frequency. For every setting of the local oscillator frequency there are **two signal frequencies** that will mix with the local oscillator to produce the required receiver i.f. Consider a local oscillator setting of 1 MHz (M.W.) with a required i.f. of 470 kHz.

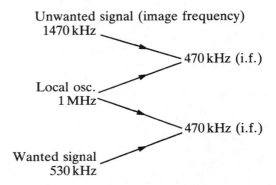

With the local oscillator tuned above the incoming signal, a station signal on 530 kHz will mix with the 1 MHz oscillator output to produce a difference frequency of 470 kHz. However, with this oscillator setting there is another station signal (if present) on 1470 kHz that will mix with the local oscillator output to create the required i.f. of 470 kHz. This unwanted signal is known as the 'image frequency' and may cause **second channel interference**.

The higher the chosen i.f., the less is the chance of the image signal actually causing interference due to the selectivity of the pre-selector or r.f. stage, see Fig. 1.7.

Adjacent Channel Interference

Another kind of interference may be caused by a station that is received close in frequency to the wanted station and is called **adjacent channel interference**, see Fig. 1.8 where f_s is the wanted station and f_a and f_b are adjacent channel signals lying close to and on either side of the wanted station and f_o is the local oscillator frequency.

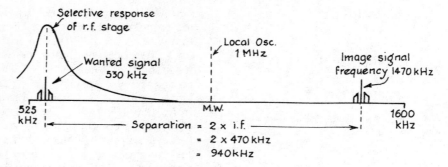

Fig. 1.7 Low response of R.F. stage to image signal frequency reduces second channel interference.

The unwanted adjacent stations, which may be of larger or smaller signal strength than f_s, if permitted to pass through the selective stages of a receiver will be heard along with the wanted signal, a situation which may be intolerable if f_a or f_b is greater in amplitude than f_s. Unlike for second channel interference, it is improbable that the selectivity of the r.f. stage will be adequate to reduce the effects of adjacent channel interference to small proportions in an a.m. radio. However, the **selectivity of the i.f. stages** may be used to reduce the effects of adjacent channel interference by appropriate selection of the intermediate frequency which may be seen from the following:

Let wanted signal = 1 MHz
and unwanted adjacent signal = 1·02 MHz.

The unwanted signal is:

$$\frac{0·02}{1.0} \times 100\% = 2\% \text{ in frequency}$$

difference from the wanted signal in the r.f. stage.

Suppose i.f. = 500 kHz and Local Osc. setting = 1·5 MHz:

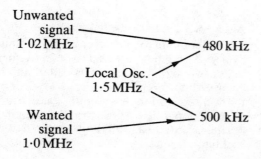

Fig. 1.8 Adjacent channel interference.

In the i.f. band, the wanted signal is frequency translated to 500 kHz (the nominal i.f.) by the mixer action and the unwanted signal becomes 480 kHz. The unwanted signal is now 0·02/0·5 × 100% = 4% in frequency difference from the wanted i.f. signal, although its absolute value is still the same as in the r.f. stage, *i.e.* 20 kHz away from the wanted signal.

Consider now the result when the i.f. = 250 kHz and the Local Osc. setting is 1·25 MHz.

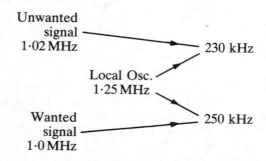

In the i.f. band the wanted signal is frequency translated to 250 kHz by mixer action and the unwanted signal becomes 230 kHz. The unwanted signal is now 0·02/0·25 × 100% = 8% in frequency difference from the wanted i.f. signal.

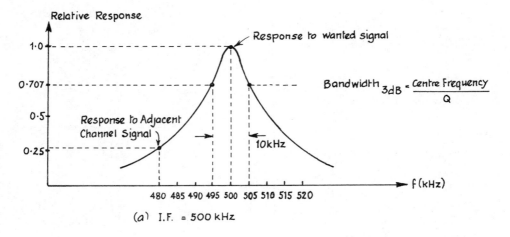

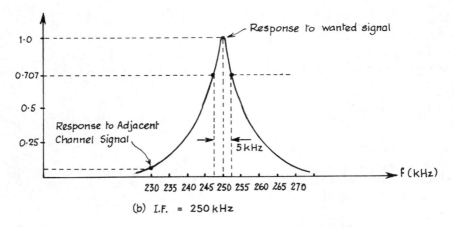

Fig. 1.9 *Effect of intermediate frequency on adjacent channel interference.*

The diagrams of Fig. 1.9 illustrate the response of the i.f. stages to the adjacent channel signal for the values considered above. With an i.f. of 500 kHz and assuming a Q-factor of 50, the response to the unwanted signal is about 0·3 of peak response, see Fig. 1.9(a). Lowering the i.f. to 250 kHz results in a reduced response of about 0·1 of peak as in Fig. 1.9(b). Here the same Q-factor has been used and it will be noted that for a given Q-factor, bandwidth is proportional to centre frequency. Thus a low value for the i.f. gives best protection against adjacent channel interference. Unfortunately, this is in direct contrast to second channel interference where a high value of i.f. gives best protection. In practice a compromise value is chosen and an i.f. of around 470 kHz is common in a.m. radio receivers.

A.M. RECEIVER CIRCUITS

Additive Mixer (Self-Oscillating)

A typical circuit of a self-oscillating additive mixer using a discrete transistor stage for a L.W./M.W. receiver is given in Fig. 1.10.

Ferrite Rod Aerial

The r.f. energy radiated from a radio transmitter consists of an alternating electric field and an associated magnetic field co-existing at right angles to one another, with

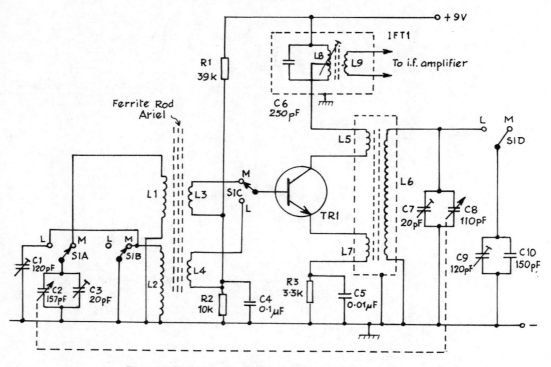

Fig. 1.10 Typical self-oscillating mixer stage with pre-selector.

both fields mutually at right angles to the direction of propagation as in Fig. 1.11. The plane containing the electric and magnetic components is referred to as the 'wavefront'.

To provide a reference, the plane containing the electric field and the direction of propagation is called the 'plane of polarisation'; the diagram shows a vertically polarised wave.

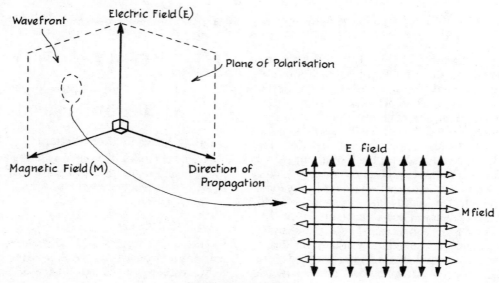

Fig. 1.11 Radio wave.

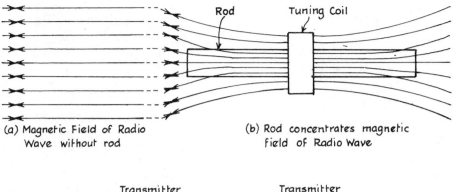

(a) Magnetic Field of Radio
Wave without rod

(b) Rod concentrates magnetic
field of Radio Wave

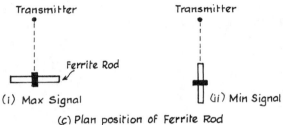

(i) Max Signal

(ii) Min Signal

(c) Plan position of Ferrite Rod

Fig. 1.12 Ferrite rod aerial.

All portable and most shelf-mounted a.m. radios incorporate an internal ferrite rod aerial which should be orientated so that it correctly intercepts the magnetic component of the radio wave for maximum transference of signal to the receiver circuits.

A ferrite rod aerial is made of ferroxcube, a material which is non-metallic, has a high permeability and a high resistivity resulting in small 'eddy current' losses.

When the ferrite rod is situated in the field of a radio wave, it concentrates the magnetic field from a large area surrounding the aerial due to its high permeability, as in Fig. 1.12. If the rod carries a coil as shown, maximum e.m.f. will be induced in the coil when it lies at the centre of the rod (since maximum flux will be linking the coil) and its orientation with respect to the transmitter is as in diagram (i) of Fig. 1.12(c).

The high permeability of the rod also increases the inductance of the coil considerably, enabling the required tuning inductance to be obtained using a small number of turns. This results in a coil of high Q (typically 200 unloaded) thus improving the selectivity of the

input tuned circuit and providing a large signal input to the mixer transistor.

The inductance of the coil may be reduced by moving it towards the end of the rod, a feature used in practice to tune the coil during r.f. alignment. Normally the L.W. and M.W. tuning coils are placed at opposite ends of the rod to minimise interaction between the coils.

Pre-Selector (R.F. Stage)

The pre-selector comprises essentially $C2$ (variable tuned) with $L1$ on M.W. and $C2$ with $L2$ on L.W., see Fig. 1.13. Trimmers $C3$ and $C1$ are included to provide frequency adjustment to the h.f. end of the tuning range of the two wavebands during r.f. aligment. A larger number of turns will be found on the L.W. coil (higher inductance) when tuned by a common value capacitance.

The values of L and C used in the pre-selector are chosen so that the tuned circuit will resonate within the selected waveband and the capacitance range of the variable $C2$ will adjust the frequency of resonance from the l.f. to the h.f. end of the band. Note that

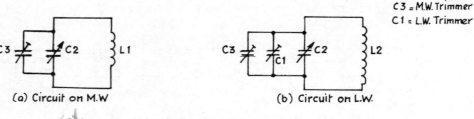

C3 = M.W. Trimmer
C1 = L.W. Trimmer

(a) Circuit on M.W.

(b) Circuit on L.W.

Fig. 1.13 Pre-selector.

with $C2$ set to its minimum value ('plates' fully unmeshed) operation will be set at the h.f. end of the band. In general the frequency of resonance of the LC pre-selector is given by:

$$f_r = \frac{1}{2\pi\sqrt{LC}} \text{ Hz.}$$

For example, with $L1 = 0 \cdot 3 \text{ mH}$ and $C2 = 80 \text{ pF}$.

$$f_r = \frac{1}{2\pi\sqrt{0.3 \times 10^{-3}\ 80 \times 10^{-12}}}$$

$$\simeq 1 \cdot 03 \text{ MHz}$$

With the above values, the voltage across $L1$ will be a maximum at $1 \cdot 03$ MHz and fall-off either side of resonance, see Fig. 1.14. Because the frequency separation between transmissions on the M.W. is only 9 kHz, the minimum bandwidth required by the pre-selector should not be less than 9 kHz.

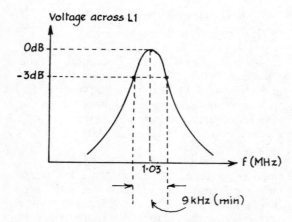

Fig. 1.14 Selectivity of pre-selector.

Mixer Stage

$TR1$ operates as a self-oscillating mixer with the signal and oscillator voltages 'summed' in the base-emitter circuit. $R1$ and $R2$ set the forward bias of $TR1$ so that operation is confined to the non-linear part of its transfer characteristic. $R3$ provides stabilisation of $TR1$ current against temperature variations and spreads in h_{FE} and is suitably decoupled to signal by $C5$.

Signal is transferred from the pre-selector tuned circuit to $TR1$ base via the coupling windings $L3$ (M.W.) and $L4$ (L.W.) wound on the ferrite rod aerial. Step-down ratios are employed between $L1$–$L3$ and $L2$–$L4$ to prevent the low input resistance of $TR1$ from unduly damping the input tuned circuit and reducing its selectivity. $C4$ 'grounds' the lower end of $L3$ and $L4$ to prevent signal loss across $R2$.

The local oscillator is connected as a Reinartz oscillator (see Volume 2) with the 'tank circuit' inductor formed by $L6$ together with feedback windings $L5$ and $L7$. The oscillator frequency determining circuit is formed by:

$L6$, $C8$ and $C7$ . . . . . .   M.W.
and $L6$, $C8$, $C7$, $C9$ and $C10$ . . .   L.W.
$C7$ = M.W. trimmer
$C9$ = L.W. trimmer

Note that $C8$ is 'ganged' with $C2$ so that the local oscillator is always 470 kHz (the i.f.) above the pre-selector tuning.

The oscillatory voltage across $L7$ is the oscillator input to the mixer and this is added to the signal voltage from across $L3$ or $L4$ in the non-linear $TR1$. The difference frequency $(f_o - f_s)$ produced as a result of the mixer action is selected by the parallel tuned circuit $L8$, $C6$ in the collector circuit which is tuned to

470 kHz. The i.f. signal is transferred to the i.f. amplifier via the secondary winding $L9$.

I.F. Amplifier

The output of the mixer stage is supplied to the i.f. amplifier which provides most of the receiver gain. Since the frequency of the mixer output always lies in the i.f. band the i.f. stages are pre-tuned, thus the gain and response of the i.f. amplifier does not vary with the frequency of the signal input to the receiver.

The i.f. amplifier serves two main functions:

(1) It must amplify the signal from the mixer to a level that will permit satisfactory operation of the demodulator stage.
(2) It must provide an i.f. selectivity curve of appropriate bandwidth and good shape to achieve a uniform response to the transmission band of frequencies, together with adequate rejection of adjacent channel interference.

A typical i.f. amplifier circuit is given in Fig. 1.15 for a discrete transistor radio receiver where two stages of i.f. amplification are used, which is most common.

The i.f. signal from the mixer output is transferred to the base of the first i.f. amplifier stage $TR1$ via the coupling winding $L9$ located in the first i.f. transformer ($IFT1$). Three i.f. transformers are employed, all pre-tuned to the i.f. and initially set during i.f. alignment by the variable ferrite cores. $TR1$ gain is controlled by the a.g.c. line with forward bias to provide class 'A' operation set by $R4$, $R5$ and the a.g.c. line voltage (a.g.c. is discussed later). $R6$ is the emitter stabilising resistor which is decoupled to i.f. by $C11$.

Amplified i.f. signal is developed across the parallel tuned circuit $L10$, $C12$ pre-tuned to the i.f. Resistor $R7$ damps the response to broaden the bandwidth to the required degree. The collector of $TR1$ is tapped into $L10$ to prevent undue damping of the tuned circuit by the output resistance of $TR1$. For the same reason, a step-down ratio is used between $L10$ and $L11$ to prevent excessive damping by the low input resistance of $TR2$ stage.

The i.f. signal is coupled to the base of the second i.f. amplifying transistor $TR2$ via $L11$. This stage has a fixed bias provided by the potential divider $R8$, $R9$ and set to give class 'A' amplification. The i.f. signal is further amplified by $TR2$ and developed across $L12$, $C15$ (pre-tuned to the i.f.) before being coupled to the demodulator via $L13$.

All of the i.f. transformers are screened to minimise magnetic or electric field coupling thereby preventing instability (oscillation) in the i.f. stages.

When i.f. amplifying stages are connected in

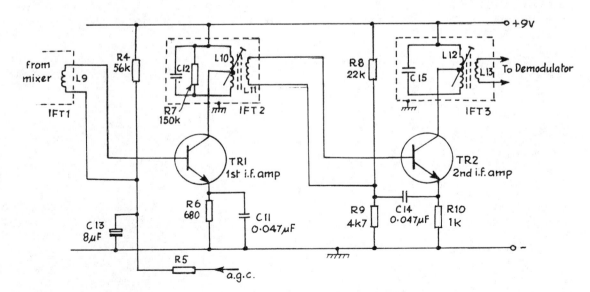

Fig. 1.15 Typical I.F. amplifier (I.F. = 470 kHz).

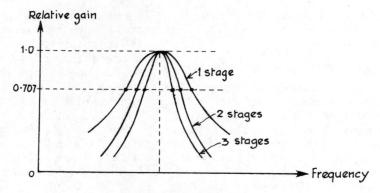

Fig. 1.16 Bandwidth shrinkage.

cascade as shown, the overall voltage gain is the product of the individual stage gains. Thus, for example, if *TR*1 stage has a gain of 20 and *TR*2 stage a gain of 18, the overall voltage gain = 20 × 18 = 360. Cascading stages also has the effect of reducing the overall bandwidth. For two cascaded stages each employing tuned circuits of identical *Q*, the bandwidth is reduced to 0·644 of that of a single stage, see Fig. 1.16.

The effect of 'bandwidth shrinkage' has to be taken into account by the circuit designer in arriving at the required overall bandwidth. It is thus not uncommon to find damping resistors (such as *R*7) used to broaden the bandwidth to the required value.

For an a.m. receiver i.f. amplifier, the required bandwidth is about 9–10 kHz, as in Fig. 1.17, with steep skirts to the response so that good rejection of adjacent channel interference is achieved.

A.M. Demodulator

The purpose of the demodulator or detector stage is to recover the original modulation impressed on the carrier at the transmitter. In an a.m. receiver the aim is to reproduce at the detector output a replica of the modulation envelope.

A typical practical circuit using a diode demodulator is given in Fig. 1.18 with waveforms illustrating operation shown in Fig. 1.19. The input to the circuit is the

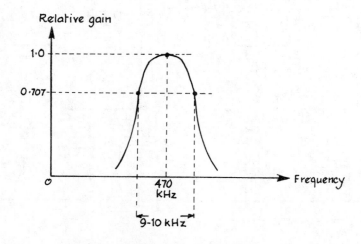

Fig. 1.17 Overall I.F. selectivity.

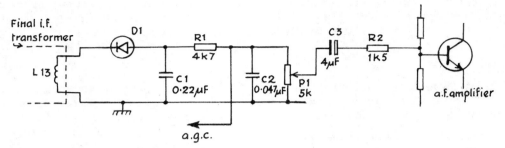

Fig. 1.18 Typical A.M. demodulator.

amplitude modulated i.f. carrier, as in Fig. 1.19(a). This is half-wave rectified by the diode $D1$ to pass on the negative half-cycles but to block the positive half-cycles. In some circuits the diode is connected the other way round without affecting the principle of operation. However, the diode connection affects the polarity of the d.c. component which is important if an a.g.c. voltage is derived from the demodulator output as in this case.

The load time constant is formed by $C1$, $R1$ and $P1$. This time constant must be long compared with the periodic time of the i.f. carrier to ensure that $C1$ does not discharge too much during the positive half-cycles, see Fig. 19(b). However, if the time constant is too long the voltage across $C1$ will be unable to follow the modulation envelope when it is falling, resulting in diagonal clipping of the modulation troughs and the introduction of distortion.

The voltage across $C1$ contains the modulation component, a d.c. component and an i.f. component plus its harmonics (constituting the i.f. 'ripple'). To remove the i.f. ripple, the i.f. filter $R1$, $C2$ is included. Thus across $C2$ the a.f. component is developed with the i.f. ripple reduced to small proportions, see Fig. 19(c).

The wanted a.f. component is fed from $P1$ (the volume control) to the a.f. amplifier via $C3$. This capacitor blocks the demodulator d.c. component to prevent it from upsetting the bias of the a.f. amplifier.

Operation of the demodulator is also affected by the input resistance of the a.f. amplifier stage. This a.c. load should be large compared with $P1$ value to avoid distortion

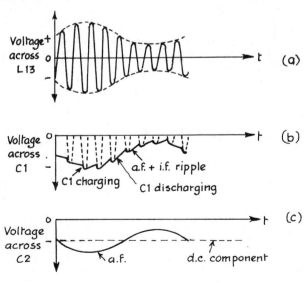

Fig. 1.19 Waveforms showing operation of demodulator.

(peak clipping). Thus to minimise variations in a.c. load with changes in setting of the volume control, the 'stand-off' resistor R2 is included.

A.G.C.

The signals arriving at the input of a radio receiver are liable to vary in amplitude and cause changes in audio output level:

(a) As the receiver is tuned from one station to another.
(b) As a result of varying propagation conditions causing the signal to fade.
(c) As a result of moving objects in the signal path.
(d) When the receiver is located in a moving vehicle.

The function of an a.g.c. system is to automatically vary the gain of the receiver to maintain a reasonably constant audio signal output power. Thus the gain of the receiver must be reduced by the a.g.c. system when a large amplitude signal is received and increased for small signal inputs. In this way, the possibility of a large increase in volume is minimised as the receiver is tuned through a powerful transmission and the effects of rapid fading that occurs with S.W. reception is smoothed out.

A.G.C. operates by varying the gain of one or more of the i.f. amplifying transistors. There are two basic methods of altering the gain of a transistor, see Fig. 1.20.

In **reverse gain control** the a.c. current gain h_{fe} is reduced as shown by decreasing the collector current, *i.e.* by **reducing the forward bias** of the transistor. Reverse gain control is used in a.m. receivers.

Some transistors are designed to exhibit a collapse in gain at high values of I_c, *e.g.* above 5 mA. Thus with this method known as **forward gain control**, the gain is lowered by increasing I_c, *i.e.* by **increasing the forward bias** of the transistor. Forward gain control is used in f.m. radio and television receivers.

A circuit example of reverse gain control is given in Fig. 1.21. Here the gain of the first i.f. amplifier is controlled by the d.c. component of the demodulated signal from across P1.

The base potential of TR1 is set by the potential divider formed by R2, R3 and P1 values. Under no signal conditions the values of R2 and R3 are chosen to give a base potential of, say, 1·7 V and an emitter voltage of 1·0 V thus providing a forward bias of 0·7 V (maximum gain).

With a large signal input there will be a large negative d.c. component of voltage developed across P1 which will reduce the forward bias of TR1 to, say, 0·6 V causing a reduction in the collector current and a lowering of TR1 gain. Conversely, if the signal strength now reduces there will be less d.c. component across P1 resulting in an increase in forward bias to, say, 0·65 V thereby increasing collector current and increasing the gain of TR1.

The l.p.f. formed by R3 and C3 removes any a.f. and i.f. fed along the a.g.c. line to TR1 base. The time constant of R3, C3 determines the speed of response of the a.g.c. system to changes in signal level.

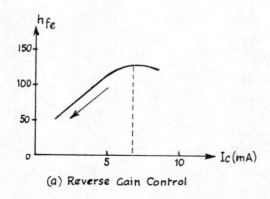

(a) Reverse Gain Control

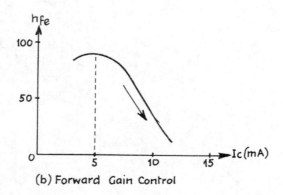

(b) Forward Gain Control

Fig. 1.20 Gain control of transistors.

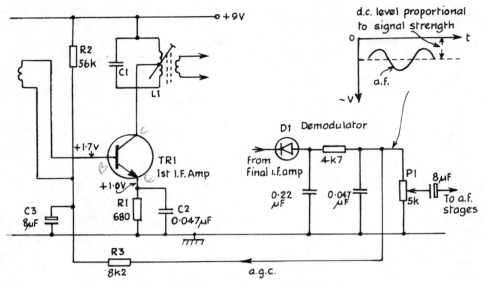

Fig. 1.21 Reverse gain control in A.M. radio.

A.F. Stages

Transistor a.m. radios employ conventional audio frequency amplifier arrangements such as that shown in Fig. 1.22 where audio power outputs from about 250mW to 3W are obtainable depending upon receiver size. For battery operated receivers, the high efficiency of class 'B' operation is adopted to conserve battery power. The audio frequency bandwidth is often restricted compared to f.m. or a.m./f.m. radios particularly so with small a.m. radios.

In the circuit of Fig. 1.22, d.c. coupling is used throughout the amplifier. Audio signals from the demodulator are fed to *TR*1 to be amplified and developed across its collector load *R*1. From here they are directly coupled

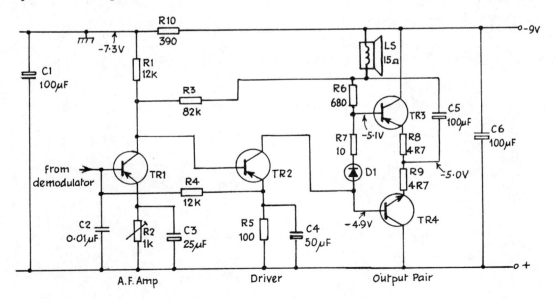

Fig. 1.22 Audio stages (portable radio).

to the base of the driver transistor *TR*2. Amplified signal produced across *R*6 is supplied to the output pair *TR*3, *TR*4 connected in a class 'B' complementary symmetry arrangement. These transistors have a small forward bias of 0·1 V applied from the bias resistor *R*7 and *D*1 to avoid cross-over distortion. The purpose of *D*1 is to compensate for falling battery voltage by maintaining a more constant bias for the output pair, thereby minimising any increase in distortion.

The emitter resistor *R*2 of *TR*1 is made variable so that the mid-point voltage at the junction of *R*8, *R*9 may be set accurately to avoid asymmetrical clipping of the audio signal at the output.

Capacitor *C*6 decouples the internal resistance of the battery to prevent instability ('motor-boating') as the battery ages (when its internal resistance rises).

F.M. RECEIVERS

An f.m. receiver deals with frequency modulated waves but employs the same superheterodyne receiver principles as outlined for the a.m. receiver, where the incoming signal f_s is mixed with the output of a local oscillator f_o to produce a difference frequency $f_o - f_s$ (the i.f.) which is usually about **10·7 MHz**. Commercial receivers are tunable over the (v.h.f.) range of **88 MHz – 108 MHz** and require a signal bandwidth of about **200–250 kHz**.

A basic block diagram of a monophonic f.m. receiver is given in Fig. 1.23 where it will be seen that the main differences to the a.m. receiver are:

(a) An r.f. amplifying stage is used.
(b) A different type of demodulator is required (f.m.).
(c) Automatic frequency control is normally fitted.
(d) The tuning may be manual or electronic.
(e) Audio signal de-emphasis is used.

R.F. Amplifier

Below about 5 MHz the noise and interference picked up in the aerial is much greater than the noise generated within the receiver and originating mainly in the mixer stage. For this reason r.f. amplification is rarely used in a.m. broadcast receivers since the incoming noise would be amplified along with the signal producing little if any improvement in signal-to-noise ratio. At high frequencies such as those employed for f.m. radio and television broadcasting, r.f. amplification is used to provide:

(a) An improvement in signal-to-noise ratio at the mixer stage.
(b) Improved selectivity for the rejection of unwanted signals, *e.g.* second channel interference.
(c) Isolation of the local oscillator from the aerial which reduces local oscillator radiation.
(d) An additional a.g.c. controlled stage which acts as a controlled attenuator on strong signals.

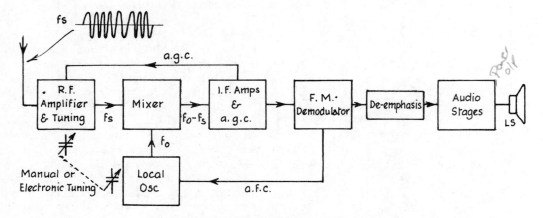

Fig. 1.23 Basic mono F.M. receiver block schematic.

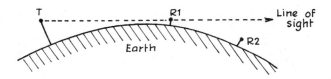

Fig. 1.24 Space wave.

Receiving Aerials for V.H.F. Radio

Communication systems operating at high frequencies, *e.g.* television, radar and v.h.f./f.m. radio use the 'space-wave' as the method of propagation. The space-wave represents the energy that travels from the transmitter in the space close to the earth, see Fig. 1.24. The range of the space-wave is chiefly determined by the height of the transmitting and receiving aerials. A receiving aerial $R1$ lies in the line-of-sight path of the transmitting aerial T and in consequence will receive its radiations. A receiving aerial $R2$ at the same height as $R1$ but located farther round the earth's circumference cannot 'see' the transmitting aerial and therefore does not pick-up the line-of-sight signal.

V.H.F. aerials for roof or loft mounting are invariably based on the half-wave dipole, see Fig. 1.25. This is a resonant type of aerial *i.e.* its rods are cut to optimum length so that it is resonant to the frequency of the energising signal. Connection to the dipole is made at the centre where the impedance is about 75 ohm providing a suitable match to standard coaxial cable of 70–80 ohm impedance. The actual overall length of the dipole is made about 5% less than the half-wavelength, calculated from:

$$\lambda = \frac{v}{f}.$$

A half-wave dipole tuned to 98 MHz (about the centre of the f.m. band) would have a length of:

$$\frac{3 \times 10^8}{98 \times 10^6 \times 2} \times \frac{95}{100}$$

$$= 1 \cdot 45 \text{ metres.}$$

In its basic form, see Fig. 1.26(a), the dipole may be used in areas of high signal strength

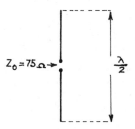

Fig. 1.25 Half-wave resonant dipole aerial.

where reflected signals are of little importance. Most local transmitters use horizontal polarisation but some transmitters use mixed polarisation. The directional performance of an aerial may be indicated by a 'polar diagram' in which the distance from the origin to the curve represents the relative strength of the received or radiated signal in that direction. As shown the plain dipole receives signal with equal strength in all directions in the vertical plane when horizontally mounted; the polar diagrams are end views of the aerial rods.

The directional performance of the basic dipole may be considerably improved by positioning additional elements close to it to form an array. The simplest array consists of a dipole and a reflector arranged in H-form, as in Fig. 1.26(b). The reflector is a continuous conductor having a length slightly greater than the dipole and placed about $\lambda/4$ from it. The addition of the reflector modifies the polar response creating maximum response in the direction X with little response in the direction Y. In consequence the beam width is reduced and the forward gain of the array is about $+4\cdot5$ dB over the basic dipole. The H-aerial can thus be used in areas of high signal strength where reflections are a problem by mounting the aerial so that (where possible) the reflected signal lies in the direction of minimum aerial response. The additional gain

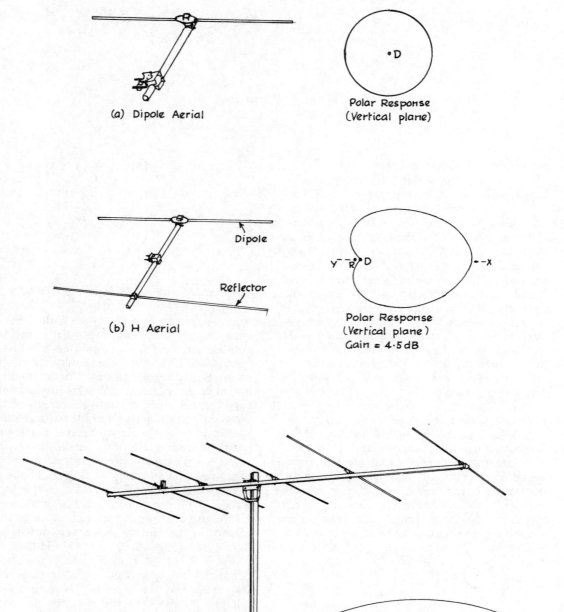

(a) Dipole Aerial

Polar Response
(Vertical plane)

Dipole

Reflector

(b) H Aerial

Polar Response
(Vertical plane)
Gain = 4·5 dB

(c) Yagi Array 6-element

side lobe

Polar Response
(Vertical plane)
Gain = 8 dB

Fig. 1.26 Aerials for F.M. radio reception (horizontally polarised).

produced by the array may also be useful at medium ranges from the transmitter.

The directivity may be improved further by fitting additional elements to the array. These additional elements are called 'directors' and are made progressively shorter than the dipole and fitted on the opposite side to the reflector. Fig. 1.26(c) shows a 6-element array consisting of a dipole, a reflector and four directors. This type of array gives a forward gain of about +8 dB over a basic dipole with a much reduced beam width. The improved directivity may assist in reducing the effects of reflections and the higher forward gain makes the aerial suitable in areas of weak signal strength.

An f.m. receiver incorporates an amplitude limiter to suppress amplitude variations (noise) of the carrier input. The degree of suppression depends upon signal strength, becoming greater as the signal delivered by the receiving aerial increases. If the signal is too weak to operate the limiter properly, turning up the volume control will only intensify the noise heard. Thus, if a good aerial is used the received programme will sound better on f.m. due to the lower level of noise that will be obtained.

To cover the three stations from the local transmitter in any area, the receiving aerial should have a bandwidth of about 5 MHz, see Fig. 1.27. A wide bandwidth is obtained by increasing the diameter of the aerial rods; the rods of an f.m. aerial should be at least 10 mm in diameter. The odd length of wire has a relatively narrow bandwidth and is no substitute for a real aerial.

A problem with the plain dipole is that its impedance is lowered when incorporated into a Yagi array. The presence of reflector and

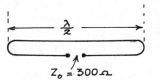

Fig. 1.28 Folded dipole.

directors may lower its impedance from 75 ohm to around 20 ohm. For this reason a **folded dipole** is often used as the main element in an array, see Fig. 1.28. Like the plain dipole, a folded dipole has an overall length of $\lambda/2$ less about 5%. The aerial consists of two conductors in parallel, sometimes called the 'folded' and 'driven' parts. If the two conductors are of equal diameter the centre impedance is raised by a factor of four to 300 ohm. When a folded dipole is featured in a Yagi array the centre impedance is lowered to around 75 ohm thus enabling a good match to be made to standard 75 ohm cable.

An f.m. aerial should be mounted as high as possible in a clear site. Metallic objects in the vicinity of the aerial may alter its polar diagram impairing its gain and directivity. This is a particular problem with loft mounted aerials since the loft space often contains water pipes, metal tanks and electrical cables. When adjusting the aerial position for maximum signal strength, always stand behind the reflector to keep the disturbance to the polar response to a minimum.

Signal De-Emphasis

It is a characteristic of frequency modulation that noise accompanying the f.m. carrier

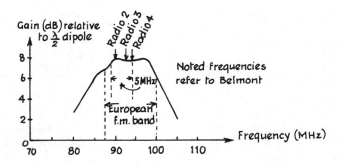

Fig. 1.27 Response of typical 6-element array to local transmitter F.M. radio stations.

causes the noise output of the receiver detector to increase with frequency as shown in Fig. 1.29(a). This results in a worsening of the signal-to-noise ratio at the higher audio frequencies.

To produce some improvement, the higher audio frequencies are given **pre-emphasis** (boost) at the transmitter as in Fig. 1.29(b). The output of the receiver demodulator will now appear as in Fig. 1.29(c), where some improvement in signal-to-noise ratio at the higher audio frequencies is evident but the tonal response of the programme signal is incorrect. This is the purpose of the receiver

de-emphasis network which restores the tonal balance of the programme signal and at the same time attenuates the noise, see Fig. 1.29(d).

The de-emphasis network usually takes the form of a *CR* low pass filter as in Fig. 1.30 and is fitted immediately following the detector in a mono f.m. receiver (in a stereo receiver it must follow the decoder). Rather than specify component values which will vary from circuit to circuit, it is more usual to quote the time constant for pre-emphasis and de-emphasis which for U.K. f.m. broadcast transmitters is $50\,\mu\text{s}$.

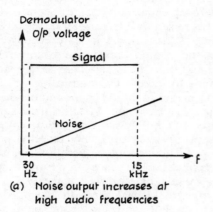

(a) Noise output increases at high audio frequencies

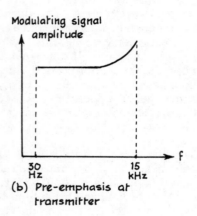

(b) Pre-emphasis at transmitter

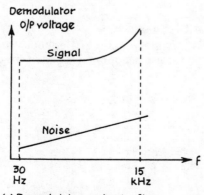

(c) Demodulator output after pre-emphasis at transmitter

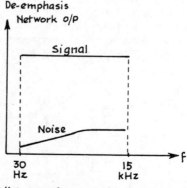

(d) Output from receiver de-emphasis network (Note improvement in signal-to-noise ratio)

Fig. 1.29 Pre-emphasis and de-emphasis.

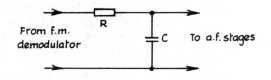

Fig. 1.30 De-emphasis network.

F.M. RECEIVER CIRCUITS

F.M. Tuner

The 'tuner' incorporates an r.f. amplifier and mixer/local oscillator stages and a typical circuit using mechanical tuning is given in Fig. 1.31.

$TR1$ is the r.f. amplifier connected in the common base mode; $C5$ grounds the base to signal frequencies. Signals from the 75 ohm aerial are coupled via $C1$ and $C2$ to the primary of the aerial input transformer comprising $L1$, $L2$. A step-up ratio is used to match to the input tuned circuit comprising $L2$, $C3$ and $C4$. This **fixed** or **pre-tuned** input circuit is damped to give a 3 dB bandwidth of about 20 MHz so that it covers the signal range of 88–108 MHz. In consequence the tuned circuit offers little 'image signal' rejection particularly when the wanted signal lies at the low end of the signal range (assuming that the

local oscillator is tuned above the signal frequency). Note that the image frequency is $2 \times 10 \cdot 7$ MHz $= 21 \cdot 4$ MHz away from the wanted signal.

Signals from the input circuit are transferred to $TR1$ emitter via the capacitive divider $C3$, $C4$. This arrangement prevents excessive damping of the input tuned circuit by the low input resistance of $TR1$. $R1$ is the emitter resistor and $R2$ provides a suitable forward bias for the transistor. A.G.C. is applied to the base of $TR1$ via $R3$.

Amplified signals are developed across the collector tuned circuit comprising essentially $L3$, $C6$. This resonant circuit is variably tuned over the range of 88–108 MHz. It has a smaller bandwidth (about 2 MHz) than the fixed tuned input circuit to provide the r.f. selectivity for 'image' signal rejection. $C6$ provides the variable tuning with the frequency limits of the tuning range adjusted by the variable $L3$ and $C7$ during r.f. alignment.

The output of the r.f. amplifier is capacitively coupled to the mixer via $C8$. $L4$, $C9$ form a series resonant $10 \cdot 7$ MHz trap to prevent i.f. break through. The 'trap' also isolates the i.f. stages from the aerial to prevent radiation at $10 \cdot 7$ MHz which may interfere with other nearby receivers.

$TR2$ is self-oscillating mixer (additive) with

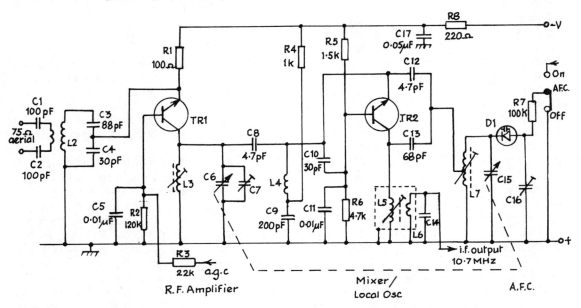

Fig. 1.31 F.M. Tuner with mechanical tuning.

forward bias provided by *R*6, *R*5 and *R*4 serving as emitter resistor. The transistor is operated in common base, the base being grounded to signals by *C*11. The oscillator frequency determining circuit is formed by *L*7, *C*15, *C*16 and *D*1 (vari-cap diode). Oscillatory energy is coupled to *TR*2 emitter from *L*7 via *C*12 and returned in-phase to *L*7 from the collector via *C*13.

The local oscillator may be tuned **above** or **below** the signal frequency by the required i.f. in an f.m. radio receiver and in this receiver it is tuned below. The variable *C*15 thus adjusts the oscillator frequency so that it is always 10·7 MHz below the signal frequency. The difference frequency $(f_s - f_o)$ resulting from the mixer action is extracted by the tuned i.f. transformer comprising *L*5, *L*6 and *C*14 in the collector of *TR*2.

A.F.C.

Local oscillators working at high frequencies, *e.g.* in f.m. radio and television receivers may significantly drift in frequency due to temperature, supply voltage or component value variations. This will cause the receiver to go off-tune resulting in distorted sound when the drift is small or complete loss of station tuning when the drift is large during f.m. reception.

To compensate for this effect, all f.m. radio and television receivers employ some form of automatic frequency control which adjusts the frequency of the local oscillator when frequency drift occurs. This is achieved within the receiver by sensing the frequency of the i.f. produced by the mixer, often at the point of the f.m. demodulator stage. If there is no drift the i.f. will be correct at 10·7 MHz. When local oscillator drift occurs the i.f. produced will either be greater than or less than 10·7 MHz, depending upon the direction of the initial drift and whether the local oscillator is tuned above or below the signal frequency.

A frequency sensitive circuit such as the f.m. demodulator may be used to convert variations of the i.f. caused by drift into a **correction voltage**. This voltage is then used to alter the capacitance of a vari-cap diode, see Fig. 1.32, connected in the local oscillator circuit so as to adjust its frequency and make the i.f. correct (or very nearly so).

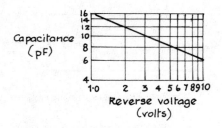

Fig. 1.32 *Typical capacitance characteristic of reverse biased P.N. diode.*

In the circuit of Fig. 1.31 the correction voltage is fed into the local oscillator via the AFC switch when it is in the 'on' position. The correction voltage must be negative w.r.t. chassis so that *D*1 is reverse biassed. Since *D*1 in series with *C*16 are effectively in parallel with *C*15, variations in *D*1 reverse bias will alter the local oscillator frequency when drift occurs.

It should be noted that manual tuning of the receiver should not be carried out with the AFC switched 'on' as the a.f.c. will tend to correct for tuning variations. It is possible to finish up apparently correctly tuned in, but with the a.f.c. at the end of its 'hold range' and unable to cope with any subsequent drift. Thus when tuning in a station the a.f.c. should be 'off'; when correctly tuned in the a.f.c. may be set to the 'on' position.

Electronic Tuning

Electronic tuning is now more common and Fig. 1.33 shows a typical arrangement to illustrate the basic idea. The r.f. amplifier, mixer and local oscillator active devices, represented by blocks, may utilise discrete bipolar or unipolar transistors or be fabricated in i.c. form.

Tuning is achieved with the aid of three vari-cap diodes fed from a common variable tuning voltage line which adjusts the frequency of three resonant circuits, two in the r.f. amplifier stage and one in the local oscillator.

In this arrangement, the r.f. amplifier is tuned at input and output which provides good selectivity and adequate rejection of the 'image' channel signal, a feature to be found in the better quality receivers. For receivers where the input circuit is fixed tuned (as in Fig. 1.31) one less vari-cap diode will be

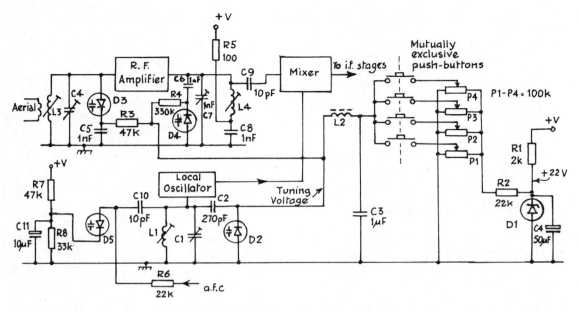

Fig. 1.33 F.M. Tuner with electronic tuning.

needed. The r.f. amplifier input tuning consists essentially of $L3$ and $D3$ and the output tuning comprises $L4$, $C6$ and $D4$. The frequency of the local oscillator is determined essentially by $L1$, $C2$ and $D2$.

To prevent unwanted tuning variations, it is essential that the tuning voltage supply is well stabilised. This is achieved by the use of the zener diode stabiliser $D1$ fed via $R1$ from the receiver supply to provide a $+22$ V stabilised tuning voltage. This voltage is developed across potentiometers $P1$–$P4$, the outputs of which may be selected one at a time by mutually exclusive push-button switches. By adjusting $P1$–$P4$ sliders to provide different tuning voltages from each, the receiver may be preset to a number of stations within the f.m. band; four in this case but a larger number may be used if desired. If continuous tuning is also required, one of the presets may be replaced by a variable potentiometer so that the tuning voltage is varied over a wide range, say, 0–22 V. To provide a visual indication of tuning, the analogue output voltage of the variable potentiometer may be converted into digital form to produce a reading in MHz on a liquid crystal display.

As a common tuning voltage line is used it is

important to prevent mutual coupling at signal frequency between the three separate circuits in the tuning line itself. This is the purpose of the isolating resistors $R3$, $R4$ and the r.f. choke $L2$ which also prevents oscillator radiation from the receiver supply voltage rail.

A.F.C. is also used for reasons previously explained but additionally to correct for small tuning errors when stations are tuned in manually. The vari-cap diode $D5$ adjusts the oscillator frequency since it together with $C10$ are, as far as a.c. is concerned, effectively in parallel with $L1$.

Frequency Synthesis Tuning

Since the radio stations picked-up in the aerial are held very accurately by the transmitter at their nominal broadcast frequencies, the actual station heard in the receiver output depends solely on the frequency of **the local oscillator**. Thus if the local oscillator frequency could be made very stable by using a crystal reference source in the receiver, precise fixed tuning could be achieved.

In a **frequency synthesis** system, the **receiver local oscillator** together with its vari-cap diode tuning **forming a voltage controlled oscillator** is

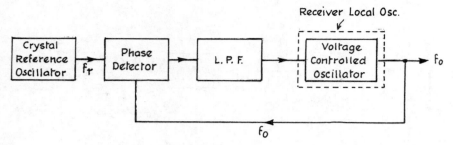

Fig. 1.34 Phase-locked loop.

made part of a **phase-locked loop** (PLL) as in Fig. 1.34.

The basic system shown comprises a crystal reference oscillator generating a frequency f_r, a phase detector, a v.c.o. generating a frequency f_o and a low pass filter.

In the phase detector f_r and f_o are compared in frequency and phase. If a frequency or phase error exists, the phase detector generates a d.c. correction voltage of magnitude and polarity that is proportional to the frequency or phase error. After filtering by the l.p.f. to remove all a.c. components, the correction voltage is supplied to the v.c.o. to vary its frequency. The action of the P.L.L. ensures that the frequency of the v.c.o. moves in such a direction that it is at the same frequency as the crystal reference oscillator. Once 'lock' has been achieved both inputs to the phase detector will be at the same frequency but with a small residual phase error existing which is necessary to maintain the d.c. control voltage to the v.c.o. Thus with this arrangement if the frequency of the crystal oscillator is, say, 4 MHz the v.c.o. will lock to this frequency.

Of course, the local oscillator frequency in a receiver needs to be altered to suit the desired station. For fixed preset tuning it will have to be set to a number of different frequencies in the range of 98·7–118·7 MHz (oscillator tuned above the signal by 10·7 MHz) in an f.m. receiver. Frequency-synthesis is thus really concerned with generating a number of discrete frequencies from a single accurate crystal reference source, either singly or simultaneously.

The refinements to the basic PLL system to produce a number of different local oscillator frequencies, generated singly from a common reference oscillator source are given in Fig. 1.35.

Two frequency dividers have now been added; a fixed divider ($\div 100$) and a programmable divider which is capable of division over a large range (512–32767) in this case.

The fixed divider following the reference oscillator divides the stable 4 MHz crystal oscillation down to 40 kHz which provides input A to the phase detector. This divider determines the smallest frequency step (resolution) that the local oscillator can be made to move.

The programmable divider following the output of the local oscillator (v.c.o.) divides the local oscillator frequency to provide input B to the phase detector. The action of the PLL is to cause input B to shift in frequency until it is of the same frequency as input A, when the local oscillator will acquire a locked condition. At this point the local oscillator will be locked to a multiple of 40 kHz; the exact frequency = the division factor of the programmable divider × 40 kHz.

Thus with the programmable divider set to give a division of 2500, the local oscillator will lock to 2500 × 40 kHz = 100 MHz. By altering the division factor of the programmable divider, the action of the PLL will be to cause the local oscillator to lock to a different frequency, see table opposite:

It will be noted that the smallest change in local oscillator frequency is 40 kHz in this case, corresponding to a change in the division ratio of one.

The scheme shown in Fig. 1.35 may be applied to the tuning of f.m. and a.m. receivers. Commercial phase locked loop i.cs produce tuning steps of 1 kHz on a.m. and

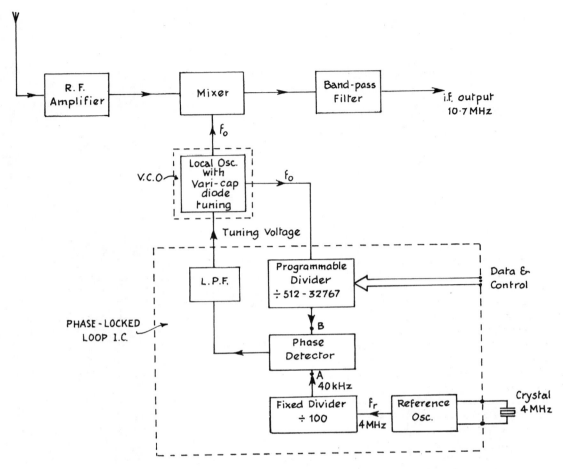

Fig. 1.35 Basic frequency-synthesis tuning system for F.M. receiver.

Programmable Divider (Division factor)	Locked frequency of local oscillator (MHz)
2500	100.00
2550	102.00
2600	104.00
2601	104.04
2602	104.08
2603	104.12

10 kHz on f.m., but use multiple phase locked loops, although the principle of operation is the same.

Sweep Search

A further application of frequency synthesis tuning is in **sweep-search** where a receiver can be made to automatically tune over a particular waveband and stop when a station of pre-determined characteristics is found. The diagram of Fig. 1.36 shows how a basic scheme may be implemented for sweep-search of the broadcast bands in an f.m./a.m. radio receiver.

When the receiver is switched-on and assuming that it has not been previously tuned, the microprocessor i.c. on instruction from the program ROM scans the keyboard waiting for a 'user command'. If, say, the 'search +' button is pressed, the program ROM outputs a sequence of stored binary

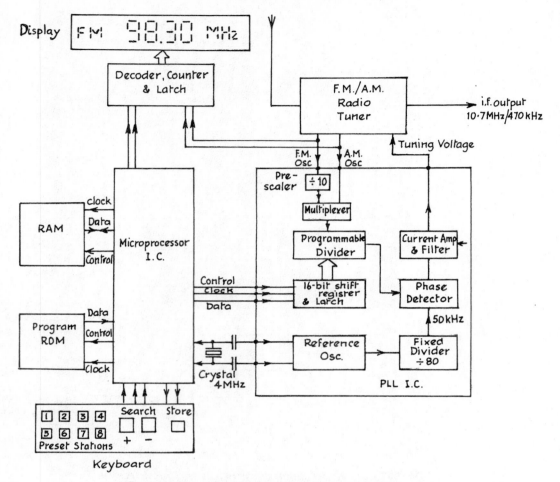

Fig. 1.36 Frequency synthesis tuning with sweep search.

numbers to the PLL. The stored binary data representing the division factors for the programmable divider is supplied to it via a 16-bit shift register and latch. This action causes the tuner to step through the selected waveband searching for a broadcast station. When a station of good signal-to-noise ratio is found, a control signal is sent from the receiver demodulator to the microprocessor causing it to stop the sequential addressing of the stored data in the ROM. A large number of separate addresses will be needed in the ROM to store the sequential data of the division factors. For example, to tune over the f.m. band from 88–108 MHz using 50 kHz tuning steps, 400 addresses will be required.

If it is desired to memorise the station that is found, the 'store' and one of the 'preset station' buttons should be pressed. These operations result in the division factor of the programmable divider for that tuning point to be stored in the RAM. The tuning point is then available for instant recall when that station is required again. A special non-volatile memory is required for the RAM and an EAROM may be used for this purpose. This type of memory can be erased by applying a high voltage of + 33 V to it and this is automatically carried out whenever the user reprogrammes the tuning points. Operating one of the 'search' keys again will cause the sequential stepping of the receiver tuning (up or down the frequency band) until another station is found, which may then be stored in the manner outlined.

An additional refinement is the capability of the system to display the exact tuning point during sweep-search and the frequency of the preset stations. This may be accomplished with the aid of a frequency counter (off-set by the receiver i.f. value) which measures the frequency of the local oscillator for indication on a liquid crystal display. A latch is used to freeze the display when a station is found during sweep-search or when preset station operation is invoked.

Sweep-search in a television receiver operates along very similar lines. However, it is necessary to use some form of **pre-scaling** (pre-division) of the television local oscillator output to enable the frequency synthesis system to utilise crystal oscillators of a few megahertz.

I.F. Stages

An example of a four-stage i.f. amplifier using discrete transistors and *LC* tuning is given in Fig. 1.37.

The circuit utilises tuned i.f. transformers (*T*1–*T*4) all with variable ferrite cores which are set during i.f. alignment so that the tuned circuits are resonant to the i.f. of 10·7 MHz. The relatively wide bandwidth required for f.m. sound transmissions of 200–250 kHz may be obtained by flattening of the i.f. transformer tuning. Some damping is provided by the input and output resistances of the transistors and the tappings on the tuned circuit inductors

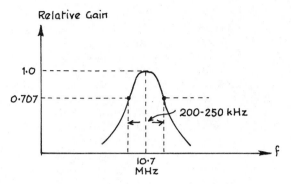

Fig. 1.38 I.F. response.

are set to give suitable damping. Additional damping is often provided by resistors connected across the i.f. transformers, such as *R*1 in this circuit.

An overall i.f. response with steep flanks is required as in Fig. 1.38 to ensure adequate rejection of adjacent channel signals. More stations now operate on the f.m./v.h.f. band; apart from the BBC national radio transmissions there are the local radio services and independent radio stations. In a local reception area, the transmission frequencies may be sepatated by about 1 MHz only, thus the i.f. gain should be well down 1 MHz either side of the centre frequency.

The wider bandwidth required reduces the stage gain and this necessitates the use of three or four i.f. stages. At 10·7 MHz there is some capacitive coupling from collector to base which may cause oscillation, this can be effectively prevented by stopper resistors connected directly to the collector terminals

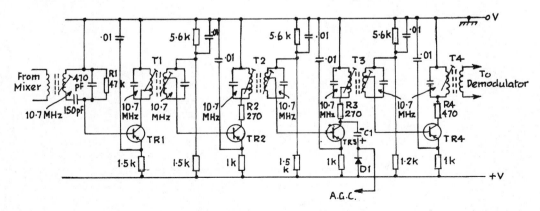

Fig. 1.37 Complete four-stage I.F. amplifier.

(*R*2–*R*4). Note that the upper supply line is connected to chasis, hence decoupling capacitors are taken to this line.

In an f.m. receiver it is desirable to remove amplitude modulation of the carrier before it is applied to the demodulator stage. Sometimes this is done with the aid of **limiting diodes** but in other cases **the i.f. amplifier will act as a limiter**. Limiting will occur in any i.f. amplifying stage if the signal amplitude is large enough, because in one direction the base-emitter will be reverse biassed and in the other direction the collector of the transistor will be 'bottomed'.

A.G.C.

An amplitude limiter operates better with a large signal input, thus it would appear that a.g.c. would be a disadvantage for limiter action. However, there are cases where cross-modulation or intermodulation can occur in the mixer stage when there is a large signal input resulting in interference. Thus it is desirable to reduce the gain of the r.f. amplifier stage on large signal inputs to the receiver.

Since the input to the demodulator tends to be of constant amplitude due to the use of limiter diodes, or the automatic limiting action of the i.f. amplifier, a.g.c. cannot normally be obtained from the demodulator stage. It must be obtained prior to limiting such as an early i.f. stage.

In the circuit of Fig. 1.37, a.g.c. is derived from the output of the third i.f. stage. *D*1 acts as a half-wave rectifier, rectifying the i.f. signal at *TR*1 collector and charging *C*1 with the polarity shown; the charge being proportional to signal strength. This voltage is fed to the r.f. amplifier stage to reduce its gain on strong signals. The input circuit of the r.f. amplifier provides a discharge path for *C*1.

Use of Ingetrated Circuits and Ceramic Filters

It is now more common to use ceramic filters to provide the i.f. bandwidth as they have a better shape characteristic than double tuned *LC* circuits. Ceramic filters do not provide any gain. They do introduce some attenuation of the signal over the 'pass band', but remove the alignment difficulty of *LC* tuned circuits.

A ceramic filter makes use of the 'Piezo-Electric' property of certain processed ceramic materials and the *Q* of such a device is much greater than can be obtained with ordinary *LC* circuits. If three quartz crystal elements are connected as in Fig. 1.39(a), bandpass characteristics similar to those shown in Fig. 1.39(b) may be obtained. The three crystal elements may be replaced by one as in Fig. 1.39(c) and if ceramic is used in place of quartz, the device is known as a **ceramic resonator**.

Ceramic filters are not tuneable but are usually colour coded; filters with the same colour coding are tuned to the same frequency.

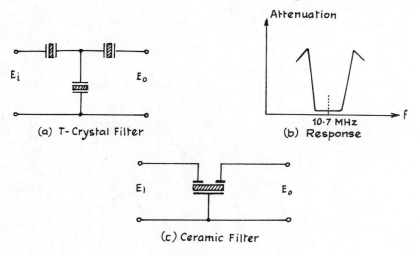

Fig. 1.39 Ceramic filter.

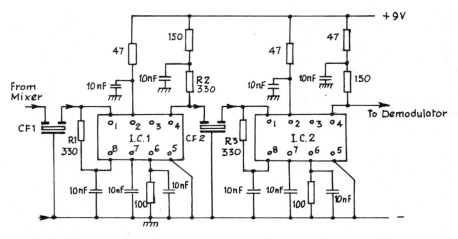

Fig. 1.40 I.F. amplifier (10·7 MHz) using integrated circuits and ceramic filters.

The filters must be matched correctly at input and output, typically 330 ohm.

The circuit of Fig. 1.40 shows how 10·7 MHz ceramic filters (*CF*1 and *CF*2) may be incorporated into an i.f. amplifier. Since the filters do not introduce any gain, the required i.f. gain is provided by the use of integrated circuits (I.C.1 and I.C.2). *CF*1 is matched at its output by *R*1 and *CF*2 is matched at input and output by *R*2 and *R*3 respectively. The high gain of the integrated circuits easily makes up for the loss introduced by the ceramic filters (about 5 dB each) and enables limiting of the signal to be achieved with moderate signal input levels. Discrete components are connected external to the i.cs. which serve as supply rail decoupling, load or biassing components *etc*.

F.M. Demodulators

Before the widespread use of integrated circuits the most common type of f.m. demodulator to be found in radio (and television) receivers was the 'ratio detector'.

Ratio Detector

A basic circuit is given in Fig. 1.41. The circuit works on the principle that the voltage

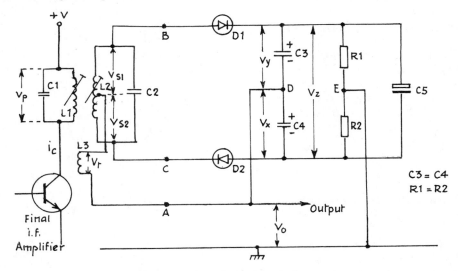

Fig. 1.41 Basic balanced ratio detector.

across the secondary $L2$, $C2$ of a tuned transformer is 90° out of phase with the primary $L1$, $C1$ at the centre frequency (10·7 MHz). In order to be able to compare the secondary voltage with the primary voltage, a tertiary winding $L3$ is added; the voltage V_t induced into $L3$ has the same phase as the primary voltage. $L2$ is centre-tapped so that V_{S1} and V_{S2} are in antiphase with one another.

The action of the circuit may be considered with the aid of phasors:

Phasors at Centre Frequency

The phasor sum of V_{S1} and V_t voltages are applied to $D1$, $C3$ whilst the phasor sum of V_{S2} and V_t voltages are applied to $D2$, $C4$. At the centre frequency these resultant voltages V_{D1} and V_{D2} are equal, see Fig. 1.42. Thus $D1$ and $D2$ conduct equally once each half-cycle of the resultant input causing the equal value capacitors $C3$ and $C4$ to acquire the same charge.

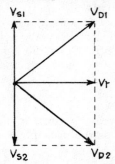

Fig. 1.42 Phasors at centre frequency (10·7 MHz).

Since $R1$ and $R2$ are of the same value, there must be equal voltages across $R1$ and $R2$ and these voltages must equal those across $C3$ and $C4$. These components form a balanced bridge circuit and the voltage between D and E will be zero. Thus at the centre frequency (no deviation),

$$V_o = 0\,V$$

Phasors When Input Is Above the Centre Frequency

When the i.f. carrier is above the centre frequency of the tuned transformer tuning, the phase angle between V_s and V_t changes to that shown in Fig. 1.43. As a result V_{D1} is now

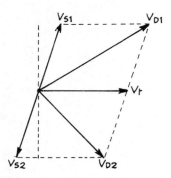

Fig. 1.43 Phasors above centre frequency (> 10·7 MHz).

greater than V_{D2} causing $D1$ to conduct harder than $D2$ and for $C3$ to acquire a greater charge than $C4$.

The sum of the voltages (V_z) across $C3$ and $C4$ which equals $V_y + V_x$ remains reasonably constant, thus the voltages across $R1$ and $R2$ (which are equal) will be approximately the same as previously. In consequence there will now be a net voltage difference between points D and E and V_o = a negative voltage.

Phasors When Input Is Below the Centre Frequency

If the carrier deviates in the other direction so that it is above the centre frequency the phasors for V_s now take up the position as shown in Fig. 1.44.

V_{D2} is now greater than V_{D1} resulting in $C4$ acquiring a greater charge than $C3$. The bridge circuit is unbalanced once again resulting in a net voltage difference between points D and E, but this time V_o = a positive voltage.

Thus as the i.f. carrier deviates either side of

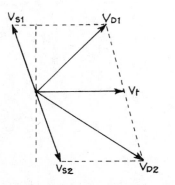

Fig. 1.44 Phasors below centre frequency (< 10·7 MHz).

the centre frequency an output voltage will be obtained of magnitude proportional to the frequency deviation with a polarity that depends upon whether the carrier is increasing or decreasing in frequency. For sine wave modulation the output V_o will be a sine wave at the modulation frequency, see Fig. 1.45.

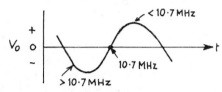

Fig. 1.45 *Output voltage varies with F.M. carrier deviation.*

It is the ratio V_x/V_y that varies during deviation of the carrier, hence the name 'ratio detector'.

Amplitude Limiting

An important feature of the ratio detector is that it does not respond to amplitude variations of the carrier. This is the purpose of $C5$, a large value capacitor (4–25 μF). The capacitor becomes charged to the mean value of the voltage across $R1$ and $R2$. Any rapid variations in the amplitude of the i.f. carrier will have little effect on this voltage due to the long time-constants on charge and discharge.

The voltage across $C1$ may be used as an indication of correct tuning during i.f. alignment. As the alignment is brought closer to correct tuning the voltage across $C5$ will increase.

Practical Circuit

A practical circuit with component values is given in Fig. 1.46. The effectiveness of a.m. rejection depends upon circuit balance in the diode circuits. As there is likely to be some difference in diode characteristics, a fixed resistor ($R2$) is placed in series with one diode and a preset ($R1$) in series with the other. $R1$ is adjusted for minimum a.m.

Capacitor $C6$ completes the circuit to chassis as regards the i.f. and across this capacitor the a.f. output is developed.

$R5$ and $C7$ form the **de-emphasis network** to correct for signal pre-emphasis carried out at the transmitter (see page 19). The network should provide a time constant of 50 μs (47 μs in this case).

A typical relationship between output voltage and frequency for a ratio detector circuit is given in Fig. 1.47. To avoid distortion the output voltage should be directly proportional to frequency, as over the range B to C. These two points should be separated by about 200–250 kHz. Point A corresponds to the unmodulated carrier (10·7 MHz).

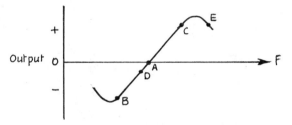

Fig. 1.47 *Characteristic of ratio detector circuit ('S' response).*

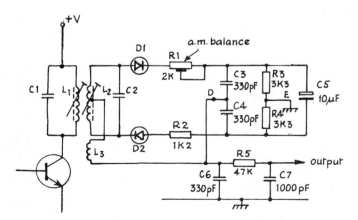

Fig. 1.46 *Practical balanced ratio detector circuit.*

If a receiver is not correctly tuned to a station, the demodulator may operate between, say, D and E and serious distortion will result.

In some circuits, point D is taken to chassis instead of point E and the audio output taken from the junction of $R3$, $R4$, the circuit operation being identical. Present with the audio output will be a **d.c. component proportional to any tuning error in the i.f.** and this may be used as a control voltage for **a.f.c.** purposes. The audio component must be filtered out before the voltage is applied to the a.f.c. circuit.

I.C. Demodulators for F.M.

Integrated circuits are now commonly used for f.m. signal demodulation, but an i.c. does not lend itself to the ratio detector circuit thus new principles are adopted.

1. Quadrature Coincidence Detector

The basic arrangement of a **quadrature coincidence detector** is shown in Fig. 1.48(a). The i.c. incorporates a limiting amplifier which produces a constant amplitude output of the i.f. signal input. This limited signal is supplied to a dual coincidence circuit, directly

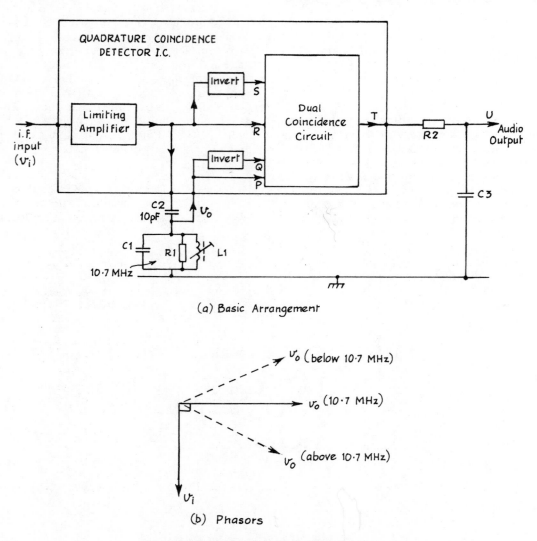

(a) Basic Arrangement

(b) Phasors

Fig. 1.48 Quadrature coincidence demodulator.

as input R and indirectly via an inverter to form input S.

The limiter output is also fed to a tuned circuit comprising $L1$, $C1$ connected externally to the i.c. via a small value capacitor $C2$. This capacitor has appreciable reactance at 10·7 MHz to which $L1$, $C1$ is accurately tuned. In consequence, at the centre frequency, the voltage across $L1$, $C1(v_o)$ is almost 90° leading in phase on the input signal (v_i), see Fig. 1.48(b).

As the frequency deviation of the carrier varies above and below 10·7 MHz, the phase of v_o relative to v_i becomes greater or less than 90°, as indicated. The output from the tuned circuit is fed directly to the coincidence circuit as input P and indirectly after inversion as input Q.

Waveforms illustrating operation of the dual coincidence circuit are given in Fig. 1.49; the limited signals are represented by rectangular waves.

One of the coincidence circuits produces an output when inputs P and S are coincident any time during the positive section of the waveforms. The other coincident circuit produces an output when inputs Q and R are coincident any time during the positive sections of these inputs. The outputs from both circuits are combined.

It will be seen that inputs P and S are time coincident during intervals AB, EF *etc* whilst inputs Q and R are time coincident during intervals CD, GH *etc*.

The output T is a rectangular wave having a repetition rate equal to **twice the i.f.** and a mark-to-space ratio, and hence a mean (d.c.) value, that varies with the deviation of the i.f. carrier. If output T is applied to a l.p.f. ($R2$, $C3$) which removes frequency components at twice the i.f. and above, the output at U will contain the variable d.c. component only, *i.e.* the demodulated audio frequency. By suitable choice of $R2$, $C3$ values the filter will also provide signal de-emphasis.

The advantages of this type of detector are:

(a) There is no fundamental component at the output of the i.f. thus less chance of i.f. instability occurring.
(b) Only a single tuned circuit is used, making alignment easier.
(c) It is linear in operation; $R1$ damps $L1$, $C1$ to produce the required bandwidth.
(d) Since it is a switching type demodulator, it does not respond to a.m.

Commercial i.cs. such as the TBA 750Q usually incorporate other circuit functions, for example, i.f. amplification, volume control and audio signal amplification. They are also

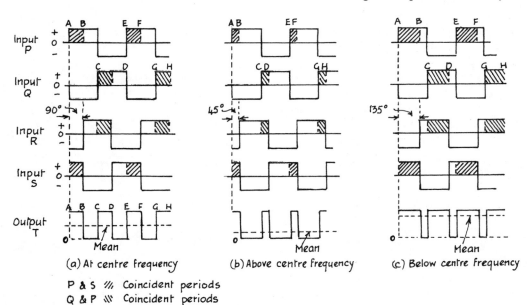

(a) At centre frequency   (b) Above centre frequency   (c) Below centre frequency

P & S ▨ Coincident periods
Q & P ▨ Coincident periods

Fig. 1.49 Operation of quadrature coincidence demodulator.

used in television receivers for sound demodulation where the tuned circuit is made resonant to 6 MHz instead of 10·7 MHz.

2. Phase Locked Loop Demodulator

The **phase locked loop** (the principle of which was described on page 24) can be used as a linear f.m. demodulator when it gives a performance similar to the quadrature detector. The essential i.c. functions are shown in Fig. 1.50.

The frequency of the v.c.o. is determined by the external components $C2$ and $C3$ with $C3$ used to set the oscillator free-running frequency to 10·7 MHz. The action of the PLL is to cause the v.c.o. to 'track' the frequency modulated i.f. input signal exactly. Once the v.c.o. is locked to the f.m. input, it is controlled by the 'error voltage' output of the low pass filter. This error voltage, resulting from the phase difference of the two inputs to the phase detector, is necessary to hold the v.c.o. frequency to that of the f.m. input. It is, therefore, evident that the error voltage must be a replica of the original audio signal modulation. Thus, at the filter output is the demodulated f.m. signal.

The active l.p.f. should have a cut-off frequency equal to the highest audio frequency (15 kHz) which is determined by the external components $R1$, $R2$, $C4$ and $C5$. Capacitor $C7$ forms part of the signal de-emphasis circuit.

With some i.cs. the v.c.o. operates at a frequency somewhat lower than 10·7 MHz thus it is necessary to convert the 10·7 MHz output of the i.f. amplifier to the lower frequency. This conversion may be carried out on the PLL chip.

A.M./F.M. RECEIVER

A number of i.cs. are available which perform the r.f., i.f. and demodulator functions of a radio receiver and a typical example giving the circuit arrangements for an A.M./F.M. radio is shown in Fig. 1.51. This diagram incorporates many of the radio circuit principles previously discussed and may serve as a useful example for 'circuit tracing' around a multi-function i.c.

A.M. Operation

The internal i.c. switches $S1$–$S4$ and the external switches $S5$–$S7$ are shown in the position for A.M. operation.

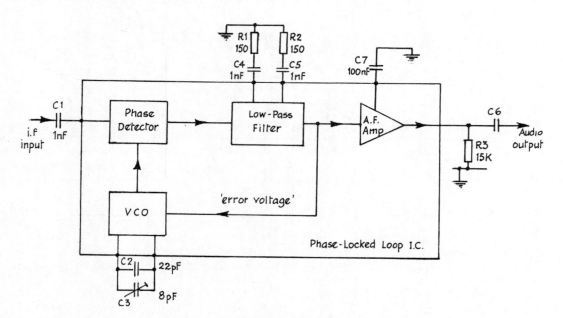

Fig. 1.50 F.M. demodulator using a PLL.

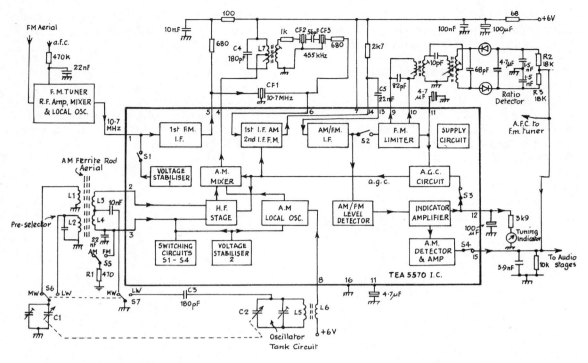

Fig. 1.51 A.M./F.M. Radio R.F./I.F. and demodulators stages using the TEA 5570 I.C.

Signals induced into the **ferrite rod aerial** are selected by $C1$, $L2$ (LW) or $C1$, $L1$ (MW) and coupled to the 'AM Mixer' via $L3$ (MW) or $L4$ (LW) and an 'H.F. Stage'. The mixer is a balanced type which requires a push-pull signal input provided by the H.F. Stage and gives improved performance. The other mixer input comes from the 'AM Local Oscillator' which has its d.c. supply regulated by 'Voltage Stabiliser 2'. The oscillator 'tank' circuit is formed by $C2$, $L5$ (MW) and $C2$, $L5$ $C3$ (LW).

I.F. signals at 455 kHz from the a.m. mixer are selected by $L7$, $C4$ and fed to the 'first AM I.F. Amp' via the **ceramic filters $CF2$ and $CF3$**, which provide the i.f. selectivity on a.m. After amplification, the i.f. signal is coupled to the common 'AM/FM I.F. Amp.' via the external capacitor $C5$. The i.f. signal is then supplied to the 'AM/FM Level Detector' which is used to give an indication of correct tuning by measuring the amplitude of the i.f. carrier. After amplification in the 'Indicator Amplifier' the measured level is fed out of the i.c. on pin 12 to a tuning indicator.

The i.f. signal is demodulated and then amplified in the 'AM Detector and Amp.' stage before being fed out on pin 15 to the audio stages. The Indicator Amplifier also supplies the '**A.G.C. Circuit**' from which control voltages are derived to vary the gain of the Mixer, first AM I.F. and the H.F. Stage.

F.M. Operation

Setting $S5$ to the FM position connects pin 3 to the common chassis line via $R1$ and this action causes the 'switching circuits' to change-over the internal switches $S1$–$S4$. Switch $S1$ (now closed) completes a path for the d.c. supply to the f.m. tuner from 'voltage stabiliser 1'.

The f.m. tuner, shown here as a single block, incorporates an **r.f. stage, mixer** and **local oscillator** and may feature **capacitive**, **inductive** or **electronic tuning**. I.F. signals at 10·7 MHz developed at the mixer output are fed into the i.c. on pin 1 to the input of the 'first FM I.F. amp.'. Following amplification, the i.f. signal is fed via the **ceramic filter $CF1$**, which provides the i.f. selectivity on f.m., to the 'second FM I.F. amplifier'. The signal is then capacitively coupled to the common 'AM/FM I.F. amp.' via C5. From this stage the i.f. signal is routed through S2 (now closed) to the **'FM limiter' where amplitude modulation is removed**.

The limited i.f. signal is fed out of the i.c. on pins 9 and 10 via external tuned circuits resonant to 10·7 MHz to a **'ratio detector'**. The demodulated f.m. signal is taken out from the junction of R2, R3 and fed to the audio stages.

The FM limiter also supplies the AGC circuit (S3 open) which provides gain control over the 'second FM I.F. amp.' only.

Tuning indication is as for a.m. operation but as S4 is now open, there will be no spurious output on pin 15 from the AM detector.

The d.c. voltages at the junction of R2, R3 in the ratio detector, which is proportional to tuning error, is used for **automatic frequency control** of the local oscillator in the f.m. tuner.

CHAPTER TWO

TELEVISION: LIGHT AND COLOUR

Objectives
1 Describe the characteristics of colour; Hue, Saturation and Luminance.
2 List primary and complementary colours. Show additive mixing principles of coloured lights. Explain use of colour triangle diagram.
3 Explain properties of light which have an important bearing on colour television.

TELEVISION IS THE art of reproducing at some distant point an instantaneous image of a scene using a system of telecommunications. In Broadcast Television the signal is radiated from a transmitting aerial which makes general reception possible, whereas with Closed-Circuit Television (CCTV) the signal is usually confined to a coaxial cable thus keeping the system 'private'.

A **scene** can be taken to mean any area or object that is capable of sending out light. Light from most scenes reaches our eyes by the mechanism of reflection. As the world about us is abundant with colour, the light emanating from everyday scenes is, of course, coloured.

For almost thirty years from the advent of television in this country, coloured scenes were reproduced as monochrome images (black and white television), but since 1967 television transmissions have permitted the reproduction of scenes in full colour detail thus providing added realism.

To obtain a clear understanding of colour television a knowledge of certain aspects of light is necessary. Thus in this chapter the important properties of light and human vision which affect the subject of television will be considered.

LIGHT AND COLOUR

Light energy is propagated from one point to another in the form of an **electromagnetic wave**, which consists of an oscillating magnetic field coexisting at right angles to an oscillating electric field as in Fig. 2.1.

Unlike sound waves, no medium is required to propagate electromagnetic waves which may pass through a vacuum. Light rays, radio waves, X-rays, cosmic rays and radiant heat all travel through space in the form of electromagnetic waves and with high velocity (3×10^8 metres per second in a vacuum). It is evident, therefore, that these different types of radiation are all essentially of the same form. What then distinguishes one form of energy from another? The properties of the different types of energy are determined by their frequency or wavelength, see Fig. 2.2. For convenience, the electromagnetic spectrum is divided into sections but the sections have no precise boundaries since the behaviour of an e.m.

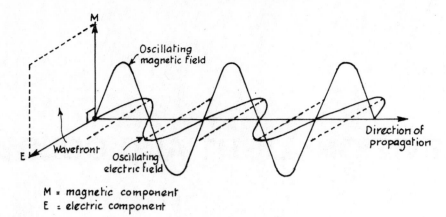

Fig. 2.1 Representation of an electromagnetic wave.

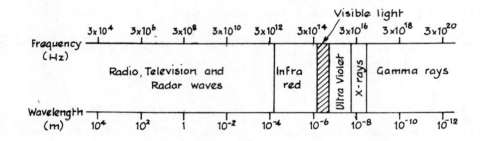

Fig. 2.2 The electromagnetic spectrum.

wave does not change sharply at given frequencies. The wavelength (λ) may be found from:

$$\lambda = \frac{v}{f} \text{ metres}$$

where f = frequency (Hz), v = velocity of e.m. waves (3×10^8 m/s) and λ = the wavelength (metres).

Visible light occupies a very small section of the e.m. spectrum in the approximate range of 380–780 nm. When all of the frequencies present in the visible spectrum reach the eye simultaneously, we see 'white' light. Thus we may regard the human eye as a 'window' for the brain in the e.m. spectrum.

Spectral Colours

When a beam of white light as in Fig. 2.3 falls on a glass prism, the ray that emerges is no longer a beam of white light but a divergent beam containing all of the colours of the rainbow and their intermediate tints. This experiment confirms that white light is not the purest form of light but on the contrary is a mixture of a vast range of colours. Each colour has a specific wavelength but the difference in wavelength between adjacent colours in the spectrum is so small that the vast range of colours present are not distinguishable by the human senses. Instead, we see a gradual blending of the numerous colour radiations which produces a graduation of distinct hues called **spectral colours**. As an aid to memory, the initial letters of the spectral colours spell the name ROY.G.BIV.

Characteristics of a Colour

There are many words in common use that we use to describe colour. Apart from colours which have their own name, *e.g.* green, red, orange *etc* there are many qualifying words

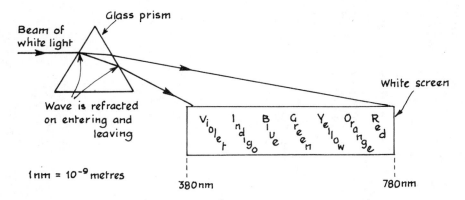

Fig. 2.3 The colour spectrum.

used such as dark blue, vivid red, pale yellow and bright green *etc*. For television purposes these descriptions are not precise enough. How, for example, can we distinguish between two slightly different shades of pale yellow? What really is the essential difference?

In television it is necessary to have an accurate way of specifying a colour so that its particular subtlety may be converted into an equivalent electrical voltage for subsequent reproduction of the original colour. Any colour may be fully described by three characteristics:

(a) Hue
(b) Saturation
(c) Luminance

(a) Hue

Hue is the quality of a colour that is most noticeable to the human senses. It is the preferred term for colour, *e.g.* when white light falls on to a red object the light reflected has a red hue, see Fig. 2.4(a). Similarly, if the object is green the light reflected has a green hue as in Fig. 2.4(b). Hue depends upon the **dominant wavelength** of the light energy and thus can be specified by quoting its wavelength in the colour spectrum.

(b) Saturation

Saturation is the quality of a colour which defines its depth. The saturation of a colour depends upon its dilution with white light. A colour which is highly saturated has most of its energy concentrated about a predominant wavelength, see Fig. 2.5 which shows a saturated red hue. When white light is added to a saturated red hue a paler shade of red is produced which we call pink. Pink has the **same hue** as red because the red wavelengths are predominant. The greater the amount of white light that is added, the paler or more **desaturated** the hue becomes. Desaturated

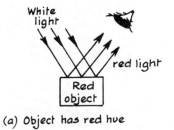

(a) Object has red hue

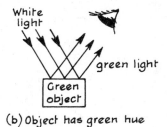

(b) Object has green hue

Fig. 2.4 Hue.

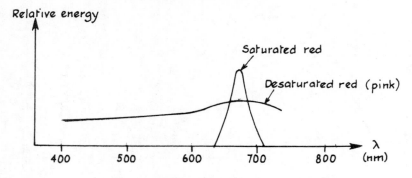

Fig. 2.5 Saturation.

hues are commonly called 'pale shades' or 'pastel colours'. Most of the colours that we see about us are desaturated by various extents.

(c) Luminance

This quality describes the brightness of a colour **as assessed by the human eye**. Consider Fig. 2.6 which shows three equal energy coloured light sources throwing out separate red, blue and green beams. To an observer moving along the line A–B the colours will not appear to be of the same brightness even though the beams are projected with equal energy.

It will be noticed that the green light will appear the brightest of the three, with the red the next brightest and the blue producing the smallest brightness sensation. The reason for this is because of the non-linear response of the human eye to lights of different colour when they are radiated with equal energy, see Fig. 2.7. It will be noted that the eye is most sensitive at about 550 nm which corresponds to a yellow-green hue. The response drops off at the red end of the spectrum and even more at the blue end.

It may be said that the three light sources were of equal brightness because of the association of brightness with 'energy level'. However, the lights **do not appear to the human eye** to be of the same brightness; they are of different **luminance levels**. Thus the sensation of brightness is more accurately defined when using the term luminance.

Non-Spectral Colours

Purple (Magenta)

This colour may be produced by mixing blue and red light. Since red and blue appear at opposite ends of the colour spectrum they do not merge with one another.

Brown

This is not a true colour but is the sensation of viewing dirty orange or dirty yellow in contrast with a brighter backgound area.

Black

Black, of course, is the absence of light energy at all wavelengths. However, due to the limited range of brightness levels that the eye can register simultaneously, dull colours may appear black when viewed near to bright

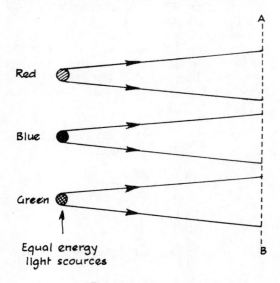

Fig. 2.6 Luminance.

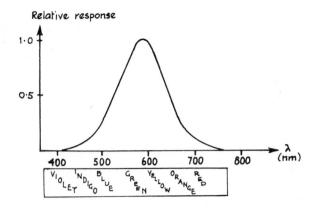

Fig. 2.7 Approximate response of eye to different colour radiations.

light. An example of this illusion is a monochrome display tube screen which when unenergised has a dull grey or green appearance. However, with the screen emitting white light, the non-energised areas of the screen appear black in contrast to the bright white areas so creating a 'black-and-white' picture.

White Light

There are many sources of so-called 'white light' but these have quite different spectral energy distributions, see Fig. 2.8. Some white light sources give out more energy towards the red end of the spectrum and are referred to as 'warm whites'. On the other hand some white light sources emit more energy at the blue end of the spectrum producing 'cold whites'.

Because the type of white light used in television studios will have a marked effect on the actual colours 'seen' by the camera, it is necessary to adopt a standard illuminant. For colour television the standard white Illuminant D_{6500} was chosen since it matches standard daylight more closely than other standard illuminants (6500°K is its colour temperature).

By using a standard white light source, more consistent colour pictures can be maintained. In setting up the white light emitted from the screen of a colour television receiver, the light output of the three phosphors is adjusted to obtain a match with Illuminant D source during 'grey-scale tracking'.

The type of white light emitted from the screen of a monochrome display tube depends upon the chemical composition of the screen phosphor coating. Some monochrome tubes emit light which matches the standard illuminant to satisfy the needs of television studios.

Colour Mixing

The principle of colour television is based on the additive mixing of three separate

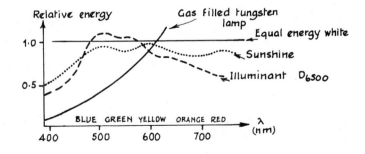

Fig. 2.8 Spectral response of various 'white light' sources.

coloured light sources. The three colours used are red (615 nm), green (532 nm) and blue (470 nm), which are referred to as **primary colours**. By mixing of the three 'primaries' in suitable proportions it is possible to reproduce nearly all of the colours that occur in nature.

If two or three of the television primary colours are projected from lamps on to a white screen so that thay partly overlap, the colour that we see in the overlap area is the result of the **additive mixing** of the original primaries, see Figs. 2.9 and 2.10.

It will be noted that:

Red	**+ Green**	**= Yellow**
Green	**+ Blue**	**= Cyan**
Red	**+ Blue**	**= Magenta**
and **Red + Blue**	**+ Green**	**= White**

Yellow, **Cyan** and **Magenta** are known as **complementary colours**. Magenta is complementary to green, cyan is complementary to red and yellow is complementary to blue. It follows that a complementary colour is one which when additively mixed with a primary, not included in the make-up of the particular complementary colour, results in white. Thus:

Green	**+ Magenta**	**= White**
Blue	**+ Yellow**	**= White**
Red	**+ Cyan**	**= White**

It should be noted that the examples shown here represent only a few of the possible colours resulting from a mixture of the primaries. For example, adding red and green lights in the right proportions results in yellow. However, if more red light is added at the expense of the green, a shade of orange will be produced. On the other hand, increasing the amount of green light will result in a shade of greenish-yellow. In fact a whole range of shades of orange, yellow and greenish-yellow may be created by mixing discrete amounts of red and green light.

The Colour Triangle

In this diagram, see Fig. 2.11, the three primary colour light sources of red, green and blue are assumed to be placed in the corners of an equilateral triangle and the light beams directed inwards. The following features of colour theory may be usefully considered from this single diagram.

(a) Additive Mixing

Yellow, magenta and cyan will be produced along the sides of the triangle due to the additive mixture of pairs of primary colours. Assuming that the primary light sources are of suitable relative intensity, white will be produced at the centre W of the triangle.

(b) Hue

As the eye travels around the circumference of the circle in the triangle, the colour of the light changes, *i.e.* the **hue** is seen to vary from red, orange, yellow, green and on to cyan *etc*.

(c) Saturation

Saturation may be defined by any straight line drawn from a corner or edge of the triangle to the centre, such as the line RW. At R the hue is assumed to be fully saturated. Movement along the line towards W causes the hue to become desaturated as more white light is added. At W the hue is fully desaturated. Thus at R we have a pure red hue which becomes paler on movement towards the centre until at W all traces of red tinting will have disappeared.

(d) Luminance

The luminosity of the colours may be considered as an axis at right angles to the triangle as shown. Looking along this line we receive the various sensations of brightness (luminance values) of the different colours within the triangle.

Colour Detail

If threads of different coloured cottons are held against a white background and viewed from about 10 metres it is dificult to identify the actual colours. The threads themselves are quite discernable, *i.e.* the eye can perceive the fine detail but the colours show up as variations of light and dark.

Thus when colour appears in **fine detail** in a scene we are only conscious of the differing luminance levels and have difficulty in recognising colours. Because in a colour television system valuable bandwidth is required to transmit the colour information (hue and saturation), it would be wasteful to transmit the colour information of fine detail if it cannot be seen. This particular characteristic of

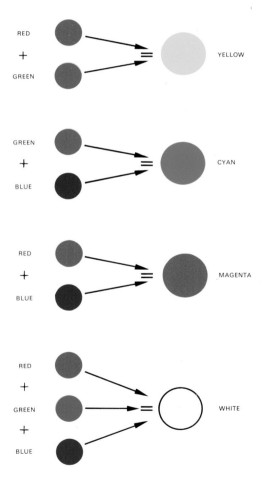

FIG. 2.9 ADDITIVE COLOUR MIXING PROCESS USING COLOURED LIGHTS

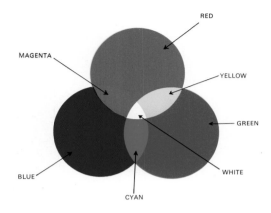

FIG. 2.10 ADDITIVE COLOUR MIXING USING THREE LANTERNS

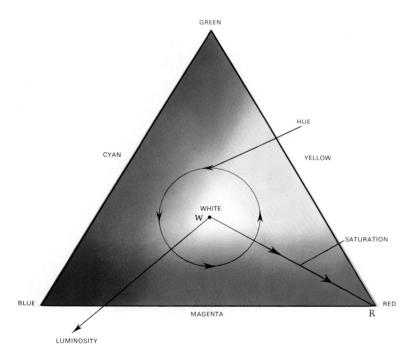

FIG. 2.11 COLOUR TRIANGLE

human vision permits hue and saturation information to be transmitted at narrow bandwidth without degrading the reproduced colour picture. On the other hand, the eye is very conscious of the luminance changes in fine colour detail, thus a comparitively wide bandwidth is required to transmit the luminance information.

Persistence of Vision

When the eye is stimulated by light from an object, the mental picture of that object does not disappear immediately if light from the object ceases to fall on the eye. The mental image tends to persist for a brief period (about ¹⁄₂₅th second) and this effect is known as the **persistence of vision**. Use of this phenomenon is made in the projection of a continuous series of still shots in a camera. The viewer does not notice the interruptions between projected shots but sees a continuous picture. This is because the viewer retains a mental image of one shot and provided the following shot is projected before the image of the last one has disappeared, a continuous picture is seen.

Another example is with the electron beam of a c.r.o. If the time base is set to a slow speed a single spot of light is seen moving across the screen. With, however, the time base speed increased to at least 25 scans per second a continuous trace of light is seen, *i.e.* each successive position of the beam is retained in the mind's eye.

Persistence of vision plays an important role in the reproduction of television pictures on a receiver screen using a fast moving electron beam which traces out 25 pictures per second to give the effect of a continuous image. With this picture rate there would be some noticeable flicker present, but this is overcome in television by using interlaced scanning (see Chapter 3).

Properties of Light which have an important bearing on Television

These may be summarised as follow:

(1) Due to persistence of vision it is possible to give the effect of a continuous picture whilst interrupting the picture 25 times each second.

(2) The eye cannot distinguish between light that is coloured because it is of a particular wavelength and a mixture of lights of different wavelengths forming the same colour. Thus only three colours red, blue and green are necessary to produce most natural colours.

(3) Certain colours appear brighter than others even when projected with equal energy. Any television system (mono or colour) must take this property of human vision into account.

(4) The eye is very sensitive to luminance changes in a scene and a comparitively wide bandwidth (0–5·5 MHz) is required to preserve the fine detail. On the other hand, the eye has difficulty in assessing the colour of fine detail which is a useful property as it means that less bandwidth is needed (0–1 MHz) to handle the colour information.

CHAPTER THREE

TELEVISION PRINCIPLES

Objectives

1 Explain how a television picture is constructed from picture elements and describe interlaced scanning.
2 State the relationship between picture rate, field frequency, number of lines and line frequency.
3 State line and field pulse dimensions and reason for blanking.
4 Explain picture resolution and determine approximate bandwidth of video signal.

THE ESSENTIALS OF a simple television system for closed-circuit operation are shown in Fig. 3.1. The television camera lens focuses an image of the scene to be televised on to the light sensitive target of the camera tube. An electrical (video) signal voltage is obtained at the camera output with an amplitude proportional to the amount of light falling on the individual small areas (called **elements** or **pixels**) of the camera tube face.

The video signal output is fed via a coaxial cable to the display monitor where, after suitable processing and amplification, it is used to intensity modulate the electron beam of the c.r.t. Thus on the screen of the display tube is developed an optical image of the original scene.

The breaking down of a scene into small areas or elements is an essential process in any television system and this will now be considered.

PICTURE ELEMENTS (PIXELS)

Consider Fig. 3.2(a) where the scene to be televised consists of a black cross on a white background, *i.e.* a monochrome scene. Suppose that the scene is divided into 48 squares of equal size. Since the scene is in monochrome there is only luminance information to be conveyed, thus each of the squares contains a certain amount of luminance information.

Assume that the camera produces 1 V ouput for the white parts of the scene and 0 V for the

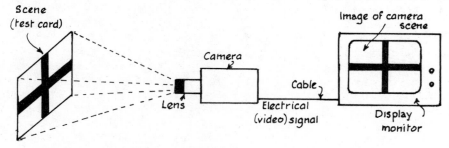

Fig. 3.1 Basic elements of a television system (closed-circuit).

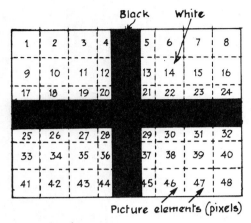

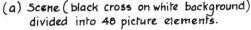

(a) Scene (black cross on white background) divided into 48 picture elements.

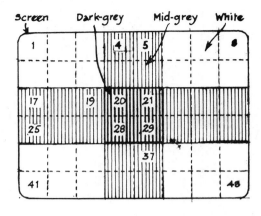

(b) Screen imaged on screen of display tube

Fig. 3.2 Breaking down the scene to be televised into picture elements (pixels). Insufficient number in this case.

black parts. Thus the following voltages will be obtained:

Square number	Output voltage
1, 2, 3, 15, 16, 46 *etc*	1·0 V (squares completely white)
4, 5, 17, 26, 44, 45 *etc*	0·5 V (sqaures half white and half black)
20, 21, 28, and 29	0·25 V (sqaures one-quarter white)

If the camera output voltage is responsible for causing the brightening or darkening of a corresponding square on the picture monitor, the image of the black cross will **not** be clearly defined, see Fig. 3.2(b). Squares 4, 5, 12, 13, 17 and 25 *etc* will be produced as mid-greys and squares 20, 21, 28 and 29 will be reproduced as darker greys, there being no sharp transistion from white to black as intended. This is because there are insufficient squares or elements to deal with the scene detail.

If the number of squares is increased by a factor of four there will be a total of 192 picture elements in the scene as illustrated in Fig. 3.3(a). As before, assume that each element gives rise to a camera output voltage which is used to brighten or darken corresponding elements on the monitor. There are now sufficient elements to deal with the scene detail, *i.e.* the picture on the monitor screen will show a sharp transition from white to black on the vertical and horizontal edges of the cross, see Fig. 3.3(b). The improvement in detail occurs only if the edges of the scene image overlap the picture elements.

The scene used in this example contains relatively large areas of constant luminance information thus only 192 elements are required to reproduce the scene on the monitor screen. If, however, there was luminance information present in the scene of an area smaller than one of the squares in Fig. 3.3(a), it would not be reproduced accurately unless a greater number of elements were employed. Thus in order **to convey very fine picture detail a large number of picture elements are required** and the larger the number the smaller is the picture detail that can be dealt with in a television system. To produce the fine detail of a 625-line broadcast television picture, approximately **5×10^5 elements** are needed.

The sub-division of the optical image produced on the face of the camera tube into a large number of picture elements is determined by the processing during manufacture

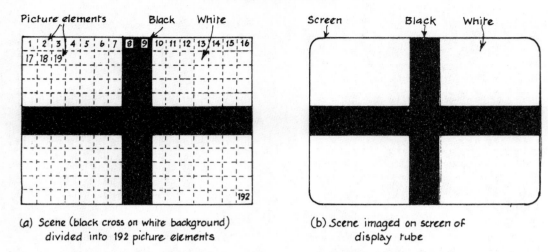

(a) Scene (black cross on white background)   (b) Scene imaged on screen of
       divided into 192 picture elements   display tube

Fig. 3.3 Increasing the number of picture elements (sufficient number in this case).

and the chemical composition of the light sensitive target of the camera tube.

SEQUENTIAL TRANSMISSION OF PICTURE INFORMATION

It is not a practical proposition to relay the information from all of the picture elements from camera to monitor simultaneously as a large number of lines or channels would be needed (5×10^5 for 625-line television). Thus a **sequential** method is used, which is really a form of 'time division multiplexing', where the information from each picture element is sent one after the other from camera to monitor over a **single** communication channel or line.

The basic idea is shown in Fig. 3.4 where for simplicity only 20 picture elements are used. The picture elements of the camera image are read in sequence from left to right starting at element 1 and proceeding to elements 2, 3, 4 and 5. At the end of the first row (line 1),

elements 6, 7, 8, 9 and 10 are 'read' completing line 2 and so on up to element 20. This process is then repeated commencing again at element 1. As each element is 'read' at the camera, the corresponding element area on the monitor screen displays the relayed information.

Clearly, the elements must be 'read' over and over again in **rapid sequence** in order to create a continuous picture on the monitor screen and to capture any movement within the scene. As long as the complete scene is read often enough (25 times per second), **persistence of vision** will ensure a continuous picture in the mind's eye.

It is essential that camera and monitor should be in step in 'reading' and displaying information as otherwise the reproduced picture may be a complete jumble. For example, if the information pertaining to element 1 of the camera is displayed in the position of element 11 on the monitor, then due to the sequential method employed, the information

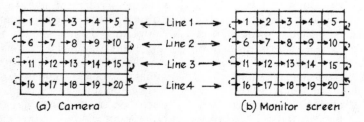

(a) Camera   (b) Monitor screen

Fig. 3.4 Sequential method of relaying picture element information.

of lines 1 and 2 of the camera will be displayed on lines 3 and 4 of the monitor. Thus the bottom half of the camera scene image will appear at the top of the monitor screen and vice-versa. Clearly, to keep camera and monitor in step there must be some form of **synchronism** between them.

SCANNING

In practice the 'reading' and displaying of element information is carried out by scanning electron beams inside the camera and display tubes. The idea of an elementary scanning system is shown in Fig. 3.5 where only eight line scans have been shown for simplicity.

Inside the camera tube an electron beam traces out a series of sloping lines across the face of the camera tube. As the beam is moving across the tube, a force is exerted on the beam causing a downward movement and this is responsible for the downward slope of the lines.

The beam commences scanning at the left-hand side of the camera face and traces out **line 1**. At the end of line 1, the beam rapidly returns to the left-hand side to commence the next **line scan** (line 2). At the end of line 2 the beam rapidly returns to commence line 3 and so on. Upon completing line 8, the full image formed on the camera tube by the lens system has been scanned. In carrying out this process the electron beam examines each element in turn and the camera produces an output voltage with an amplitude proportional to the light information at each element. When the electron beam reaches the end of

line 8, it quickly returns to the top and repeats the scanning process again starting with line 1. The movement of the beam from top to bottom constitutes what is known as the **field scan**.

At the monitor the same scanning process is adopted using an electron beam which scans the screen of the monitor display tube. As the beam travels across and down the screen, the beam is made more or less intense by the voltage output of the camera, thus causing a larger or smaller light output from the screen.

Interlaced Scanning

Persistence of vision ensures that continuous pictures are observed if a picture rate of 25 pictures per second is used. However, with this rate there would be some noticeable flicker present particularly in bright areas of the picture. To overcome flicker it is necessary to raise the rate to 50 pictures per second. Unfortunately this would speed up the whole scanning process resulting in more information being packed into a shorter time interval and in consequence a doubling of the video bandwidth.

Since transmission bandwidth is at a premium, alternative ways were considered to get over the flicker problem without resorting to 50 pictures per second. This led to the introduction of **interlaced scanning**, a system used internationally for broadcast television and CCTV.

In an interlaced scanning system an odd number of lines must be used, *e.g.* 625 lines, 525 lines *etc*. An example of an 11-line system

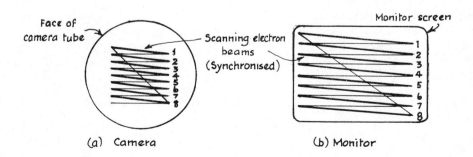

Fig. 3.5 *Use of electron beam for sequential 'reading' and display of element information (simple scanning).*

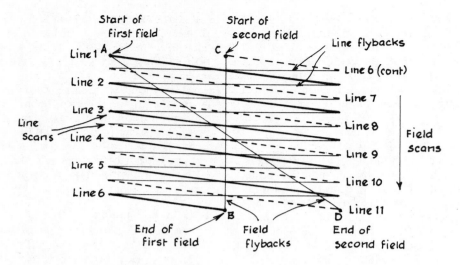

Fig. 3.6 Interlaced scanning in an 11-line system.

is shown in Fig. 3:6. The complete picture is divided into two distinct **fields** each containing 5½ lines.

Scanning commences at *A* with the beam tracing out lines 1, 2, 3 and 4 *etc*. At the end of each line, **line flyback** occurs causing the beam to rapidly return to the left-hand side of camera and monitor tubes. Due to the effects of the **field scan** the beam is also subjected to a downward deflection at the same time.

Half-way through line 6 the first (odd) field is completed and **field flyback** commences at point *B*. The beam now returns to the top of the screen and the camera tube. Assuming that the field flyback is instantaneous, the other half of line 6 will now be completed as shown when the second (even) field commences at point *C*. Because of the half-line, scanning lines 7, 8 and 9 *etc* now interlace with lines 1, 2, 3 and 4 *etc* of the first field.

This action continues until the end of line 11 at which point the second field scan is completed. At *D* field flyback occurs and the beam is returned to the starting point *A*.

This action is repeated over and over again at the **picture rate of 25 pictures per second. Each picture is thus composed of two interlaced fields with a field scan rate of 50 scans per second. In 625-line television** there are, of course, 625 scanning lines thus each field is composed of **312½ lines.**

Interlaced scanning tricks the eye into believing that every part of a scene is repeated 50 times per second when in fact each element of the scene is only being flashed up on the screen 25 times per second.

The diagram of Fig. 3.7 shows a small area of picture detail (about two beam widths). With interlaced scanning, line x on, say, the odd field causes the top half of the picture detail to brighten up, and ⅟₅₀th of a second later on the even field, line y causes the lower half of the detail to brighten up. Although it takes ⅟₂₅th of a second for the whole of the detail to be shown, **a part** is being flashed up on the screen every ⅟₅₀th of a second.

In a non-interlaced, 25 pictures per second system, lines x and y will occur in the same

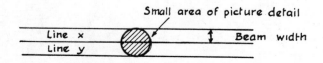

Fig. 3.7 Optical 'trick' of interlaced scanning.

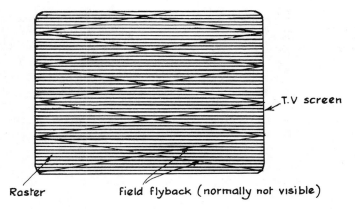

Fig. 3.8 The raster (no picture modulation).

field scan. Thus the upper and lower portions of the picture detail will brighten up in a time interval of two consecutive lines, but will not brighten up again until ¹/₂₅th of a second later on the next field scan.

Raster

If the brightness control of a television receiver is turned up when there is no picture modulation, the scanning lines produced by the electron beam of the display tube can be seen, as in Fig. 3.8. The pattern of lines visible on the screen is called the **raster**. In practice the field flyback is not instantaneous as depicted in Fig. 3.6 and also because the line time-base operates continuously, the electron beam traces out a zig-zag path during field flyback. This is normally not visible since the field flyback (also the line flyback) is blanked out.

Deflecting the Electron Beam

Magnetic deflection of the electron beam is employed in both camera and display c.r.t. using two pairs of scan coils (**line** and **field** scan coils) which set up magnetic fields at right angles to one another. With a display c.r.t. the two sets of coils are mounted around the glass neck so that their resulting magnetic fields influence the path taken by the single electron beam in a monochrome c.r.t., or the three electron beams in a colour c.r.t.

The diagram of Fig. 3.9(a) shows the disposition of the magnetic fields produced by the line and field scan coils in a display c.r.t. The horizontal field pattern produced by the field coils causes vertical deflection of the beam whilst the vertical magnetic field pattern created by the line scan coils causes horizontal deflection of the beam.

In either the horizontal or vertical directions the movement of the beam must be at a **linear rate during the scan** and rapid later on during the flyback. To achieve this, linear sawtooth current waveforms must be supplied to both sets of scan coils, See Fig. 3.9(b).

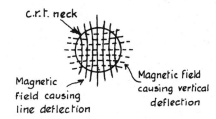

(a) Deflecting magnetic fields at right angles

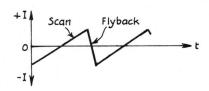

(b) Current waveform required for magnetic deflection (sawtooth)

Fig. 3.9 Magnetic deflection.

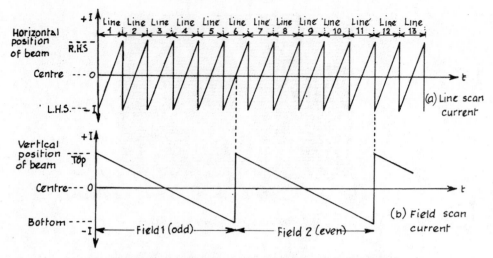

Fig. 3.10 Scanning waveforms for an 11-line interlaced system.

Scanning current waveforms for interlaced scanning using an 11-line system (for simplicity) are illustrated in Fig. 3.10. Here it has been assumed that both field and line flyback occur instantaneously. In practice the field flyback time is about ¹⁄₂₀th of the field scan time. Within limits, the duration of field flyback is quite arbitrary and does not have to be an exact number of line durations as at first may be thought. Provided the field flyback time is the same on odd and even fields, satisfactory interlacing will occur.

VIDEO SIGNAL AND SYNCHRONISING PULSES

Voltage Range

The composite video signal for the British 625-line system over a period of one television line is shown in Fig. 3.11. The video luminance signal occupies the range between 28% and 100% of the full voltage amplitude whilst the range between 0% and 28% is taken up by the sync. pulses. This provides a picture/sync. voltage ratio of about 2·5 : 1. This ratio is

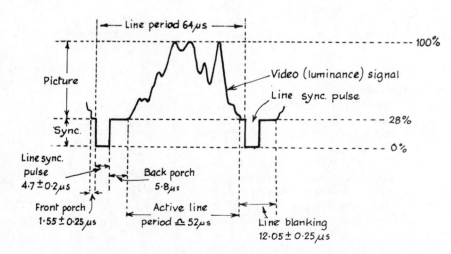

Fig. 3.11 Luminance signal waveform for 625-line system (line dimensions).

chosen so that when at some remote receiver where the signal level is weak, the receiver time bases will fail to synchronise at the same time as the picture signal-to-noise ratio falls to such a level that the picture ceases to be of viewable quality. The levels of 28% and 100% represent zero luminance (black) and maximum luminance (peak white) respectively.

The video signal can have any arbitrary value between 28% and 100% and on a normal scene each line of video information will be different from the preceding one. When 'scoping' the line waveform of such scene using an ordinary c.r.o., the display will show **superimposed** lines of information. As the video content is different line-to-line, the displayed video will appear very fuzzy. The line sync. pulses being of repetitive shape will be quite distinct. When the scene information is repetitive line-by-line as with some test pictures, *e.g.* a 'grey-scale', the video information of the displayed waveform will also be distinct.

Line Dimensions

With 625 lines and 25 pictures per second, the **line frequency = 625 × 25 = 15625 Hz**.

Therefore the **line period** $= \dfrac{1}{15625} = 64\,\mu\text{s}$.

Not all of the $64\,\mu\text{s}$ line period is active, *i.e.* carries picture information. During the **line blanking period** no picture information is transmitted. Any spurious signals generated by the camera between the end of one scanning line and the commencement of the next are suppressed by means of a 'blanking pulse' which is added to the video signal in the camera. The line blanking period can be divided into three sections:

(a) Front porch

This is a brief period $(1 \cdot 5\,\mu\text{s})$ just before the commencement of each line sync. pulse. It serves as a 'cushioning' period for the video circuits in camera and receiver allowing them to settle down before the commencement of the sync. pulses. The level of the video signal at the end of a line of video information is quite arbitrary. Electronic circuits cannot change their voltage state instantaneously and

the front porch allows sufficient time for the voltage to fall from 100% to 28% level before the line sync. pulse commences. Without this interval, the sync. pulses may be late in starting following lines ending at high voltage level compared with the sync. pulses following lines ending at low voltage level, resulting in faulty line timebase synchronisation.

(b) Line Sync. Pulses

This pulse is used to synchronise the line timebase in the receiver with that in the camera. The leading edge of the pulse initiates the commencement of **line flyback**. A duration of $4 \cdot 7\,\mu\text{s}$ is allowed for the pulse and during this time the electron beams in camera and receiver will be in a retrace stroke.

(c) Back Porch

This period provides a further 'grace' period for the line timebase in the receiver to complete its flyback before picture information recommences on the next line. This is necessary due to variations in the design of the line output stage used in different makes of receiver. The back porch may also be used as a brief sampling period for measuring the amplitude of the sync. pulses for a.g.c. purposes in the receiver.

Field Sync. Pulses

With 25 pictures per second and 2 fields per picture, the **field frequency = 2 × 25 Hz = 50 Hz**.

Therefore, the **field period** $= \dfrac{1}{50}\text{s} = 20\,\text{ms}$.

Field sync. pulses at a rate of 50 per second are required to synchronise the field timebase in the receiver. It might at first be thought that a single long pulse of, say, 1 ms could be used. Although this will work and is used in industrial CCTV systems it is not entirely satisfactory since during the period of the pulse there are no sync. pulses to keep the line timebase in synchronism. This may appear to be unimportant, but without any line sync. during the field flyback period the line timebase may drift in frequency causing the first few lines at the top of the picture to be laterally displaced. Thus a system must be used which maintains the line timebase in synchronism

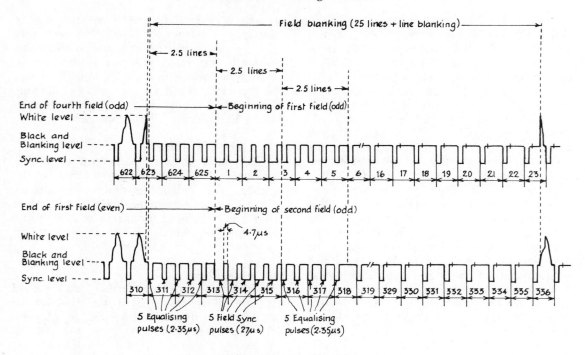

Fig. 3.12 Field synchronising waveform (System I).

during the field flyback period. A further complication arises due to the use of interlaced scanning, the conditions being dissimilar at the end of alternate fields. The diagram of Fig. 3.12 shows the complex 625-line field waveform which overcomes the difficulties mentioned above. The essential features are:

(a) Field Sync. Pulses

At the end of each field there are five broad 27 μs pulses occurring at half-line intervals. In the receiver these pulses are used to build up a field locking pulse which initiates the flyback of the field timebase oscillator.

(b) Equalising Pulses

A group of five 2·3 μs equalising pulses are added before and after the field sync. pulse train in each field. These pulses are included to ensure that the field locking pulse generated in the receiver has precisely the same shape on odd and even fields to achieve good interlace of the two fields. The need for these pulses is because of dissimilar conditions at the end of odd and even fields.

(c) Field Blanking Pulses

During the two groups of equalising pulses plus the field sync. pulses (7½ lines in total) and a further 17½ lines in each field, picture information is suppressed. Thus for **25 lines in each field no picture information is transmitted**. This period is known as the **field blanking interval** and allows adequate time for the receiver field timebase to complete flyback.

In each complete picture period there are therefore **50 lines not bearing picture information**. Thus the number of **active lines** in 625-line television is 625 − 50 = **575 lines**.

The field blanking interval also provides a valuable additional communication channel which is 'invisible' to the viewer, provided that during this time interval the electron beam of the receiver c.r.t. is cut-off (blanked). This period is used for national test signals on lines 19 and 20 of one field and lines 332 and 333 of the following field. Additionally, lines 10–17 on one field and lines 324–331 on the next field are used for **Teletext signals** of the IBA's ORACLE and BBC's CEEFAX services. The effect of the teletext signals on a normal picture may be observed if the receiver picture height is reduced, when a few lines of random 'bright-ups' may be seen at the top of the screen.

PICTURE RESOLUTION

The **resolution** or **definition** of a television system is a measure of its ability to resolve fine picture detail. The definition of a reproduced picture depends upon both the **horizontal** and **vertical resolution** of the system.

Horizontal resolution is a measure of the ability to reproduce luminance changes along a line such as *xy* in Fig. 3.13(a) and depends upon the frequency bandwidth of the system. The finer the vertical stripes, the faster the system will have to respond to reproduce them clearly, and the larger the video bandwidth required.

Vertical resolution is a measure of the ability to reproduce fine detail along a line such as *rs* in Fig. 3.13(b). To reproduce horizontal detail such as this, a large number of scanning lines is required and the more there are, the better the vertical resolution.

Vertical Resolution

In a 625-line system there are 575 active lines as has been noted. It would appear that

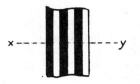

(a) Vertical stripes used for assessing horizontal resolution

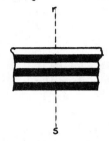

(b) Horizontal stripes used for assessing vertical resolution

Fig. 3.13 Horizontal and vertical resolution.

the vertical resolution would be that obtainable from 575 lines, but in practice it is less than this figure.

This is because the relative positioning of the scanning electron beam in the camera to horizontally disposed picture information affects the resolution, see Fig. 3.14.

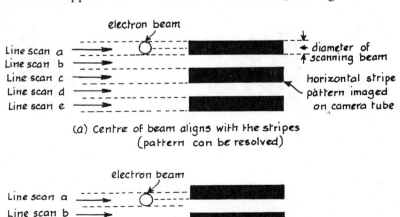

(a) Centre of beam aligns with the stripes (pattern can be resolved)

(b) Centre of beam aligns with horizontal edge of stripes (pattern cannot be resolved)

Fig. 3.14 Effect of beam alignment with ultimate stripe pattern.

If the beam is aligned as in Fig. 3.14(a) the pattern can be resolved. On the other hand, if the beam is disposed as in Fig. 3.14(b) the pattern cannot be resolved. With the beam in intermediate positions between these two extremes some loss of vertical resolution will result.

The positioning of the scanning beam to such picture detail will depend how accurately optical positioning and camera scan geometry is set and maintained. Statistical and subjective testing suggests that the effective number of lines is about 0·7 of the total number of active lines. This factor (0·7) is known as the **Kell factor**. Thus assuming a Kell factor of 0·7, the maximum vertical resolution obtainable in a 625-line system is $0.7 \times 575 = 402.5$ lines (say 402 lines).

Horizontal Resolution

An obvious aim in designing a television system would appear to be to make the horizontal resolution the same as the vertical resolution. With a maximum vertical resolution of 402 lines (see above) per active picture height, the horizontal resolution to match it is also 402 lines per active picture height.

Now the horizontal resolution is determined by the video bandwidth, and to find out what bandwidth is needed consider Fig. 3.15. This diagram shows a checker board pattern of alternate white and black squares which is to be reproduced on the screen of the television receiver. There are 402 squares down the vertical side of the board, this number representing the maximum practical vertical resolution. Each square has sides equal to the

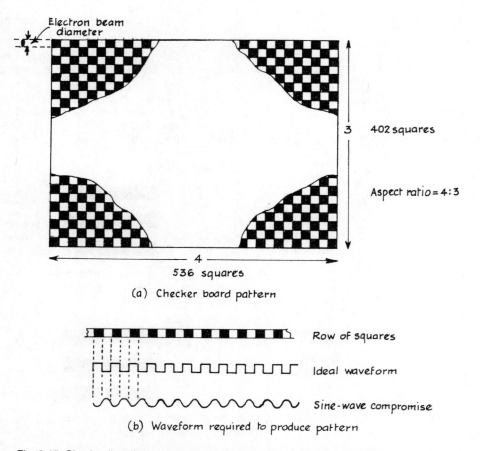

(a) Checker board pattern

(b) Waveform required to produce pattern

Fig. 3.15 Checker board pattern to access highest video frequency required.

diameter of the electron beam and represents the ultimate pattern for testing the resolution.

In television the ratio of **Picture Width : Picture Height**, called the **Aspect Ratio**, is **4 : 3**. Therefore, the number of squares along the horizontal side of the board is $4/3 \times 402 = 536$.

Thus 536 squares have to be scanned by the beam in the time period of the active line, $52\,\mu s$. To reproduce such a pattern, the video signal waveshape is ideally a square wave, see Fig. 3.15(b). To handle this waveshape would place too great a demand on the system in terms of bandwidth. A reasonable technical compromise is to accept a sinewave response. Note, however, that each cycle corresponds to **two** squares. Thus the number of cyclic changes across each picture line is $536/2 = 268$. Therefore, the periodic time of one cyclic change $= 52/268\,\mu s = 0 \cdot 194\,\mu s$. Thus the frequency of the cyclic changes is:

$$\frac{1}{0 \cdot 194 \times 10^{-6}}\ \text{Hz} = 5 \cdot 15\,\text{MHz}.$$

This figure is reasonably close to the upper video frequency of $5 \cdot 5\,\text{MHz}$ transmitted in the 625-line signal. Thus the following expression may be used for determining the approximate highest video frequency required.

Highest video frequency =

$$\frac{\text{No. of active lines} \times \text{aspect ratio} \times \text{Kell factor}}{2 \times \text{duration of one active line}}$$

CHAPTER FOUR

THE COLOUR CAMERA AND OUTPUT SIGNALS

Objectives

1 Explain the operation of a simple colour camera and deduce the primary signal outputs on colour bars.
2 State the luminance signal equation and construct a grey-scale waveform for colour bars.
3 Describe the operation of a 4-tube colour camera.

BASIC COLOUR CAMERA

THE FIRST PROCESS in a colour television system is to break down the light coming from the scene into its constituent components of red, blue and green light. The essential arrangement for a 3-tube colour camera, which was the first type to be used in colour television broadcasting is given in Fig. 4.1.

To split the light into its basic components of red, green and blue light, the camera uses two

special mirrors called **dichroic mirrors**. These mirrors are designed to pass particular light wavelengths but to reflect others.

Light from the scene passes through a common lens system and falls on the dichroic mirror M1 which passes red and green light but reflects the blue component. The blue light is reflected by a silvered surface mirror M3 on to the face of T1, the 'blue' camera tube.

The red and green light passing through M1

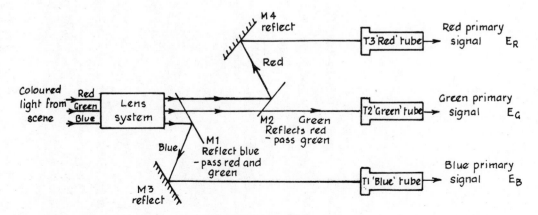

Fig. 4.1 Basic arragement of a 3-tube colour camera.

fall on another dichroic mirror M2 which passes green light on to the face of the 'green' camera tube T2, but reflects the red light. Another silvered surface mirror M4 then reflects the red component on to the face of the 'red' camera tube T3. Other correcting filters are normally required but these are not essential to the basic idea of operation.

Each camera tube has its own electron beam and deflection system. The separate colour images formed on the sensitive target layer of the three camera tubes must be scanned in synchronism at the line and field rates to produce two interlaced fields during each picture period. As the images are scanned, video signal voltages are produced simultaneously at the output of each camera tube. These output signals are called **primary signals** (since they relate to the three 'primary' colours) and are designated E_R, E_G and E_B.

Primary Signal Waveforms

Three examples will be considered here:

Example 1

With the monochrome test picture of Fig. 4.2 consisting of a white cross on a black background there will be no output during the black areas of the picture. However, during the white parts, all three camera tubes will produce an output since the colour camera breaks the white light into its three constituent components of red, green and blue light. If the standard white of Illuminant 'D' is used and is at maximum intensity, the camera outputs are each adjusted to give $1 \cdot 0$ V of signal.

Example 2

The waveform diagram of Fig. 4.3 shows the primary signal outputs for colour bars at 100% amplitude (max intensity) and 100% saturation (pure hues). These waveforms may be deduced from the theory of **additive colour mixing**. For example, since white light is composed of red, green and blue light, there will be outputs from all three camera tubes on the white bar. Also, since yellow is composed of red and green light there will only be outputs from the 'red' and 'green' camera tubes during the yellow bar *etc*. It should be noted that **transmitted colour bars** are **100% amp and 95% saturated** which, for example, would result in a small output from the blue camera tube on the yellow bar because of the presence of a small amount of white light that produces the desaturation.

Since each colour bar is continuous from the top of the screen to the bottom, the primary signal waveforms will be repetitive line-by-line.

The colour bar signal is a useful test signal source for colour receivers as the near fully saturated colours provide a stringent test of the colour handling circuits. The colour bar signal also gives rise to more easily recognisable and repetitive waveforms within the receiver.

Instead of using a colour bar test card and colour camera, the primary signal waveforms for the colour bars may be generated electronically. With, say, a master square wave oscillator working at $76 \cdot 923$ kHz, four complete cycles would be produced in the active line period of $52 \, \mu s$ and the oscillator output could be used for producing the E_B waveform. By dividing this output by a factor of 2 (using a bistable), the E_R waveform may be produced. Using a further divide-by-two stage the E_G waveform may be obtained. Of course, the output of the master oscillator must be muted during flyback periods. Electronic generation of the colour bar signal is used to confirm the correct operation of colour encoding and decoding equipment.

Example 3

The waveform diagram of Fig. 4.4 shows the primary outputs from the colour camera for a normal scene. It has been assumed here that all of the colours are fully saturated except for the light blue sky. Thus during the periods corresponding to the sky during the line scan A–B, there will be some output from the 'red' and 'green' tubes but a greater output from the 'blue' tube since the camera is 'looking at' a desaturated blue (Blue + White).

Forming a Luminance Signal

A colour television system designed for national use must be **compatible**, *i.e.* monochrome receivers should be able to tune into the colour transmission and extract the necessary signal information to produce a good monochrome image. The primary signal

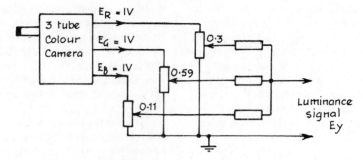

Fig. 4.5 Forming the luminance signal when a 3-tube colour camera is used.

outputs of the 3-tube camera contain hue, saturation and some luminance information. However, **individually** these signals do not contain sufficient scene luminance information to produce a good black and white picture on a monochrome receiver. The method adopted to produce a luminance signal with a 3-tube camera is shown in Fig. 4.5.

The primary signal outputs from the camera video amplifiers are adjusted so that they are nominally $1 \cdot 0 \,\text{V}$ on the standard white illuminant D at maximum intensity. Portions of the primary signals are then taken from the potentiometer sliders to form the luminance signal. The actual portions taken are $0 \cdot 59$ of E_G, $0 \cdot 3$ of E_R and $0 \cdot 11$ of E_B. When added together in the resistive matrix shown they give the luminance signal E_Y which can be written as:

$$E_Y = 0 \cdot 3\,E_R + 0 \cdot 59\,E_G + 0 \cdot 11\,E_B$$

The particular portions taken to form the luminance signal are related to the relative contribution towards luminance of the colour phosphors used on the colour display tube.

Consider the formation and value of the luminance signal for the individual colours of the colour bars:

White	$E_Y = 0 \cdot 3$	$+\ 0 \cdot 59$	$+\ 0 \cdot 11$	$=$	$1 \cdot 00\,\text{V}$
Yellow	$E_Y = 0 \cdot 3$	$+\ 0 \cdot 59$	$+\ 0 \cdot 00$	$=$	$0 \cdot 89\,\text{V}$
Cyan	$E_Y = 0 \cdot 00$	$+\ 0 \cdot 59$	$+\ 0 \cdot 11$	$=$	$0 \cdot 70\,\text{V}$
Green	$E_Y = 0 \cdot 00$	$+\ 0 \cdot 59$	$+\ 0 \cdot 00$	$=$	$0 \cdot 59\,\text{V}$
Magenta	$E_Y = 0 \cdot 3$	$+\ 0 \cdot 00$	$+\ 0 \cdot 11$	$=$	$0 \cdot 41\,\text{V}$
Red	$E_Y = 0 \cdot 3$	$+\ 0 \cdot 00$	$+\ 0 \cdot 00$	$=$	$0 \cdot 30\,\text{V}$
Blue	$E_Y = 0 \cdot 00$	$+\ 0 \cdot 00$	$+\ 0 \cdot 11$	$=$	$0.11\,\text{V}$
Black	$E_Y = 0 \cdot 00$	$+\ 0 \cdot 00$	$+\ 0 \cdot 00$	$=$	$0 \cdot 00\,\text{V}$

The luminance signal waveform during one line of the colour bars is shown in Fig. 4.6. It will be noted that the steps on the waveform from left to right are in decreasing order of luminance. This is as intended since the colours in the colour bars are arranged in reducing luminance intensity from left to right.

The diagram of Fig. 4.7 shows the image produced on the screen of a monochrome receiver during the transmission of colour bars, resulting from the luminance waveform. The same display will be present on the screen of a colour receiver if the colour is turned 'off'. This image is known as a **grey-scale** display.

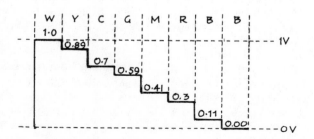

Fig. 4.6 Luminance signal E_Y for colour bars (grey-scale waveform).

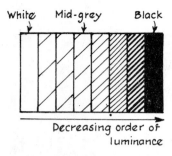

Fig. 4.7 Grey-scale display.

A 4-tube Colour Camera

One problem with the 3-tube camera is that in order to obtain a luminance signal of adequate sharpness, the separate images of the red, green and blue tubes must be very closely registered with one another. To overcome this and other problems the 4-tube

camera was designed, the extra camera tube being used to develop the luminance signal.

The diagram of Fig. 4.8 shows one arrangement which is basically a combination of a 3-tube colour camera and a monochrome camera. Light focussed by the lens system falls on a semi-silvered mirror M1 which reflects some of the light on to the face of T1, the luminance camera tube. This tube is given a spectral response to approximately match that of the human eye and provides at its output a separate luminance signal at high definition. The light passing through M1 is split into its three basic coloured components by the action of the dichroic mirrors M2 and M3.

Thus, as for the 3-tube camera, separate colour images are produced on T2, T3 and T4 which provide the primary signals at their outputs. With modern cameras, prisms with dichroic surfaces are used in place of the dichroic mirrors to provide a more compact optical system.

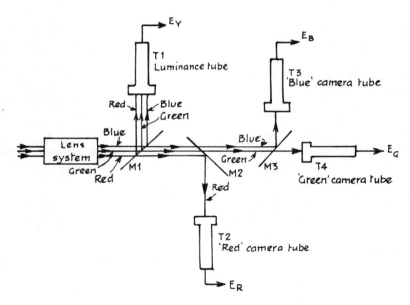

Fig. 4.8 A 4-tube colour camera (separate tube used for the luminance signal).

CHAPTER FIVE

ENCODING THE COLOUR SIGNAL

Objectives
1 State the reasons for the use of colour-difference signals.
2 Show how luminance and colour difference signals are formed in a simple colour camera system.
3 Explain what is meant by frequency interlacing.
4 State the frequency used for the chrominance sub-carrier.
5 Describe suppressed-carrier and quadrature modulation and production of the chrominance signals.
6 State the need for signal weighting and define V and U signals.
7 Describe the PAL system and the purpose of the burst signal.

THE DIAGRAM OF Fig. 5.1 shows the primary signal output of a 3-tube camera together with the luminance signal obtained by matrixing as discussed in Chapter 4.

It was seen in Chapter 3 that for satisfactory monochrome operation, the luminance signal requires a video bandwidth extending from 0 Hz up to 5.5 MHz. During a colour television broadcast extra information called the **chrominance** or **colouring** signal has to be transmitted. Because extra channels or bandwidth could not be spared to accommodate the chrominance signal, it became vitally important to find a way of fitting the chrominance

signal within the normal monochrome bandwidth of 0–5·5 MHZ.

Another important consideration is that the signals sent out during a colour television broadcast must be composed in such a way that a monochrome receiver is able to pick up a suitable signal in order to produce a good monochrome picture; a feature referred to as **compatibility**.

Also, since not all transmissions are in colour, the colour television system must have **reverse compatibility** so that a colour receiver is able to display a good quality monochrome image.

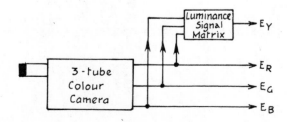

Fig. 5.1 Primary and luminance signals from a simple camera.

To satisfy the above requirements the primary signals are not directly transmitted. The actual signals transmitted are:

(1) E_Y **luminance signal**

(2) $\left. \begin{array}{l} E_R - E_Y \\ E_B - E_Y \end{array} \right\}$ **colour difference signals**

(1) This signal is transmitted at wide bandwidth (0–5·5 MHz) and provides the signal information to produce a good black and white image on monochrome and colour receivers.

(2) These signals are transmitted at narrower bandwidth (0–1 MHz) and together with the luminance signal provide all the necessary information to produce a well defined colour image on the screen of a colour receiver.

Although in a colour television system we start off at the camera end by generating **primary signals which are eventually required to drive the colour display tube in the receiver**, these signals are not transmitted directly for the following reasons:

(1) As previously noted the primary signals contain hue, saturation and some luminance information of the scene. The luminance signal is created to carry all the luminance information so it would be very inefficient to duplicate this information by sending out primary signals.

(2) Using the colour-difference signal method we need only transmit two signals extra to the luminance signal thus making the task of fitting the chrominance information within the normal monochrome bandwidth an easier one.

To drive a colour display tube at the receiver the E_R, E_G and E_B signals are required. However, if the colour-difference and luminance signals are available at the receiver, the primary signals may be **recovered** as can be seen from the following simple algebraic addition:

$$(E_R - E_Y) + E_Y = E_R$$
$$(E_B - E_Y) + E_Y = E_B$$

Also, if $E_G - E_Y$ is available as well at the receiver

$$(E_G - E_Y) + E_Y = E_G.$$

It will be noted that $E_G - E_Y$ is not transmitted, but this too can be recovered at the receiver by adding together suitable portions of the $E_R - E_Y$ and $E_B - E_Y$ signals as will be explained later.

COLOUR-DIFFERENCE SIGNALS

$E_R - E_Y$ and $E_B - E_Y$

The principle involved in the production of the red and blue colour-difference signals is illustrated in Fig. 5.2. A 3-tube camera has again been used in this diagram as it helps to show more clearly some of the basic relationships between the various signals.

The primary signal outputs of the camera are fed to the resistive matrix comprising $R1$,

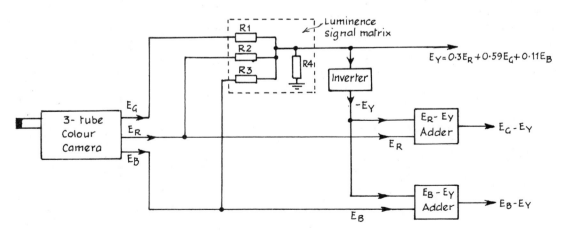

Fig. 5.2 Producing the colour difference signals.

$R2$, $R3$ and $R4$ to produce the luminance signal. The resistor values are chosen to select the correct proportion of each primary signal, *e.g.* $R2$ and $R4$ provide 0.3 of E_R. The luminance signal output of the matrix is then inverted to produce a $-E_Y$ signal. This signal is fed to two adders where it is added separately to the E_R and E_B signals. As a result of the additions, $E_R - E_Y$ and $E_B - E_Y$ signals are available at the adder outputs.

It should be noted that a colour-difference signal is simply the subtraction of electrical voltages and has nothing to do with coloured light. The result of the subtraction of the luminance signal voltage from the primary signal voltages for the colour bars are shown in Fig. 5.3. The corresponding video signal waveforms for the colour bars are given in Fig. 5.4.

The merits of the colour-difference signal method are:

(1) When the transmission is in monochrome, the colour-difference signals automatically disappear. Thus no coloured noise will appear on the screen of the colour display tube from the chrominance channel of the receiver.

(2) The colour-difference signals are true colour signals, *i.e.* they carry hue and saturation information only, the luminance information being carried by the luminance signal. This is referred to as the 'constant luminance' principle which means that the luminance of the light emanating from the screens of a mono-chrome receiver and a colour receiver is exactly the same when both are tuned to the same colour transmission, even though one picture is in monochrome and the other is in colour.

$E_G - E_Y$ Signal

There is no need to transmit the $E_G - E_Y$ signal because of a fundamental relationship that exists between all three colour-difference signals. This may be seen from the following:

Now
$$E_Y = 0.3E_R + 0.59E_G + 0.11E_B \quad (5.1)$$
and
$$E_Y = 0.3E_Y + 0.59E_Y + 0.11E_Y \quad (5.2)$$

Subtracting (5.2) from (5.1) we have
$$0 = (0.3E_R - 0.3E_Y) + (0.59E_G - 0.59E_Y) + (0.11E_B - 0.11E_Y)$$
or
$$0 = 0.3(E_R - E_Y) + 0.59(E_G - E_Y) + 0.11(E_B - E_Y)$$

Thus
$$0.59(E_G - E_Y) = -0.3(E_R - E_Y) - 0.11(E_B - E_Y)$$

Dividing both sides by 0.59
$$(E_G - E_Y) = -0.51(E_R - E_Y) - 0.19(E_B - E_Y)$$

Thus if the red and blue difference-signals are available in the receiver, the green difference-signal may be obtained by adding

	W	Y	C	G	M	R	B	B
E_R	1.0	1.0	0.00	0.00	1.0	1.0	0.00	0.00
E_B	1.0	0.00	1.0	0.00	1.0	0.00	1.0	0.00
E_G	1.0	1.0	1.0	1.0	0.00	0.00	0.00	0.00
E_Y	1.0	0.89	0.7	0.59	0.41	0.3	0.11	0.00
$E_R - E_Y$	0.00	+0.11	-0.7	-0.59	+0.59	+0.7	-0.11	0.00
$E_B - E_Y$	0.00	-0.89	+0.3	-0.59	+0.59	-0.3	+0.89	0.00
$E_G - E_Y$	0.00	+0.11	+0.3	+0.41	-0.41	-0.3	-0.11	0.00

Fig. 5.3 Table showing colour-difference signal values for 100% amp., 100% sat. colour bars.

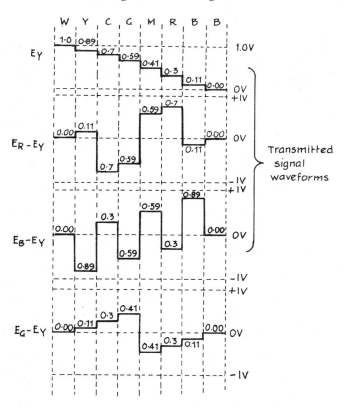

Fig. 5.4 Colour-difference signal waveforms for colour bars.

-0.51 of $(E_R - E_Y)$ to -0.19 of $(E_B - E_Y)$. The minus sign simply indicates a phase reversal of the red and blue difference-signals. The red and blue difference-signals were selected for transmission rather than any other combination of two colour-difference signals as these provide the best signal-to-noise ratio (compare signal amplitudes in Fig. 5.4).

FREQUENCY INTERLEAVING

Now that the form the colour information takes during a colour television broadcast has been established, it is appropriate to show how the chrominance information is accommodated within the normal luminance signal bandwidth.

The luminance signal has a bandwidth extending from 0 Hz to 5·5 MHz and it would appear that this band is full, thus, there would be no room for extra information. However, if the luminance signal is analysed it is found that not all frequencies in the range of 0–5·5 MHz are present. Only those frequencies which are harmonics of the **line frequency** are produced, see Fig. 5.5(a), and these are of diminishing amplitude up to the limit of the band (5·5 MHz). Around each line frequency harmonic are clusters of components at field and picture frequency, but these are only of significant amplitude close to the line frequency multiples. There are, therefore, **frequency spaces** created which may be used to carry additional information.

The chrominance signal is fitted into the frequency spaces of the luminance signal. The basic idea is to amplitude modulate a **sub-carrier** with the **colour-difference signals**, using a sub-carrier frequency which fits between two adjacent line multiples of the luminance signal. Balanced modulators are used, thus the actual sub-carrier is suppressed. However, the side-frequencies remain and since they too are related to line frequency,

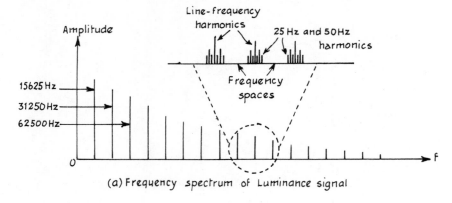

(a) Frequency spectrum of Luminance signal

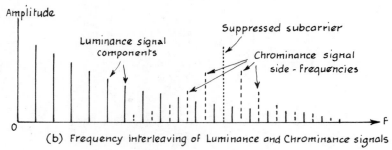

(b) Frequency interleaving of Luminance and Chrominance signals

Fig. 5.5 Fitting the chrominance information into the luminance signal bandwidth.

they interleave with the harmonic components of the luminance signal as shown in Fig. 5.5(b). This **frequency interleaving** allows the luminance and chrominance signals to share the same video frequency band.

Choice of Colour Sub-carrier Frequency

As far as a monochrome receiver is concerned, the chrominance side-frequencies or sidebands represent interference and as such cause dot patterning of the raster lines. The higher the frequency of the chosen sub-carrier the finer is the dot patterning produced and the less is its annoyance value. This may be appreciated from the diagrams of Fig. 5.6 where sine wave modulation of a monochrome receiver raster at various frequencies is considered.

In each of these diagrams, the sine wave will brighten up the trace during one half-cycle and blacken it out on the other half-cycle. As the frequency of the sine wave is increased from 50 Hz to approximately 117 kHz in these diagrams, the visibility of the pattern is seen to reduce. Raising the sine wave frequency to, say, several MHz will reduce the visibility even further as there will be many more cyclic changes occurring across each line display period.

Now, the colour-difference signals are in the range of 0–1 MHz thus the chrominance sidebands extend 1 MHz either side of the chosen sub-carrier. Therefore, to accommodate the upper sideband of the chrominance signal, the sub-carrier frequency cannot be higher than 4·5 MHz. Thus somewhere in the range of 4·0–4·5 MHz would appear to be most suitable. In the PAL system, the sub-carrier frequency is made 283¾ times the line frequency plus 25 Hz which may be written as:

$$f_{sc} = (283 \cdot 75 \times 15625) + 25 \text{ Hz}$$
$$= 4 \cdot 43361875 \text{ MHz} \ (\approx 4 \cdot 43 \text{ MHz})$$

SUPPRESSED-CARRIER MODULATION

It has been noted that the colour-difference signals are modulated on to a sub-carrier of approximately 4·43 MHz but the sub-carrier is

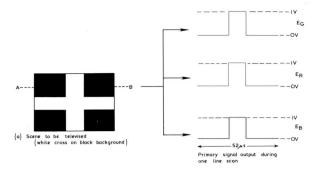

FIG. 4.2   PRIMARY SIGNAL OUTPUTS OF 3-TUBE CAMERA (E_G, E_R AND E_B) FOR TEST
PICTURE

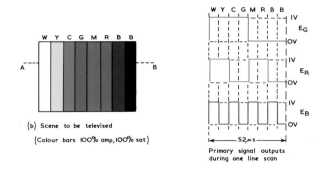

FIG. 4.3   PRIMARY SIGNAL OUTPUT OF 3-TUBE CAMERA FOR COLOUR BARS

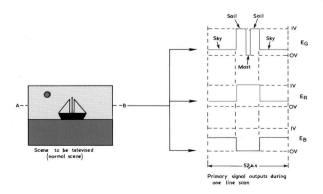

FIG. 4.4   PRIMARY SIGNAL OUTPUTS OF 3-TUBE COLOUR CAMERA (E_G, E_R AND E_B)
FOR NORMAL SCENE

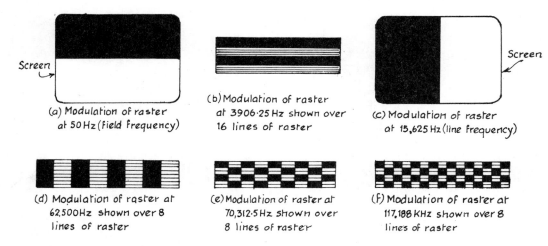

(a) Modulation of raster at 50 Hz (field frequency)

(b) Modulation of raster at 3906·25 Hz shown over 16 lines of raster

(c) Modulation of raster at 15,625 Hz (line frequency)

(d) Modulation of raster at 62,500 Hz shown over 8 lines of raster

(e) Modulation of raster at 70,312·5 Hz shown over 8 lines of raster

(f) Modulation of raster at 117,188 KHz shown over 8 lines of raster

Fig. 5.6 *Effect of sine-wave modulation of raster at various frequencies on monochrome receiver screen.*

suppressed, thus a balanced modulator is used.

With a suppressed-carrier or balanced modulator there is no output when the modulating signal is zero, see Fig. 5.7 where sine wave modulation is assumed. When the modulating signal is present the output consists of **side-frequencies only**. The amplitude of the output varies in accordance with the amplitude of the modulating signal, but it should be noted that **each time the modulating signal changes polarity, the phase of the output changes by 180°**, see Fig. 5.7(ii).

Clearly, if the waveform of Fig. 5.7(ii) were fed to an ordinary diode demodulator, the detected output would be a very distorted version of the original modulation, because the carrier is 'missing'. Thus to reconstitute the original modulation, the carrier must be made **available** at the receiver when suppressed carrier operation is employed. Fig. 5.7(iii) shows the output from an ordinary amplitude modulator for comparison with Fig. 5.7(ii).

In practice the modulating signal is not a sine wave but a colour-difference signal. An example of the modulator output when receiv-

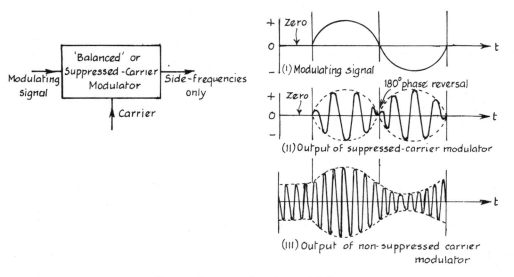

Fig. 5.7 *Suppressed carrier modulation.*

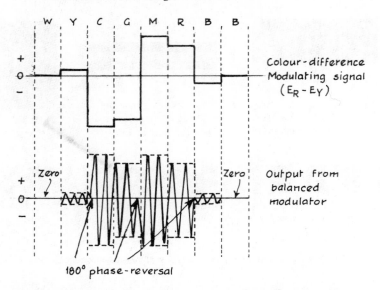

Fig. 5.8 Example of balanced modulator output with colour-difference modulating signal.

ing $E_R - E_Y$ modulation (for the colour bars) is given in Fig. 5.8. The main points to note are:

(1) The output has an amplitude proportional to the amplitude of the colour-difference signal, thus there will be no output on monochrome when the colour-difference signal disappears.

(2) A 180° phase reversal occurs each time the colour-difference signal changes polarity.

Suppressed-carrier modulation is used in preference to ordinary amplitude modulation since with the former there is no large amplitude carrier to cause interference to monochrome reception. The sidebands, of course, produce some dot patterning but this is not so objectionable as it is at its worst only on fully saturated colours.

QUADRATURE MODULATION

It has been explained how the luminance and chromonance signal information is fitted into the same frequency band using frequency interlacing. Now, the colour information is conveyed by **two** colour-difference signals. Thus the problem is how to simultaneously modulate a common sub-carrier with the two colour-difference signals and to be able to

separate them at the receiver. The problem is resolved by using **quadrature modulation**.

A basic arrangement for a quadrature modulator is shown in Fig. 5.9. In the balanced modulator A, the $E_B - E_Y$ signal modulates a 4·43 MHz sub-carrier, thus at x the output consists of side-frequencies only. Meanwhile in balanced modulator B the $E_R - E_Y$ signal modulates a sub-carrier having precisely the same frequency but advanced in phase by 90° on the sub-carrier input to modulator A. The output of modulator B at y will also consist of side-frequencies only but these will differ in phase to the sideband output of modulator A by 90° – hence the term 'quadrature modulation'.

A carrier (f_c) amplitude modulated by a sine wave signal (f_m) may be represented by three phasors as in Fig. 5.10(a). With suppressed-carrier operation, the carrier phasor is omitted leaving just the side-frequency phasors. This representation is used in Fig. 5.10(b) which shows the side-frequency output of modulators A and B. The resultant of the side-frequency output at x is the phasor $R1$ whilst the resultant of the side-frequency output at y is the phasor $R2$. When the outputs of the two modulators are combined the resultant is given by phasor $R3$. This combined resultant represents a particular hue and saturation as

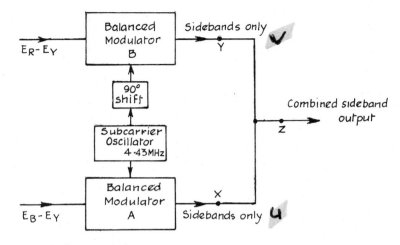

Fig. 5.9 Quadrature modulation.

determined by the respective amplitudes and polarities of the colour-difference signals.

When dealing with the operation of a balanced modulator it was noted that the phase of the output changed by 180° whenever the modulating signal changed polarity. Since the colour-difference signals may have either positive or negative polarity, the phase of the combined resultant may lie in any of the four quadrants of Fig. 5.11.

The actual phase position of the combined resultant in any quadrant is dependent upon the relative amplitudes of the side-frequencies, but these are directly proportional to the amplitudes of the colour-difference signals. Thus the colour-difference signal values may be plotted directly on the axes.

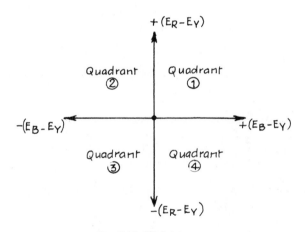

Fig. 5.11 Modulator axes.

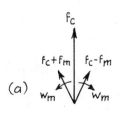

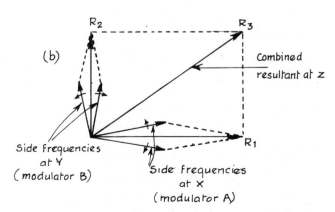

Fig. 5.10 Combining the modulator outputs.

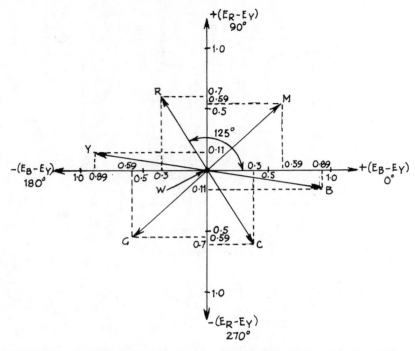

Fig. 5.12 Phase positions for the colour bars 100% amp., 100% sat. (non-weighted).

Phasors for the Colour Bars

The phase position for the colour bar hues are shown in Fig. 5.12. The position of each phasor is obtained by finding the resultant of the $E_R - E_Y$ and $E_B - E_Y$ values (given in the table of Fig. 5.3) for the various hues. The following points may be noted from this diagram:

(1) The **hue** of a colour determines the **phase position** of the resultant phasor. In angular measurement this is taken from the reference axis $+ (E_B - E_Y) = 0°$. For example, the red phasor makes an angle of approximately 125° with respect to the $+ (E_B - E_Y)$ axis.

(2) The **length** of the resultant phasor is determined by the **saturation** and **amplitude** of the colour. A fully desaturated hue (white) has a position at the origin.

(3) Complementary colours are diametrically opposite their associated primary colours, *e.g.* magenta is opposite to green.

(4) If the phasor of a complementary colour is added to the phasor of its associated primary, the result is zero, *i.e.* white which is in accordance with additive colour mixing.

(5) By projecting from a particular phasor to the diagram axes, the relative amplitudes of the resultants of the side-frequency components may be found.

In practice, Fig. 5.12 has to be modified on account of 'weighting' which will be considered next.

WEIGHTING

The combined chrominance signal output of the balanced modulators together with the luminance signal also sync. pulses and burst (see later) are fed to the main u.h.f. carrier modulator. This waveform consists of the chrominance information 'riding' on the luminance modulation as in Fig. 5.13(a).

As far as monochrome operation is concerned, the normal limits of modulation are 100% corresponding to the sync. pulse tips and peak white at 20% (see Chapter 6). For certain colours, the combined signal amplitude greatly exceeds the normal permissible

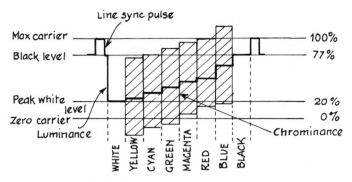

(a) Non-weighted chrominance signals
(100% AMP, 100% SAT Colour bars)

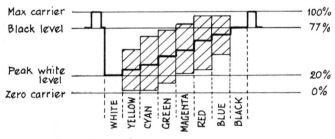

(b) Weighted chrominance signals

Fig. 5.13 Weighting.

limits of modulation as shown. To prevent this, the colour-difference signals are reduced in amplitude prior to being fed to the balanced modulators. The attenuation of the colour-difference signals is called **weighting** and the weighted colour-difference signals are re-named **V and U signals** where:

$$V = 0.877 \ (E_R - E_Y)$$
$$\text{and} \quad U = 0.493 \ (E_B - E_Y).$$

After weighting, the combined luminance and chrominance signal waveform is as in Fig. 5.13(b) where it will be noted that the chrominance signal component no longer exceeds the sync. pulse tips or reaches the zero carrier level.

The weighting process does not cause any

difficulty with the display colour as it is a simple matter in the receiver to restore the colour-difference signals to their correct levels by adjusting the gains of the appropriate channels; a process called **de-weighting**.

V and U Signals

From now on we shall be concerned mainly with V and U signals rather than $E_R - E_Y$ and $E_B - E_Y$ signals. The weighting process is shown in Fig. 5.14(a) where the inputs to the balanced modulators are now V and U signals or attenuated colour difference signals. Because of this the modulation axes are redesignated V and U axes as shown in Fig. 5.14(b).

Using the V and U modulation axes we may

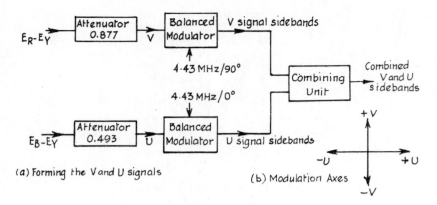

(a) Forming the V and U signals

(b) Modulation Axes

Fig. 5.14 V and U signals.

now plot the approximate phase positions and amplitudes of the colour bars, using the values from Table 5.1.

The circle diagram of Fig. 5.15 shows the phase position of the colour bars and should be used in preference to that of Fig. 5.12 since it deals with the transmitted weighted signals. Any colour present in a broadcast scene may be specified on this diagram. It should now be appreciated that the **phase** of the combined chrominance sidebands is very important, since a change in phase will result in a change in the hue.

As previously explained, the modulator outputs consist of sidebands centred on a suppressed carrier of 4·43 MHz and as such are sine wave type signals. The diagrams of Fig. 5.16 show the waveforms for the *V*, *U* and combined sidebands which are referred to as **chrominance signals**. The *V* and *U* chrominance signals assume the relative values which are given in Table 5.1. The amplitude of the combined *V* and *U* chrominance signal for each bar may be calculated from:

$$\sqrt{V^2 + U^2}$$

For example, on the yellow bar $V = 0.096$ and $U = 0.439$.

Thus the resultant amplitude:

$$= \sqrt{(0.096)^2 + (0.439)^2}$$
$$= 0.45$$

These waveforms may be observed in the receiver decoder prior to synchronous demodulation of the *V* and *U* components.

THE PAL SYSTEM

A major disadvantage of quadrature modulation is that any phase shift occurring in the combined chrominance signal will cause the wrong colours to be displayed in the receiver.

For example, consider the transmission of a particular red hue which is represented by the phasor R_t in Fig. 5.17. This signal has a true *V* component of v_t and a true *U* component of u_t. Suppose that somewhere in the transmitting-to-receiving link a phase advance occurs causing the signal to take up the new phase position represented by the phasor R_e. This 'error' signal R_e has a *V* component v_e which is

Table 5.1 V and U values on colour bars (100% set, 100% amp)

	W	Y	C	G	M	R	B	B
$E_R - E_Y$	0·000	+0·110	−0·700	−0·590	+0·590	+0·700	−0·110	0·000
V	0·000	+0·096	−0·614	−0·517	+0·517	+0·614	−0·096	0·000
$E_B - E_Y$	0·000	−0·890	+0·300	−0·590	+0·590	−0·300	+0·890	0·000
U	0·000	−0·439	+0·148	−0·291	+0·291	−0·148	+0·439	0·000

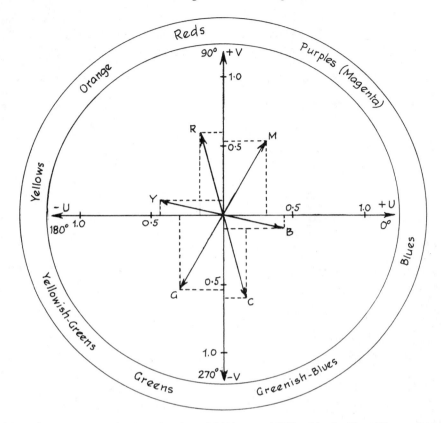

Fig. 5.15 Approximate phase positions for colour bars (100% amp., 100% sat.) using V and U axes (weighted signals).

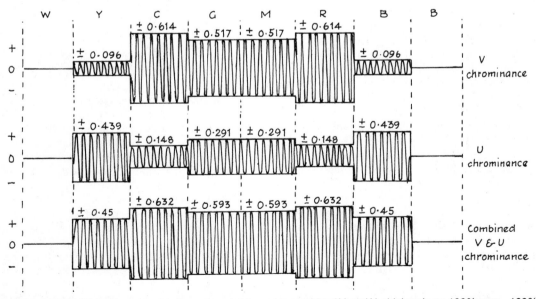

Fig. 5.16 V and U sideband outputs of balanced modulators plus combined V and U sidebands on 100% amp., 100% sat. colour bars.

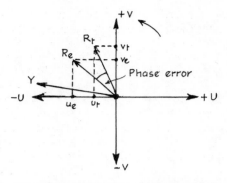

Fig. 5.17 *Effect of phase error in transmitted signal.*

smaller than intended but a *U* component u_e which is larger than intended. After these components have been detected at the receiver, the display would show an incorrect hue, somewhere between red and yellow producing a shade of orange. Unfortunately, the eye is very sensitive to variations in hue (particularly on flesh tones) and it is generally considered that humam vision can detect hue variations caused by phase errors of about 5°.

Phase errors would not be such a serious matter if any phase shift occuring was the same for all transmitted colours, for then a control could be fitted to adjust the phase of the sub-carrier oscillator in the receiver. There is, however, a type of phase shift which is level dependent, *i.e.* the amount of phase shift introduced depends upon the level or amplitude of the chrominance signal (note that the chrominance signal 'rides' on a luminance signal of varying level). With differing amounts of phase error for various colours it would be impossible to correct all the colours simultaneously with the aid of a single receiver control. Although level dependent phase error can be reduced by careful design it cannot be wholly eliminated. Because of the problems associated with phase errors, a modification to quadrature modulation was introduced in U.K. colour broadcasts called **PAL (phase alternation line)**.

The basic idea of PAL is to **invert the V component of the transmitted chrominance signal on alternate lines**. The diagram of Fig. 5.18(a) shows as an example a red hue having a + *v* component and a − *u* component. On odd lines the phasor for red is sent out as shown. On even lines a red hue is transmitted as in Fig. 5.18(b). The phasor now

has a − *v* component but the *U* component is unaltered. Thus the transmitted phasor on even lines is a mirror image (about the *U* axis) of the transmitted phasor for odd lines. This simple modification overcomes the effect of phase errors. Of course, on even lines the received phasor is incorrect so **at the receiver the V component must be reinverted** to put matters right.

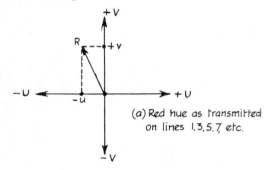

(a) Red hue as transmitted on lines 1, 3, 5, 7 etc.

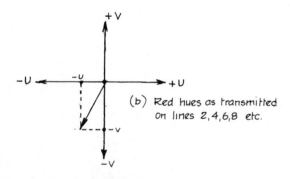

(b) Red hues as transmitted on lines 2, 4, 6, 8 etc.

Fig. 5.18 *Diagrams showing basic idea of PAL.*

The schematic given in Fig. 5.19 shows the arrangement used at the transmitter for inverting the *V* component on alternate lines. The sub-carrier is fed to the balanced modulators as previously described, but into the sub-carrier path to the *V* modulator is placed the inverting switch called the **PAL switch**. This switch is driven at half-line rate (7·8125 kHz – usually abbreviated to 7·8 kHz in technical literature). On odd lines the sub-carrier input to the *V* modulator is advanced by the normal 90° on the sub-carrier input to the *U* modulator (0°). On even lines the PAL switch inverts the sub-carrier so that it is at 270° with respect to the *U* modulator sub-carrier input. When the sub-carrier input to the *V* modulator changes

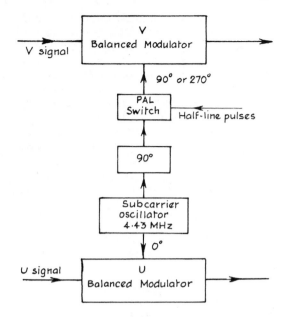

Fig. 5.19 Inverting the V signal component.

phase by 180°, so does the side-frequency output.

Receiving PAL Signals

Zero Phase Error

Phasors for normal operation, *i.e.* no phase error in the received signal are shown in Fig. 5.20. Here we are considering the transmission of a red hue, assumed to be sent out on all lines.

Figure 5.20(a) shows the transmitted and received phasor $R1$ for odd lines and Fig. 5.20(b) the transmitted and received phasor $R2$ for even lines. Since the phase of the received signal on even lines is incorrect it is necessary **in the receiver to reinvert the V component of $R2$**. This is shown in Fig. 5.20(c) where the V component has been reinverted we have the correct phasor $R3$ for the red hue.

In the PAL-D receiver (D stands for delay-line), the phasors of the odd and corrected even lines are added together electrically and the resultant signal after suitable processing is used to produce colour on the display c.r.t. This is shown in Fig. 5.20(d) where phasors $R1$ and $R3$ have been added vectorally to produce a resultant $R4$. Note that $R4$ makes the same angle θ with the $+ V$ axis as $R1$ and $R3$, *i.e.* the hue is correct but is twice the length of $R1$ or $R3$. The increase in amplitude of the V and U components which are now $+ 2v$ and $- 2u$ is not important as this may be corrected by an adjustment to the gain of the colour signal channels in the receiver.

To be able to take an electrical average of the chrominance signals from odd and even lines, it is necessary to 'store' the chrominance signal of each line so that it can be compared (averaged) with the chrominance signal of the

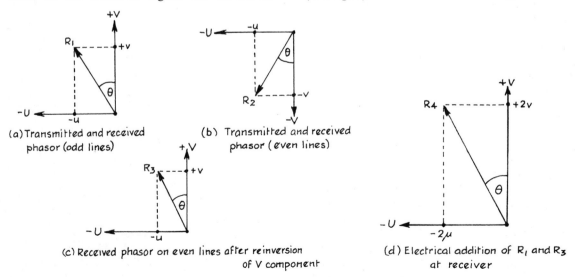

Fig. 5.20 Diagrams showing effect of PAL when there is no phase error (normal operation).

following line. This is carried out by the **PAL delay line** in the receiver which provides **a time delay equal to one line period of 64 μs.**

Phase Error Present

The diagrams of Fig. 5.21 show the effect of the PAL modification when the received signal has a phase error.

Suppose that a red hue R_t is transmitted on all lines but during transmission a phase advance occurs so that the actual signal transmitted is R_e. This is shown in Fig. 5.21(a) and (b) for odd and even lines where R_e is advanced on R_t by a small angle. Thus the

phasors of the received chrominance signals on odd and even lines will be as in Fig. 5.21(c) and (d).

In the receiver, the V component of the even line signal is reinverted, thus the even line phasor is now as in Fig. 5.21(e).

If the chrominance signals of Fig. 5.21(c) and Fig. 5.21(e) are added together electrically, we get the result shown in Fig. 5.21(f). The even line signal has a phase which is lagging the true phase for red whilst the odd line signal is advanced on the true phase for red. However, the phase of the electrical resultant is correct and a true red hue will be displayed.

Note that the amplitude of the V and U

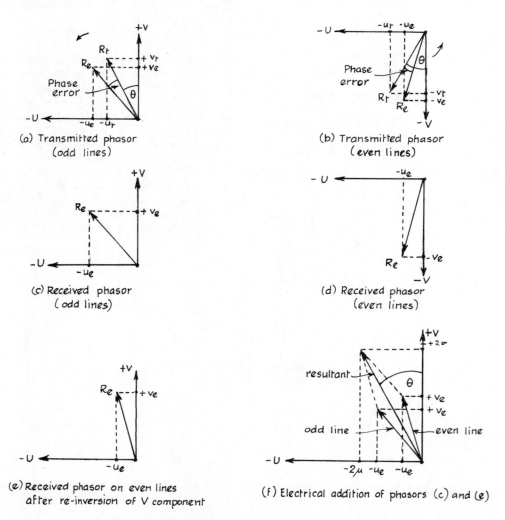

Fig. 5.21 *Diagrams showing effect of PAL when there is a phase error in the received signal.*

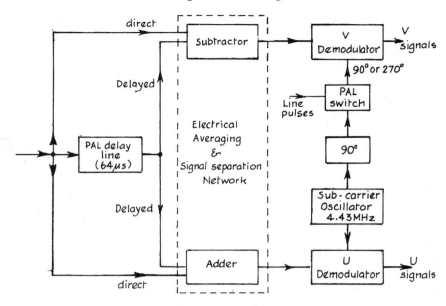

Fig. 5.22 The heart of a PAL decoder.

components of the resultant are less than when there is no phase error (compare with Fig. 5.20(d)) thus the displayed signal will be slightly **desaturated**.

Thus when a phase error occurs in the transmitting or receiving link, the effect of PAL is to cancel out the phase error resulting in the display of correct hues but with some small desaturation. Fortunately, the eye is not so sensitive to small desaturation errors.

The block schematic of Fig. 5.22 shows the essential processes of a receiver PAL decoder including the PAL delay line, but will not be considered in detail in this volume.

COLOUR BURST SIGNAL

This signal is transmitted to enable two important functions to be carried out in the receiver decoder:

(1) With suppressed-carrier operation, the sub-carrier must be made available at the receiver for successful demodulation of the chrominance signal information as previously stated. Not only must the locally generated sub-carrier be of the same frequency as that used in the transmitter, but it must also be of the same phase. Clearly, there must be some form

of synchronisation between the transmitter and the receiver sub-carrier oscillators. **This synchronisation is performed by the colour burst signal**. The burst signal consists of approximately **10 cycles of the sub-carrier** transmitted on the back porch of the line sync. pulses, see Fig. 5.23.

At the receiver these burst cycles are picked out by a gating circuit and then used to control the frequency and phase of the locally generated sub-carrier.

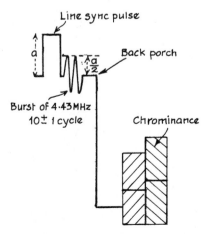

Fig. 5.23 The colour burst.

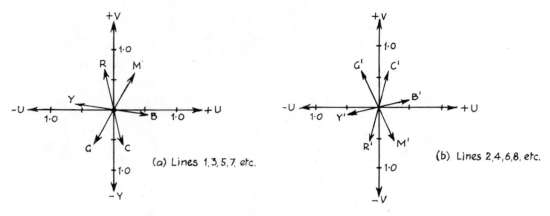

Fig. 5.24 *Phases of colour bar signals on odd and even lines (weighted values).*

(2) An additional function performed by the colour burst is **to keep the PAL switch in the receiver decoder in-step with the PAL switch at the transmitter**. The reason for this may be appreciated by considering Fig. 5.24 which shows the PAL colour bar phasors transmitted on odd and even lines. The function of the receiver PAL switch is to reinvert the V component of the received signal on **even** lines. If, however, the receiver PAL switch is out of step with that of the transmitter it may invert the V component on **odd** lines, resulting in the display of incorrect colour on all lines (normal red flesh tones would turn 'green').

The additional information required to keep the receiver PAL switch in step is conveyed by the **phase** of the burst signal, see Fig. 5.25. On odd lines the burst phase is 45° lagging on the − U axis whilst on

even lines its phase is 45° leading on the − U axis. At the receiver this so called 'swinging burst' which is in sympathy with the V signal switching, gives rise to an **identification (ident) signal** which is used to synchronise the receiver PAL switch.

PAL ENCODER SCHEMATIC

The important features of the PAL system of colour television discussed in this chapter may now be summarised with the aid of the block schematic given in Fig. 5.26.

The colour camera breaks down the scene to be televised into its three basic components of red, green and blue light. Each camera tube produces at its output a primary signal voltage having an amplitude proportional to the amount of coloured light falling on its face. In block 1 portions of the primary signal are matrixed together to form the luminance signal E_Y. In addition, the E_Y signal is subtracted from the E_R and E_B signal voltages to obtain the colour difference signals $E_R − E_Y$ and $E_B − E_Y$. The colour difference signals are then weighted (attenuated) in blocks 2 and 3 to produce the **V and U baseband signals** where $V = 0.877 (E_R − E_Y)$ and $U = 0.493 (E_B − E_Y)$. The V and U baseband signals are then fed to balanced modulators via filters which limit the bandwidth to the required value of 0 − 1 MHz.

In blocks 6 and 7 the V and U signals amplitude modulate a common sub-carrier of 4.43 MHz, but with the sub-carrier input to the V modulator in phase quadrature to the

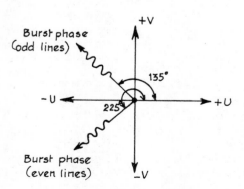

Fig. 5.25 *The swinging burst.*

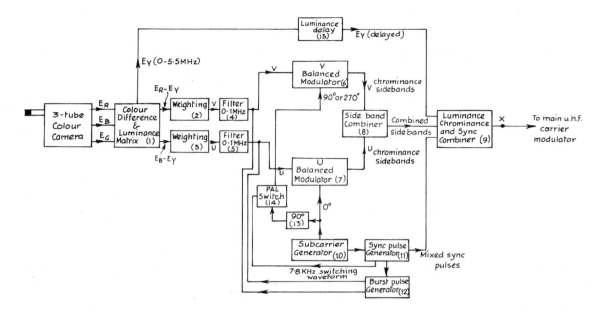

Fig. 5.26 Arrangement of PAL encoder.

sub-carrier input to the U modulator. The sub-carrier is generated in block 10 and fed directly to the U modulator but via a 90° phase advance network (13) and the PAL switch to the V modulator. The PAL switch (14) is required to invert the phase of the V component on alternate lines. Since balanced modulators are used, the sub-carrier is suppressed thus the output of each modulator consists of side-frequencies only centred on 4·43 MHz. The V and U chrominance signal sidebands are then combined in block 8 and subsequently fed to block 9 where they are combined with the luminance and sync. signals.

The line and field sync. pulses also blanking and equalising pulses are generated in block 11 with their timing controlled by frequency division of the sub-carrier output from block 10. The sync. pulse generator also supplies a 7·8 kHz switching waveform for the PAL

switch and line frequency pulses to the burst generator (12). The burst pulse generator supplies pulses of opposite polarity at line frequency having durations confined within the back porch period to the V and U modulators. These pulses produce bursts of the sub-carrier at the modulator outputs. On odd lines the individual bursts have phases of $+V$ and $-U$ which, after combination in block 8, produce a burst at 135°. On even lines, due to the reversal in phase of the sub-carrier input to the V modulator, the phases of the individual bursts are $-V$ and $-U$ which after combination provide a burst of 225° as is required.

Before the luminance signal is combined with the other signals in block 9 it is delayed briefly for about 1 μs in block 15. This delay is necessary so that all signals arrive at the input to block 9 together, since the V and U signals are restricted in bandwidth compared to the luminance signal, *i.e.* they have longer rise and fall times than the luminance signal.

The diagram of Fig. 5.27 shows the **composite video waveform** appearing at point X during one television line of the colour bars. A colour receiver requires all four components (a), (b), (c) and (d) to produce a well defined colour image on its screen. A monochrome receiver when tuned to the same colour transmission requires only components (b) and (d). If the transmission is in monochrome then components (a) and (c) will not be transmitted.

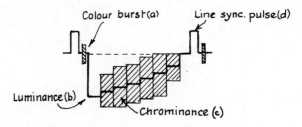

Fig. 5.27 Composite signal at X (Fig. 5.26) during the transmission of colour bars.

CHAPTER SIX

THE TRANSMITTED SIGNAL

Objectives

1 Show the modulation levels used for the vision signal and draw a typical modulated carrier waveform.
2 Explain why vestigial sideband transmission is used.
3 Show the 625-line System I frequency spectrum and state the spacing between vision and sound carriers.
4 State the bandwidth occupied by each television channel and show the extents of Band 4 and 5.

THE SECTION OF the vision transmitter dealing with the modulation of the radiated carrier will accept either monochrome or colour signal modulation. During a colour programme, the input to block 1 of Fig. 6.1 is the composite video waveform consisting of luminance, chrominance, colour burst and sync. On the occasions when the programme is a black-and-white film or video recording, the input to block 1 is the luminance and sync. waveform only.

Amplitude modulation is used for the vision carrier which for **625-line terrestrial trans-** **missions lies in the u.h.f. band**. To obtain good frequency stability, the u.h.f. carrier is derived from a crystal oscillator working at a sub-multiple of the u.h.f. carrier which is raised to the required radiated frequency by the use of frequency multiplier stages. Amplitude modulation of the u.h.f. carrier takes place in block 3.

Modulation Levels

The modulation levels which were originally set by the needs of monochrome operation are

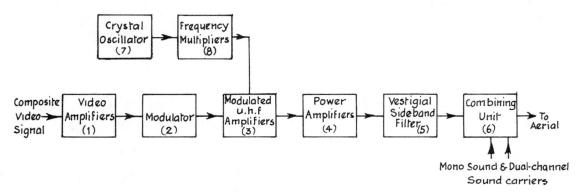

Fig. 6.1 Basic television transmitter.

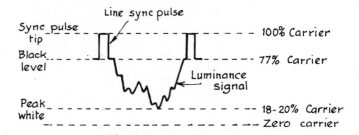

Fig. 6.2 Modulation levels for the monochrome (luminance) signal.

shown in Fig. 6.2. Maximum carrier (100% modulation) occurs on the sync. pulse tips whilst a minimum carrier of 18–20% modulation corresponds to peak white. Black and blanking are set at 77% modulation. This type of modulation is sometimes referred to as 'negative modulation' since increasing the amplitude of the video signal reduces the carrier amplitude.

It may appear wasteful not to make use of the full range of modulation levels by limiting peak white at around 20% but there is a good reason for this. In the receiver, a technique called **intercarrier sound** is used where an intercarrier sound i.f. of 6 MHz (also 6·552 MHz for stereo sound) is produced by beating the vision and sound i.f.s together. If the vision carrier was returned to zero during modulation there would be no intercarrier i.f. produced causing loss of sound.

The modulation levels on 100% amp, 95% saturated colour bars are shown in Fig. 6.3. In spite of the weighting given to the chrominance signal, the monochrome lower limit of 20% is exceeded for some hues. There is, however, some residual carrier present to meet the needs of intercarrier sound at the receiver. In a typical colour programme the lower levels of 6% will not be reached since

the colours will rarely be at full amplitude and highly saturated as for the colour bars which provide a critical test of the colour television system.

The output of block 3 in Fig. 6.1 is the amplitude modulated u.h.f. carrier. Examples of the modulated carrier for monochrome and colour operation are given in Fig. 6.4 and Fig. 6.5. It should be noted that the chrominance modulation is a sine wave type modulation (side bands of 4·43 MHz imposed on the luminance levels).

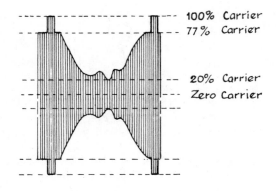

Fig. 6.4 Typical modulated carrier waveform showing sync. and luminance signal envelope.

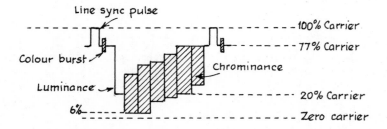

Fig. 6.3 Modulation levels on 95% saturated colour bars.

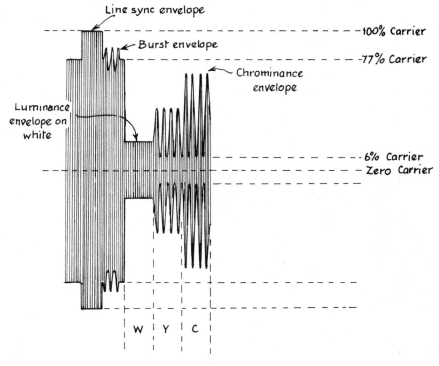

Fig. 6.5 Modulated carrier showing part colour bar modulation.

VESTIGIAL SIDEBAND OPERATION

We have seen that the video bandwidth of the luminance signal extends from 0 Hz (d.c.) up to 5·5 MHz. With amplitude modulation of the vision carrier we therefore get two sets of sidebands as shown in Fig. 6.6(a) producing an overall bandwidth of 11 MHz. Double sideband transmission was used in the early 405-line system but is rather wasteful of bandwidth. Some of the side-frequencies of one sideband (upper or lower) may be removed leaving a 'vestige' or 'trace' of that sideband and this idea is used in all modern systems. In the British 625-line system the lower sideband is attenuated as in Fig. 6.6(b) with only the lower side-frequencies down to 1·25 MHz below the carrier remaining. This results in a considerable saving in bandwidth for the vision signal, thereby allowing more channels to be accommodated in the bands allocated to television broadcasting.

A further saving in bandwidth could be achieved if one of the sidebands was completely suppressed, resulting in single sideband operation and it may be asked why this is not

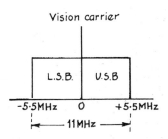

(a) Double sideband operation

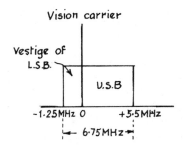

(b) Vestigial sideband operation

Fig. 6.6 Diagrams showing the bandwidth saving by employing vestigial sideband working.

done. With single sideband operation it is found that the receiver detector output contains some distortion due to the suppression of one of the sidebands. This distortion increases rapidly with depth of modulation thus single sideband operation is only acceptable for low levels of modulation. For the luminance signal it is the low frequency components that cause high modulation depths, whereas the high frequency components (fine scene detail) result in relatively low levels of modulation.

Vestigial sideband operation is, in effect, a compromise between the bandwidth problem of double sideband operation and the distortion problem of single sideband working, as Fig. 6.7 more clearly shows. The high video frequencies from $+1\cdot25\,$MHz to $+5\cdot5\,$MHZ are transmitted by means of the single upper sideband whereas the lower video frequencies of $0\,$Hz to $1\cdot25\,$MHz (which cause the greatest depths of modulation) are transmitted by both sidebands.

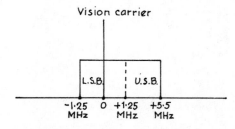

Fig. 6.7 Vestigial sideband working using D.S.B. (0–1·25 MHz) and S.S.B. (1·25 MHz–5·5 MHz).

The vestigial sideband characteristic is achieved by passing the double sideband output of the modulated u.h.f. amplifier through a filter, block 5 of Fig. 6.1, which removes part of the lower sideband.

Receiver Response for Vestigial Sideband Working

Because of the presence of both sidebands for video frequencies from 0–$1\cdot25\,$MHz, a receiver with a uniform response would produce double the output at its detector for these frequencies compared with modulation frequencies in the range of $1\cdot25$–$5\cdot5\,$MHz since these are transmitted in only one sideband.

It is thus necessary to correct for vestigial

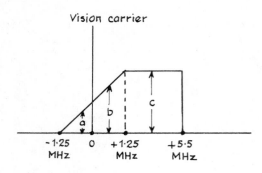

Fig. 6.8 Receiver response required to correct for vestigial operation.

sideband transmission in the receiver by shaping its response as in Fig. 6.8 which shows the ideal form.

Clearly, the sum of symmetrically disposed side-frequencies on either side of the vision carrier in the range of 0–$1\cdot25\,$MHz such as a and b will equal the amplitude of the side-frequency components from $1\cdot25$–$5\cdot5\,$MHz such as c, *e.g.* a + b = c. In consequence, a receiver with this type of response will provide from its demodulator the same amplitude of output signal over the range of 0–$5\cdot5\,$MHz.

625-LINE TELEVISION FREQUENCY SPECTRUM

The diagram of Fig. 6.9 shows the frequency spectrum of a single channel for the U.K. 625-line System I television signal.

Vision Signal

In the vestigial sideband vision signal, side-frequencies are transmitted in full up to $5\cdot5\,$MHz in the upper sideband and then are rapidly attenuated. In the lower sideband, side-frequencies are transmitted in full up to $1\cdot25\,$MHz at which point attenuation is applied giving complete suppression at $1\cdot75\,$MHz.

During colour transmissions the chrominance signal which embraces $4\cdot43\,$MHz $\pm1\,$MHz in the video baseband will, upon modulation of the u.h.f. carrier, appear in the upper sideband of the transmitted vision signal. The chrominance signal has full amplitude sidebands extending up to $5\cdot5\,$MHz and down to about $3\cdot1\,$MHz producing a full level

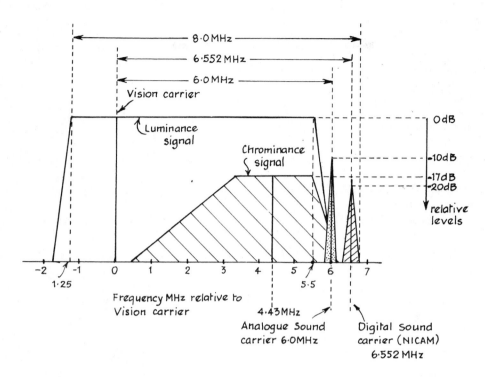

Fig. 6.9 625-line system I frequency spectrum of television signal (single channel) including analogue (mono) sound and digital (stereo) sound signals.

bandwidth of approximately 2·3 MHz but is radiated 17 dB below the level of the luminance signal.

Sound Signal

(a) Mono

A mono sound channel is provided by **frequency modulating** a u.h.f. carrier fixed at 6 MHz above the vision carrier. The f.m. sound carrier produces a maximum deviation of ±50 kHz and the audio signal which extends up to 15 kHz is given pre-emphasis at the transmitter using a 50 μs time-constant.

(b) Stereo

High quality stereo sound has now been added to the System I transmitted signal for reproduction in television receivers equipped with a special NICAM decoder.

The stereo channel audio signals extending up to 15 kHz are digitally encoded and the two channels are simultaneously sampled at a rate of 32 kHz using 14-bits per sample. The high data rate generated by 14-bits per sample is companded (reduced) using a **NICAM (near-instantaneous companding audio multiplex)** format which reduces the bit rate to 10-bits per sample so that the signal can be accommodated within the television channel bandwidth. The companding is done in such a way that it can be re-instated to 14-bit accuracy at the receiver decoder.

For transmission, the dual-channel sound data packets are converted into a series of parallel dibits (two bits) which cause **differential quadrature phase shift modulation** of a u.h.f. carrier placed **6·552 MHz above the vision carrier**. All of the digital sound information is conveyed by means of **four phase changes** (90° apart) **in the u.h.f. carrier**.

Some important frequencies and relationships of the 625-line System I transmission are:

Channel bandwidth : 8 MHz
Mono sound carrier relative to vision carrier : 6 MHz
Stereo sound carrier relative to vision carrier : 6·552 MHz
Chrominance sub-carrier relative to vision carrier : 4·43 MHz

U.H.F. TELEVISION CHANNELS

The 625-line television broadcasts are transmitted in Bands 4 and 5. The u.h.f. Band 4 extends from 470 MHz – 582 MHz, whilst Band 5 covers the range of 614 MHz to 854 MHz. Tables 6.1 and 6.2 show the television channels and their frequencies.

The diagram of Fig. 6.10 shows three adjacent channels. During certain signal propagation conditions it is possible for channels either side of the selected channel to cause interference. Protection against this type of interference is made by including adjacent channel rejection in the receiver i.f. stages. If, for example, channel 28 is the channel in use, the sound carrier of channel 27 and the vision carrier of channel 29 may cause interference; these are called the **adjacent channel sound** and the **adjacent channel vision** respectively.

Table 6.1 Band 4 Channels and Frequencies.

	Channel	Frequency Range (MHz)	Vision Carrier (MHz)	Mono sound Carrier (MHz)
	21	470–478	471·25	477·25
	22	478–486	479·25	485·25
	23	486–494	487·25	493·25
	24	494–502	495·25	501·25
	25	502–510	503·25	509·25
Aerial	26	510–518	511·25	517·25
Group A	27	518–526	519·25	525·25
(Red)	28	526–534	527·25	533·25
Channels	29	534–542	535·25	541·25
21–34	30	542–550	543·25	549·25
	31	550–558	551·25	557·25
	32	558–566	559·25	565·25
	33	566–574	567·25	573·25
	34	574–582	575·25	581·25

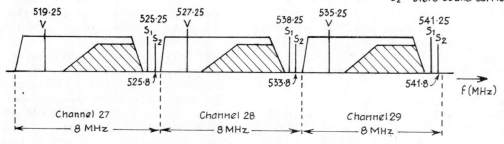

V   Vision Carrier
S_1 Mono Sound Carrier
S_2 Stero Sound Carrier

Fig. 6.10 Three adjacent band 4 channels.

Table 6.2 Band 5 Channels and Frequencies.

	Channel	Frequency Range (MHz)	Vision Carrier (MHz)	Mono sound Carrier (MHz)
	39	614–622	615·25	621·25
	40	622–630	623·25	629·25
	41	630–638	631·25	637·25
	42	638–646	639·25	645·25
Aerial Group B (Yellow) Channels 39–51	43	646–654	647·25	653·25
	44	654–662	655·25	661·25
	45	662–670	663·25	669·25
	46	670–678	671·25	677·25
	47	678–686	679·25	685·25
	48	686–694	687·25	693.25
	49	694–702	695·25	701·25
	50	702–710	703·25	709·25
	51	710–718	711·25	717·25
	52	718–726	719·25	725·25
	53	726–734	727·25	733·25
	54	734–742	735·25	741·25
	55	742–750	743·25	749·25
Aerial Group C (Green) Channels 50–66	56	750–758	751·25	757·25
	57	758–766	759·25	765·25
	58	766–774	767·25	773·25
	59	774–782	775·25	781·25
	60	782–790	783·25	789·25
	61	790–798	791·25	797·25
	62	798–806	799·25	805·25
	63	806–814	807·25	813·25
	64	814–822	815·25	821·25
	65	822–830	823·25	829·25
	66	830–838	831·25	837·25
	67	838–846	839·25	845·25
	68	846–854	847·25	853·25

Aerial Group E (Brown) Channels 39–68

Aerial Group D (Blue) Channels 49–68

These carriers being close to the channel in use produce intermediate frequencies in the receiver which lie close to the bandpass of the i.f. stages.

Local Station Channels

Each local area transmitter is allocated four channels. The lowest channel is called $\underline{n}$ and the other channels are usually arranged according to the format of $\underline{n+3}$, $\underline{n+6}$ and $\underline{n+10}$ or alternatively $\underline{n+4}$, $\underline{n+7}$ and $\underline{n+10}$. Some examples of local station channels are given in Table 6.3.

It will be noted that some transmitters are allocated the same channel numbers, *e.g.* Emley Moor and Wenvoe. Mutual (co-channel) interference does not normally occur between such transmitters since they are far enough apart geographically.

Including the highest and lowest channel in any group of a particular transmitting station, there are 11 channel spacings. Thus, to receive the four local programmes efficiently, a receiving aerial should have a bandwidth of $11 \times 8\,\text{MHz} = 88\,\text{MHz}$.

Table 6.3 Examples of Local Station Channels.

	BBC 1	IBA 1	BBC 2	IBA 2	Aerial Group
Crystal Palace*	26	23	33	30	A red
Emley Moor	44	47	51	41	B yellow
Belmont	22	25	28	32	A red
Winter Hill	55	59	62	65	C green
Mendip	58	61	64	54	C green
Wenvoe	44	41	51	47	B yellow

* Non-standard group.

CHAPTER SEVEN

RECEIVING AERIALS FOR TELEVISION

Objectives

1 Explain the main features of space wave propagation at u.h.f.
2 Describe the main features of Yagi arrays for reception of television signals.
3 State the need for matching to the feeder cable and outline the operation of attenuators, signal splitters and diplexers.

SPACE WAVE

TERRESTRIAL TELEVISION BROADCASTS are radiated using the **space-wave**, as for v.h.f.-f.m. radio broadcasts discussed in Chapter 1. Television reception is thus limited to the line-of-sight path of the transmitted wave, see Fig. 7.1. With a transmitting aerial height of 1000 feet, the distance to the horizon is about 38 miles.

Clearly, a high elevation is desirable for the transmitting aerial as it will 'see' a more distant horizin thereby increasing the service area. It is important that the maximum power radiated from the aerial should not be horizontal to the earth as it will never reach the earth at all. The transmitting aerial is thus designed **to tilt the beam downwards by half or three-quarters of a** **degree** so that maximum power is directed towards the edges of the service area.

The area served by a television transmitter may be greater that the distance to the horizon, due mainly to the phenomenon of 'diffraction'. When an electromagnetic wave strikes the terrain at the horizon it is diffracted, *i.e.* it spreads downwards. The idea is shown in Fig. 7.2 which compares the effect for u.h.f. and v.h.f. waves. The longer the wavelength of the transmission the more the diffraction. At Band 5 frequencies the diffraction is small. Thus, beyond the horizon it is possible to pick up the television wave but the field strength falls off rapidly particularly so at u.h.f. where the area beyond the horizon is in deep shadow.

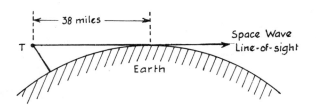

Fig. 7.1 Horizon of 38 miles from transmitting aerial of height 1000 feet.

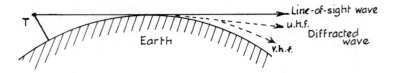

Fig. 7.2 Diffraction of wave at horizon increasing transmitter service area.

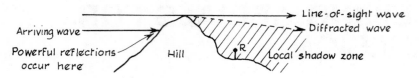

Fig. 7.3 Local shadow zone created by large hill.

Another important factor affecting the propagation of the television signal is the terrain of the country in the path of the wave, especially at high frequencies. Hills, large buildings and forests *etc.* can create local shadow zones as illustrated in Fig. 7.3. A receiving aerial lying deep in the shadow zone will be starved of signal. It is this effect more than diffraction which reduces the service area of u.h.f. transmissions compared with v.h.f. transmissions. Trees are a serious obstacle to u.h.f. propagation particularly when in full leaf. It appears that the branches introduce more loss of signal than the trunks. Thus, if it is impracticable to raise the receiving aerial above the trees, it may be beneficial to lower it provided that this did not encounter any other obstruction.

Effect of the Troposphere

Reception in the fringe area of a transmitter is affected by refraction of high angle waves from the transmitting aerial by the troposphere, see Fig. 7.4.

The **troposphere** is the region of changing weather and clouds extending from sea level up to an altitude of about 10 miles. Refraction of television waves by this part of the earth's atmosphere is caused by the reducing permitivity, and hence refractive index with increasing height, of the water vapour content in the troposphere. Refraction by the troposphere thus causes some signal energy to travel around the earth into the shadow zone of the line-of-sight signal.

It may be thought that the effect of tropospheric propagation would be beneficial as regards fringe area reception. However, signals refracted by the troposphere vary in amplitude with changing weather conditions and cause fading, resulting in unreliable reception. Thus the service area of a transmitter is limited by signals received via the troposphere.

Signals propagated by the troposphere are

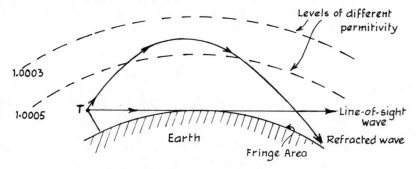

Fig. 7.4 Refraction by the troposphere.

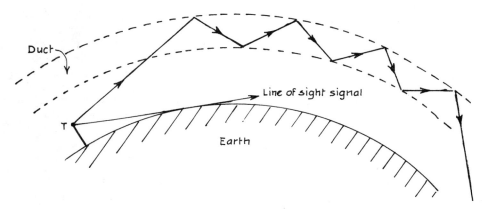

Fig. 7.5 Duct propagation.

important for another reason. During stable weather conditions following a hot day, a 'duct' is formed between layers in the troposphere which 'traps' the signal and causes many reflections as indicated in Fig. 7.5. In such conditions the signal can be propagated over distances up to several hundred miles.

These 'ducted' signals can cause interference between stations operating on common channels (**co-channel interference**), in spite of the fact that for the normally received signal, co-channel transmitting stations are far apart geographically.

Co-channel interference may be reduced by:

(1) Using different polarisations for co-channel stations, *e.g.* horizontal polarisation for one station and vertical polarisation for the co-channel station. This does not give complete protection because propagation effects cause cross-polarisation.
(2) 'Off-setting' the transmitter frequencies by one-thirds or two-thirds of line frequency which reduces the visibility of the interfering pattern.

RECEIVING AERIALS

Aerials intended for terrestrial television reception at u.h.f. are invariably based on the **half-wave dipole** which was considered in Chapter 1.

The overall length of a half-wave dipole at 500 MHz (Band 4) would be about:

$$\frac{3 \times 10^8}{500 \times 10^6 \times 2} \times \frac{95}{100} = 28 \cdot 5 \, \text{cm}$$

and at 800 MHz (Band 5) would be approximately:

$$\frac{3 \times 10^8}{800 \times 10^6 \times 2} \times \frac{95}{100} = 17 \cdot 8 \, \text{cm}$$

A transmitter radiates a certain number of kilowatts of energy which is dissipated in the form of a 'field' that becomes weaker as it progresses from the transmitter. The field can be expressed as the p.d. set up between any two points lying parallel to the electric component and spaced one metre apart. It is usually quoted in mV or μV per metre. The higher the frequency of the transmission, the shorter is the length of the dipole and hence the smaller the field that the aerial intercepts. For example a half-wave dipole operating at 800 MHz of length 17·8 cm (as calculated above) and suitably orientated in a field of 5 mV per metre would have an induced voltage (on open-circuit) of:

$$\frac{17 \cdot 8}{100} \times 5 \, \text{mV} = 0 \cdot 89 \, \text{mV}.$$

In practice the actual voltage would be about two-thirds of this value, since not every part of the dipole is of the same 'usefulness' in intercepting the wave. The current and voltage distribution in a half-wave dipole is shown in Fig. 7.6. It will be seen that the current is at maximum at the centre and zero at the ends and has a sinusoidal distribution. The average

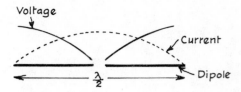

Fig. 7.6 Voltage and current distribution in half-wave dipole.

value of a half-sine wave is $\frac{2}{\pi}$ (approx $\frac{2}{3}$). Not all of the voltage as calculated above will actually reach the receiver (see later). Thus for equally radiated powers, the signal picked up in a Band 5 half-wave dipole is considerably less than that induced in a Band 2 half-wave dipole.

Because of its small signal pick up and poor directivity the plain half-wave dipole is rarely used on its own for television reception at u.h.f. but is usually incorporated into a Yagi array employing a reflector and a number of directors.

Yagi Arrays

When a plain dipole is incorporated into a Yagi array its centre impedance is lowered from 75 ohm to around 20 ohm and for this reason a 'folded dipole' is used as the main element in the array as was explained in Chapter 1.

A **folded dipole** is two half-wave dipoles connected in parallel provided the spacing between the two is small compared with the wavelength. If the diameters w_1 and w_2 are the same as in Fig. 7.7(a) the centre impedance is

increased by a factor of four to 300 ohm. When incorporated into a Yagi array of suitable design this impedance may be lowered to around 75 ohm to provide a good match to 75 ohm coaxial cable. By making the diameters unequal, the centre impedance of the folded dipole can be varied over a large range (greater or smaller than 300 ohm). Advantage is taken of this in the design of arrays having many directors and in some arrays, the folded dipole is made from a single sheet of metal, suitably cut and bent to provide unequal width conductors as in Fig. 7.7(c).

A typical 10-element u.h.f. Yagi array is shown in Fig. 7.8. This uses a folded dipole as the main element, eight directors and a 4-rod reflector unit (counted as one element) mounted at right angles to the boom. A multi-rod reflector is a common feature with a u.h.f. array and is used to maintain a high front-to-back ratio over the full bandwidth of the aerial. Some aerial manufacturers mount the reflector unit at an angle to the boom as a corner unit which provides uniform channel performance, ensuring a high front-to-back ratio and at the same time cutting down on wind resistance. In other designs, the reflector is made from a metal sheet with slotted apertures.

Typical parameters for three group A u.h.f. Yagi arrays are given in Table 7.1.

U.H.F. aerials must have a bandwidth of at least 88 MHz for reception of the four local programmes, and in selecting an aerial for a particular group its performance over the channels concerned is important. The solid curve of Fig. 7.9 shows what may occur with

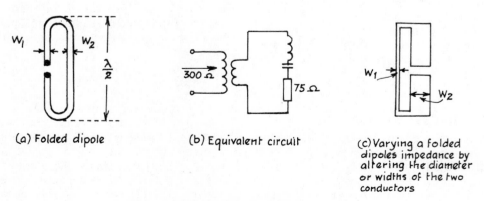

(a) Folded dipole   (b) Equivalent circuit   (c) Varying a folded dipoles impedance by altering the diameter or widths of the two conductors

Fig. 7.7 The folded dipole.

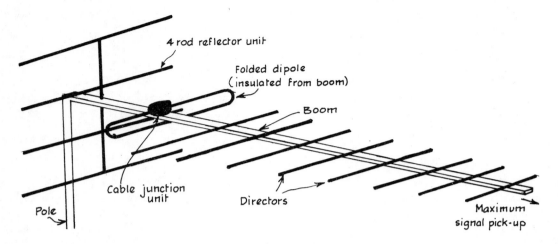

Fig. 7.8 10-Element U.H.F. aerial.

Table 7.1 U.H.F. Aerial parameters.

No. of Elements	Use	Forward gain	Front/Back ratio	Beam width
6	Areas of good signal strength	9·5 dB	25·2 dB	50°
13	Medium range reception	13·0 dB	27·2 dB	38°
18	Long range reception	14·7 dB	30·7 dB	32°

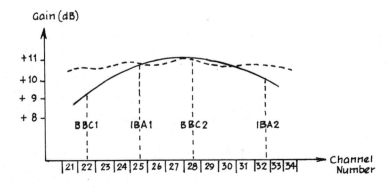

Fig. 7.9 Variation in aerial gain over four local programmes.

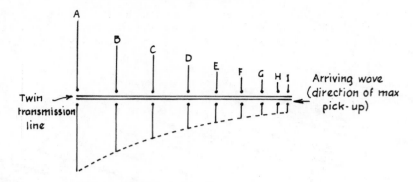

Fig. 7.10 Principle of log periodic aerial.

some aerial designs where the gain falls off at the extremities of its coverage. This may cause unwanted luminance and colour variations between different programmes. The dotted curve shows what might be expected from an aerial of good design where variations are within 1 dB over the full group of channels.

A development of the Yagi array is the **Log-periodic** aerial which consists of a series of dipoles having lengths and spacings which decrease in a logarithmic manner as shown in Fig. 7.10. All the dipoles are connected to a common transmission line which in practice is formed by a double boom. Each dipole has shorter dipoles on one side and longer dipoles on the other so it behaves like a Yagi array.

Consider a wave arriving as shown having a frequency which corresponds to the resonant frequency of dipole C. As the wave moves along the array it first meets the shorter non-resonant dipoles I, H, G, F *etc* to which it gives up energy. As the wave progresses it gives up more and more energy to the intercepting dipoles until it reaches dipole C

where maximum energy is yielded. The next element that the wave 'sees' is dipole B which behaves like a conventional Yagi reflector, thus the rest of the array to the left of dipole B contributes little to the aerial operation.

As the frequency of the arriving wave is reduced, making, say, dipole B the resonant one, more of the array is involved in its operation. If the frequency is reduced then fewer dipoles are involved. Thus the log-periodic aerial is capable of operating over a wide bandwidth (limited only by the physical size of the array).

Each dipole is connected to the double boom as illustrated in Fig. 7.11. Like the Yagi array, the log-periodic aerial has a high front-to-back ratio and good directivity and so is suitable for rejecting unwanted signal reflections or interference. Because of its wide bandwidth capabilities this type of aerial may be designed to cover any aerial group in the u.h.f. band. At least one aerial manufacturer offers a log-periodic aerial which covers all of the u.h.f. channels. This feature is particularly

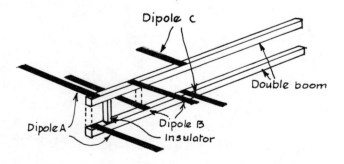

Fig. 7.11 Connection of the dipole rods to the double boom in a log periodic aerial.

useful when the aerial is to be used in different locations, *e.g.* with a receiver fitted in a touring caravan.

Aerial Mounting

An outdoor aerial mounted clear of any obstructions and above roof-top always provides the stronger signal. When assessing the signal strength of a roof mounted aerial always stand behind the reflector and well clear of the array.

Because of its compactness, a u.h.f. aerial may be mounted in the loftspace for those who are obliged to use an indoor aerial. However, the signal is about 10 dB lower than the above roof mounted array (about 5 dB is due to loss of height and 5 dB due to attenuation through the roof material). Apart from this there may be further deterioration due to the presence of electrical wiring, metal pipes, water tanks *etc* which upset the polar response of the aerial and cause reflections resulting in ghost images.

Since the outer conductor of the coaxial feeder cable is at or near earth potential, the cable should run from the main element junction unit **along the boom** and **down the pole** of the array **keeping it well away from the aerial elements** to avoid disturbance of the polar response.

Room or 'set-top' aerials are available in a variety of designs. Some consist of a small Yagi array whilst others use a pair of circular or square elements arranged as a main element-reflector system. Although there is a measure of directivity with these simple arrays, the performance is greatly influenced by positioning. A 'set-top' aerial may suffer a signal loss of about 25 dB compared with the 'above roof' aerial. Most of this is due to loss of aerial height, but some is due to attenuation through outside walls, party walls or partition walls. Reflections from objects and people inside the room tend to introduce variations in signal which can be most disturbing when people move about.

Multipath Reception (Ghosting)

Television signals reflected by buildings, gas holders and land masses *etc* may cause ghost images to appear on the receiver screen. The diagrams of Fig. 7.12 show two possible reflected signal paths. In both cases a 'direct' and a 'reflected' signal arrive at the receiving aerial.

Since the direct and reflected signals travel over different path lengths, there will be a time difference between the receipt of the two signals at the receiver. In addition, there will be an amplitude difference, with the direct signal generally being the larger of the two. This may not always be so as the direct signal may suffer a greater attenuation than the reflected signal depending upon the intervening terrain in the two signal paths.

The speed of travel of radio waves is 186,000 miles per second or 0·186 miles per microsecond and the time taken for the receiver c.r.t. beam to travel across the screen is 52 μs (the active line scan). Hence if the ghost image was displaced from the main image by a complete line it would correspond to a difference in path length of:

$$52 \times 0.186 \simeq 9.7 \text{ miles.}$$

Thus with a screen 18″ wide, each inch of displacement corresponds to:

$$\frac{9.7}{18} \simeq 0.5 \text{ mile}$$

This might be worth remembering as it may

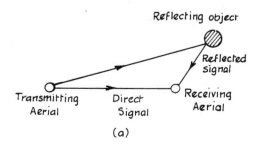

(a)

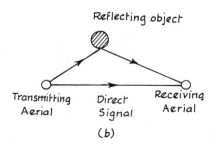

(b)

Fig. 7.12 Reflections causing ghost images.

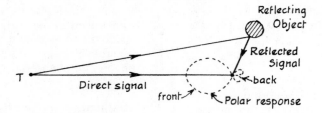

(a) Use of aerial front-to-back ratio

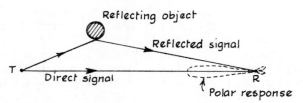

(b) Use of aerial with narrow beam width

Fig. 7.13 Minimising pick-up of reflected signal.

help in determining what is causing the ghost image.

Ghost images may be positive or negative depending upon the relative phases at the receiver of the arriving direct and reflected signals. The effect is most noticeable on the luminance information where the ghost image is black following a white main image (negative ghost image), or white following a white main image (positive ghost image).

The effects of ghost images of the type illustrated in Fig. 7.12 may be reduced by positioning and choice of aerial array. Fig. 7.13(a) shows how a directional array may be used to deal with a reflected signal originating from an object at the back of the aerial. Here the reflected signal is diminished by the high front-to-back ratio of the aerial. By using a more directional array, the reflected signal in Fig. 7.13(b) is diminished by the narrow acceptance angle of the aerial.

Metal objects, *e.g.* other aerials, poles and metal gutters *etc* close to the aerial may upset the polar response which can lead to ghost images, so a site should be chosen which is well clear of such objects. Short-term ghosting by nearby objects often gives rise to 'soft' vertical edges to the picture.

Another cause of reflections is from flying aircraft ('aircraft flutter'). Waves reflected from a moving aeroplane give rise to a varying time (phase) difference between the receipt of the direct and reflected signals, which causes large changes in the resultant signal and produces a 'pumping' effect on the picture. Aircraft flutter takes place at a few cycles per second but the effects depend upon the speed of the aircraft and whether it is moving down the beam or across it. From the aerial point of view there is little that can be done to avoid this effect.

FEEDER CABLE

The feeder cable connected between the aerial and receiver input, see Fig. 7.14 is employed to transfer the received signal energy from aerial to receiver with minimum loss of signal power.

The two conductors need not be parallel wires as shown but may take the form of a wire

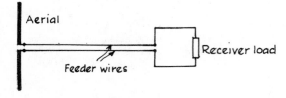

Fig. 7.14 The feeder cable.

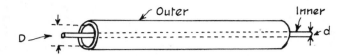

Fig. 7.15 Coaxial cable.

braid outer conductor and an inner (coaxial) conductor separated by insulation, as illustrated in Fig. 7.15.

Coaxial cables for television have been standardised in the U.K. and the dimensions are such that the impedance is 75 ohms. Although having disadvantages, the coaxial cable has the advantage that the outer conductor may be at earth potential and thus screen the inner. The impedance of 75 ohm was not decided by accident. The ratio of D to d determines the impedance and with air insulation it was found that the ratio which provides the minimum loss is one that results in an impedance of 75 ohms.

Matching

In order that maximum signal power is delivered to the receiver, it is necessary to match from the aerial terminals to the coaxial feeder and from the coaxial feeder to the receiver input. Thus if a coaxial cable of 75 ohms characteristic impedance (Z_o) is used, the aerial impedance and the receiver input impedance must also be 75 ohms for maximum power transfer, see Fig. 7.16.

Under the matched condition **only half of the available aerial voltage will arrive at the receiver**. Consider a practical example of a Yagi array with a forward gain of 9·5 dB operating at 800 MHz and lying in a field strength of 5 mV/metre. The length of the aerial main element would be 17·8 cm and 9·5 dB represents a voltage gain of 2·99. Thus the open-circuit e.m.f. of the aerial is:

$$\frac{17·8}{100} \times 5 \times 2·99 \times \frac{2}{3} = 1·77\,\text{mV}$$

(the factor ⅔ is discussed on page 90)

Thus the signal arriving at the receiver input will be $1·77/2 = 0·89\,\text{mV}$ (approx).

The above assumes a perfect feeder cable, *i.e.* no losses. In practice the cable introduces an attenuation, typically about 2 dB per 10 metre length for 'low-loss' coaxial cable using cellular polythene insulation.

When the feeder cable is correctly terminated by its Z_o as in Fig. 7.16, signal energy is dissipated in the receiver input impedance as fast as it is propagated down the cable from the aerial. Under this condition voltage and current in the cable is the same everywhere (neglecting feeder losses).

If, however, there is a mismatch between cable and receiver impedance then when the 'forward signal' arrives at the receiver it is reflected back down the cable towards the aerial. As a result the 'forward' and 'reflected' waves produce interference effects which causes 'in-phase' and out-of-phase' voltage and current distribution or **standing waves** down the cable.

The main effects of mismatch are:

(1) Loss of signal power at the receiver.
(2) Radiation from the feeder cable possibly resulting in interference and patterning.
(3) Incorrect impedance at receiver input which may upset receiver tuning resulting in possible 'overshoot' or 'smearing' of the picture image.
(4) Ghosting.

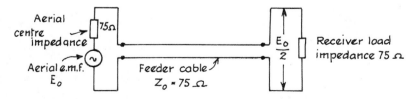

Fig. 7.16 Matched aerial–receiver system.

Since the impedance of the feeder cable is dependent on the ratio of D to d, it is important that during installation the cable is not 'squashed' when it is stabled as this will alter the impedance at that point producing a possible mismatch.

ATTENUATORS, SPLITTERS AND DIPLEXERS

Attenuators

In areas of very high signal strength it may be necessary to fit an attenuator between the aerial down lead and the receiver input socket to prevent overloading of the receiver.

A T-type attenuator is shown in Fig. 7.17. In designing an attenuator to provide a given attenuation of the input signal, the impedance seen 'looking' into the attenuator from either direction must be the same (usually 75 ohm for television). The values of the resistances are:

$$R_1 = \frac{R(A-1)}{A+1}; \ R_2 = \frac{R(2A)}{A^2-1}$$

where R is the nominal impedance of the system, *e.g.* 75 ohm and A is the ratio of input-to-output signal.

For example, suppose $R = 75$ ohm and an attenuation of 18 dB (8:1) is required.

$$R_1 = \frac{75(8-1)}{8+1} = 58{\cdot}33 \, \Omega \ (56 \, \Omega)$$

$$R_2 = \frac{75(2 \times 8)}{8^2-1} = 19{\cdot}04 \, \Omega \ (20 \, \Omega)$$

Since the values are not critical, the nearest preferred value resistors (shown in brackets) may be used. Although this simple attenuator may easily be constructed, it should be noted that the self-inductance of the resistors and stray capacitance may, at u.h.f., result in an attenuation quite different from the calculated

value. Commercial attenuators (in-line attenuators) are often designed for use at v.h.f. and u.h.f. They are usually of the coaxial type and are available with fixed attenuation levels, *e.g.* 6 dB, 12 dB, 18 dB *etc.*

Splitters

It may be necessary to operate more than one receiver from a common aerial system. The receiver inputs cannot be connected in parallel without upsetting the matching. Two receivers may be operated from a single aerial using a 'splitter unit' employing three resistors as shown in Fig. 7.18.

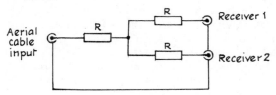

Fig. 7.18 Two-way splitter unit.

The value of each resistor is the same and may be calculated from:

$$R = \frac{n-1}{n+1} Z_o$$

where n is the number of receivers and Z_o is the nominal impedance of the system (usually 75 ohm). Thus for a two-way splitter:

$$R = \frac{2-1}{2+1} \times 75 = 25 \text{ ohm}$$

To operate three receivers (using four resistors) each resistor would be:

$$R = \frac{3-1}{3+1} \times 75 = 37{\cdot}5 \text{ ohm}$$

In both cases the nearest preferred value resistors would be used. If an output is not

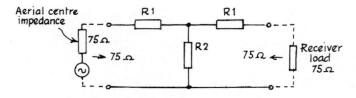

Fig. 7.17 T–Attenuator.

required it should be terminated with a 75 ohm resistor so as to maintain correct matching.

Operating receivers in this way obviously reduces the signal to each receiver. With two receivers there is a 6 dB loss of signal voltage at each output compared with the available input to the splitter unit. For three receivers the loss is about 10 dB. Thus when a large number of receivers are to be supplied from a common aerial system more elaborate arrangements are necessary and distribution amplifiers become essential.

Feeder Extensions

To operate a single receiver in one of two locations, the feeder may be extended as shown in Fig. 7.19. In position A the extension feeder is not in use. In position B, the cable from A to B is plugged into the socket at A. More than two operating positions may be provided simply by repeating the extension arrangement between position A and B.

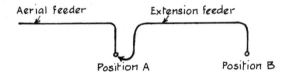

Fig. 7.19 Providing two operating positions for a television receiver.

Combining and Dividing Units

If two aerials are to be combined in a common down-lead, a 'combiner' or 'diplexer' must be used. The aerials cannot be connected directly in parallel as the matching would be upset, also there may be a problem with ghost

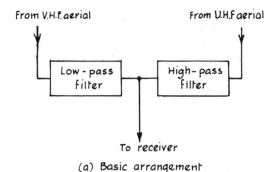

(a) Basic arrangement

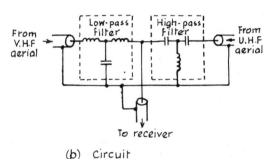

(b) Circuit

Fig. 7.20 Combining unit (diplexer).

signals as each aerial will pick up some signal to which the other aerial is resonant.

It may be necessary to combine a Band 2 v.h.f. radio aerial with a Band 4/5 u.h.f. television aerial into a common down lead and the arrangement in Fig. 7.20 may be used. The combiner consists of two T-type filters, one being a high pass and the other a low pass. Each aerial thus 'sees' the feeder cable via its associated filter but the aerials do not 'see' one another. Fig. 7.21 shows the response of a typical v.h.f./u.h.f. combiner with a crossover frequency of about 350 MHz.

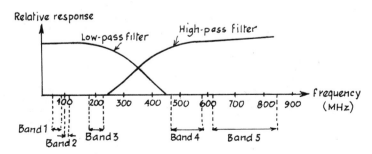

Fig. 7.21 Response of v.h.f/u.h.f. diplexer.

At the receiver end of the cable the Band 2 and Band 4/5 signals must be separated from one another and fed to the respective receivers. Since a combiner is reversible in action it may be used to separate the signals in the down-lead as shown in Fig. 7.22. It is now called a 'divider'; the essential difference between a combiner and a divider is one of construction. A combiner has to be rugged and weather-proof since it is normally mounted outdoors, whereas a divider is normally mounted indoors and has a more pleasing appearance.

All combiners and dividers introduce some loss but this is usually small in a well designed unit. Whether the arrangement shown in Fig. 7.22 is used or separate down-leads from the two aerials, depends upon the installation. If the feeder run is short, separate down-leads may be the better arrangement; but with a long feeder run it may be more economical to use a combiner and divider. It should be noted that any existing feeder previously used at v.h.f. may not be suitable at u.h.f. owing to the higher cable attenuation at u.h.f.

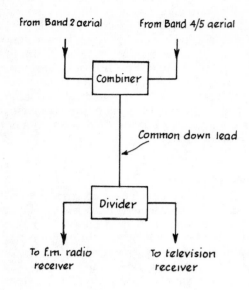

Fig. 7.22 *Use of combiner and divider units.*

CHAPTER EIGHT

TELEVISION RECEIVER BLOCK DIAGRAMS

Objectives
1 To show by means of a block diagram how advanced technical features and facilities fit into the overall scheme of a television receiver system and to give reasons for the adoption of the standard Peritelevision connection system.
2 To establish a basic block diagram for a colour television receiver to embrace the circuits and techniques to be described in the remaining chapters of this volume.

A GOOD BLOCK diagram enables the servicing technician to quickly become familiar with the path of the signal and its processing in various parts of the complete circuit. This is particularly important in today's complex receiver designs where integrated circuits are used to perform most of the circuit functions, some of which are not directly related to the position of the i.c. in the circuit diagram layout. Unfortunately a block schematic is not always included with the service information and the technician has to fall back on basic block schematics memorised earlier.

GENERAL COLOUR TELEVISION RECEIVER SCHEMATIC

The general block diagram of Fig. 8.1 shows the main sub-systems and advanced features that may be found in a domestic colour television receiver. The arrangement is not based on a particular television receiver since each receiver design will incorporate its own unique features, but is intended as a general guide to show how many current technical features fit into the overall television receiver scheme.

Frequency synthesis tuning under the control of a microprocessor program stored in a ROM is now a common feature. After initial tuning to local channels, the tuning data is permanently stored in a RAM which is powered by a lithium or nickel-cadmium battery when the receiver is switched 'off'. Using commands from either the infra-red remote control transmitter or from the receiver front panel keyboard, the microprocessor may control all switching functions within the receiver and adjustment of 'analogue controls' such as brightness, colour and contrast.

Many receivers now incorporate a teletext decoder as a standard sub-system to enable the display of text and graphics from the CEEFAX and ORACLE binary data signals transmitted in the field blanking intervals. A 'fastext' facility is often provided to enable the viewer to select certain related or linked pages very quickly using four prompts which are displayed in different colours.

With display tube designs reaching the

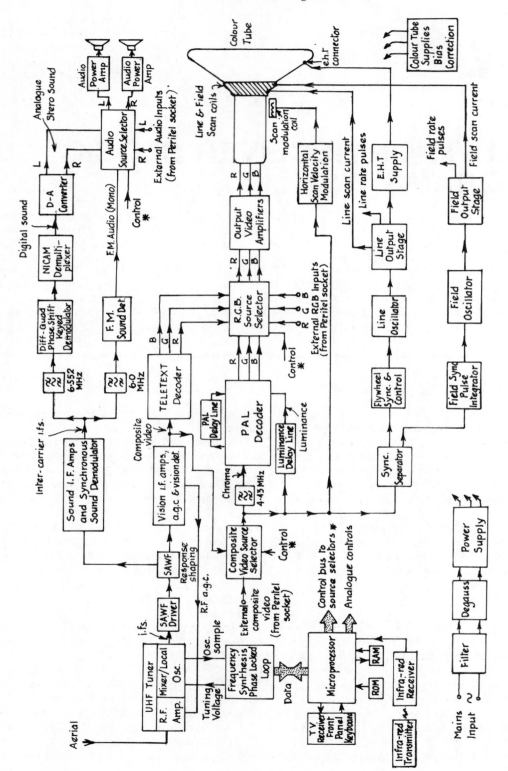

Fig. 8.1 General block diagram showing the main sub-system and features to be found in a colour television receiver.

limits of possible definition, some receivers may employ 'velocity scan modulation' techniques to enhance picture definition by using an auxiliary horizontal scan coil driven by a differentiated luminance signal.

Receivers fitted with NICAM boards now offer stereo sound as an option to the normal mono sound. Using the NICAM system it is possible to receive up to three separate languages; one in each NICAM channel and the other on the normal mono sound channel with selection of the chosen language via the remote hand unit. Some designs offer further enhancement of the sound reproduction by arranging for extra speakers to be connected between the L and R audio amplifiers to provide 'Surround Sound'.

With the use in the home of other audio and visual sources such as home computers, electronic games and video cassette recorders *etc*, it is increasingly common to find television receivers equipped with baseband inputs (and outputs). Digital signal sources such as electronic games and computers provide R–G–B signals of high definition and quality and such signals may be directly coupled to the television receiver. This avoids the degradation of signal quality that would occur if the baseband signals were modulated onto a u.h.f. carrier in the PAL format and applied to the aerial input in the normal way. For sources such as video cassette recorders, the video signal is normally available only in composite PAL form and the video signal can be introduced directly to the PAL decoder.

SCART or Peritelevision Connector

Interconnection between items of domestic audio-visual equipment of different manufacture is made easier if a standard interface system is adopted. The most comprehensive base-band interface to emerge is the **SCART** system proposed by the French SCART committee. It is also known as the **Peritel** system and includes a 21-pin connector (Euroconnector) which provides for the transfer of composite video (PAL, SECAM and NTSC), R–G–B base-band signals, stereo audio and binary data control signals between the television receiver and external equipment.

The use of a Peritel plug and socket system is not limited to a single external device as any number of Peritel sockets can be provided on the back of the television receiver with a control capability of addressing the desired external unit. The uniquely configured 21-pin socket connector is shown in Fig. 8.2 together with the standardised status of the pins. The system not only specifies the pin status but also the level and impedance expected from the external signal source.

Typical uses of the Peritel 21-pin socket connector include:

(1) **Mono/Stereo Audio Input** from radio and tape recorders *etc*.
(2) **Stereo Audio Output** to Hi-Fi equipment.
(3) **Composite Video Input** from video cameras, games and recorders.
(4) **Composite Video Output** to video recorder or monitor.

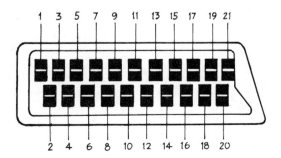

Fig. 8.2 SCART or Peritelevision socket.

Table 8.1 Peritel socket standardised status of pins.

Pin Number	Status	Level/Impedance
1	Audio output (R)	500 mV r.m.s. (2 V max) $\leqslant 1\,\mathrm{k\Omega}$
2	Audio input (R)	500 mV r.m.s. (2 V max) $\geqslant 10\,\mathrm{k\Omega}$
3	Audio output (L)	500 mV r.m.s. (2 V max) $\leqslant 1\,\mathrm{k\Omega}$
4	Audio common	
5	Blue component common	
6	Audio input (L)	500 mV r.m.s. (2 V max) $\geqslant 10\,\mathrm{k\Omega}$
7	Blue component input	0·7 V pp $\pm 3\,$dB (75 ohm)
8	Mode switching (Television/Video)	Television 0–2 V (logic 0) Video 9·5–12 V (logic 1)
9	Green component common	
10	No connection	
11	Green component input	0·7 V pp $\pm 3\,$dB (75 ohm)
12	No connection	
13	Red component common	
14	No connection	
15	Red component input	0·7 V pp $\pm 3\,$dB (75 ohm)
16	Rapid blanking switching	0–0·4 V (Television) 1–3 V (RGB)
17	Video common	
18	Rapid blanking common	
19	Composite video output	1 V pp $\pm 3\,$dB (75 ohm)
20	Composite video input	1 V pp $\pm 3\,$dB (75 ohm)
	Composite sync. input	0·3 V pp (75 ohm)
	Luminance input	1 V pp $\pm 3\,$dB (75 ohm)
21	Cable screen	

(5) **RGB Input** from video cameras, games and computers *etc*.

BASIC COLOUR TELEVISION RECEIVER SCHEMATIC

A basic block diagram for a colour television receiver is given in Fig. 8.3. It will be seen that this is similar to the diagram of Fig. 8.1 except that the Teletext decoder and Nicam stereo sound sub-systems have been omitted in addition to advanced technical features such as scan velocity modulation and external source selection.

The schematic of Fig. 8.3 will be used as an introduction to television receiver technology and should be referred to and studied in parallel with the information given in the remaining chapters. The PAL decoder will be treated as a single block as its internal functions will not be considered in any great detail in this volume. However, for those who need to have a grasp of its basic operation, the decoder schematic of Fig. 8.4 is included together with an outline description.

PAL DECODER OUTLINE DESCRIPTION

Waveforms given on the diagram of Fig. 8.4 illustrate the decoder operation during the receipt of standard colour bars.

The output of the vision detector contains the composite picture signal, *i.e.* luminance, chrominance, subcarrier burst and sync. pulses which are fed *via* an emitter-follower stage block (1) to a video amplifier block (2). In this stage the chrominance and burst signals are extracted from the composite waveform using a fairly low Q tuned circuit. This tuned circuit has a bandwidth of approximately

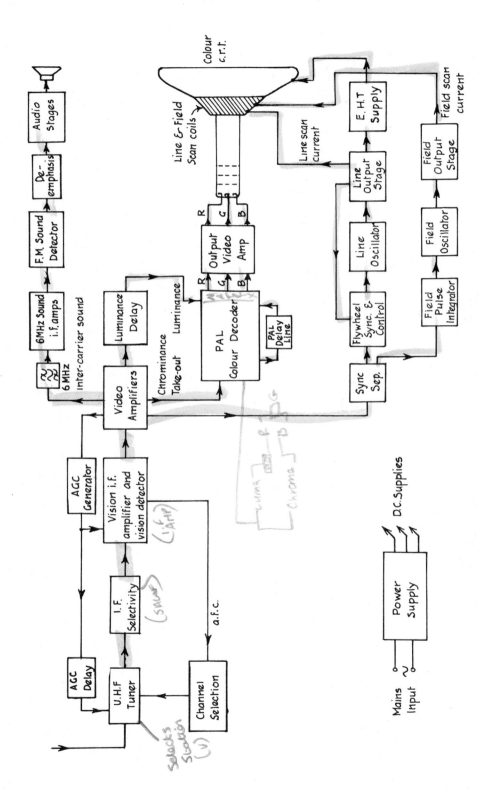

Fig. 8.3 Basic colour receiver block diagram.

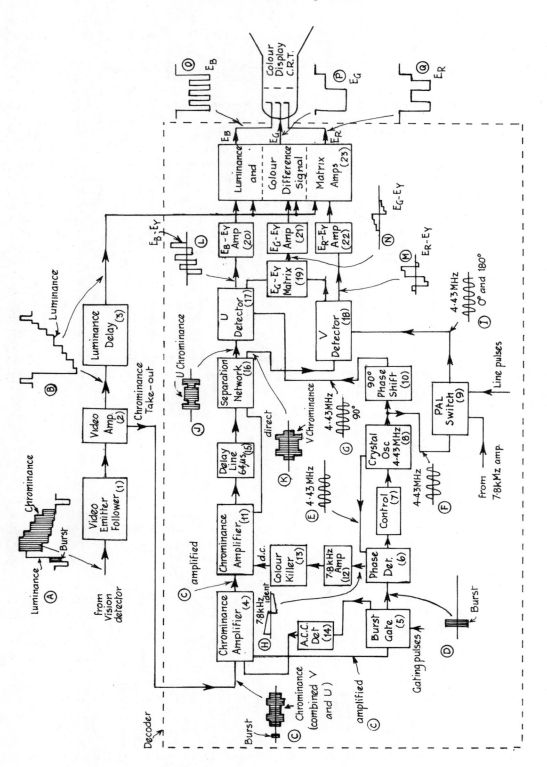

Fig. 8.4 Basic PAL decoder block schematic.

± 1 MHz centred on 4·43 MHz and embraces the chrominance and burst signals. The same tuned circuit may also be used to prevent the chrominance and burst from reaching the luminance channel. Thus the output of the video amplifier contains luminance and sync. signals only which are passed *via* the luminance delay stage to block (23) in the decoder.

The chrominance signal fed to block (4) in the decoder contains frequencies extending from approximately 3·43 MHz up to 5·43 MHz and so contains a small amount of luminance signal energy extracted, together with the chrominance signal in block (2). However, the luminance signal energy has an insignificant effect upon the decoder operation. Burst and chrominance are amplified in block (4) which has two outputs. One is fed to a further stage of amplification block (11), and the other to block (5) which will be dealt with first.

(1) Burst Signal Path

It is required to separate the burst signal from the chrominance information so that the burst may be used to synchronise the crystal oscillator, block (8), the output of which is used to recreate the subcarrier (suppressed at the transmitter). Without this subcarrier the chrominance information cannot be detected. The burst gate stage is fed with gating pulses and operates only when the pulses are present. These pulses, which are usually derived from delayed line flyback pulses, having a timing and duration that corresponds to the period of the burst signal, *i.e.* the back porch period. Thus, only the burst signal appears at the output of block (5). The burst signal is then fed to the phase detector, block (6), which also has another input (a continuous sine wave) from the crystal oscillator. The frequency and phase of the burst and oscillator inputs are compared in the phase detector. If there is an error, a correction voltage is fed *via* the control stage (7) which corrects the frequency and phase of the subcarrier oscillations.

(2) Crystal Oscillator Output

A subcarrier oscillation is now positively locked to the burst signal and the output of the oscillator is supplied to the two chrominance signal detectors [blocks (17) and (18)]. Block

10 provides a 90° phase shift so that detection of the *U* signal component (which is at 90° to the *V* signal component) takes place correctly. The subcarrier input to the *V* detector comes from the PAL switch (9). The purpose of this stage is to reinvert the *V* signal component on alternate lines to deal with the PAL signal (remember the *V* signal component is reversed on alternate lines at the transmitter). Block (9) is really two separate stages. It contains a bistable oscillator operating at 7·8 kHz which is triggered by 15·625 kHz line pulses (note that a bistable oscillator divides by two). The output of the bistable oscillator is used to reverse the phase of the subcarrier input block (8) on alternate lines. This is often achieved by using the bistable output to alternately cause one of a pair of diodes to conduct, thereby passing normal (0°) and inverted (180°) subcarrier to the output. To keep the PAL switch in step with the *V* signal alternations at the transmitter, block (9) is fed with a 7·8 kHz locking input from the 7·8 kHz amplifier block (12). This stage is fed with the 'identification signal' derived at the output of the phase detector due to the effects of the 'swinging burst'. The identification signal is an approximate square wave and the purpose of block (12) is to amplify the fundamental component of 7·8 kHz.

(3) Chrominance Signal Path

Return now to block (4) and consider the other output of the first chrominance amplifier which is fed to block (11). The gain of the first chrominance amplifier is normally controlled by an a.c.c. (automatic chrominance control) voltage derived by rectifying the burst signal in the a.c.c. detector of block (14). The a.c.c. voltage maintains a constant burst signal amplitude by controlling the gain of block (4) regardless of changes in amplitude of the signal input to the decoder. Block (11) provides further amplification of the chrominance signal to drive the delay line in block (15). The second chrominance amplifier is operational only during colour transmissions, *i.e.* on monochrome transmissions the stage is cut off. This is achieved by providing the forward bias for this transistor amplifying stage from the colour killer stage. Block (13) rectifies the output of the 7·8 kHz amplifier and the resulting d.c. is used to bias on block (11). As there is no output from the 7·8 kHz amplifier during monochrome transmissions (no swinging burst present), the chrominance channel is cut off or 'killed'. This prevents coloured noise from spoiling the monochrome picture. The burst signal present at the input to block (11) is not required and may be removed by applying a suitable gating pulse to this stage to cut it off during the burst period.

The amplified chrominance signal output of block (11) feeds the delay line (15) and the separation network (16). The delay line provides the necessary line period delay of $64\,\mu\text{s}$ so that an electrical average of adjacent transmitted lines of chrominance information may be taken. To produce this comparatively long delay, an ultrasonic delay line is used. In the separation network the 'delayed' and 'direct' inputs are electrically averaged and at the same time the V and U components of the signal are separated from one another.

Separated U and V signal components are then fed to their respective detectors (17) and (18) which also receive subcarrier inputs as previously described. These stages synchronously detect the V and U chrominance signals to provide colour-difference signals at their outputs.

(4) Colour-Difference Signal Path

The $E_B - E_Y$ and $E_R - E_Y$ colour-difference signals (0–1 MHz) appearing at the outputs of the detectors are fed to blocks (20) and (22) where they are amplified. Suitable portions and polarities of the $E_B - E_Y$ and $E_R - E_Y$ signals are also fed to the $E_G - E_Y$ matrix where they are combined to form the $E_G - E_Y$ signal. Block (21) provides amplification of the $E_G - E_Y$ signal. De-weighting of the signals is normally carried out at the

detector outputs by adjusting the gains of the $E_B - E_Y$ and $E_R - E_Y$ channels (the gain of the $E_B - E_Y$ channel is increased relative to the $E_R - E_Y$ channel).

In block (23) which contains three separate amplifying stages, the colour-difference signals from blocks (20), (21) and (22) are matrixed with the luminance signal to provide the primary signals E_R, E_B and E_G. These signals are fed to the cathodes of the tricolour tube to drive the three guns (primary signal drive). On monochrome, when there are no colour-difference signals, the drive to the three guns consists of the luminance signal only.

Variations in decoder design are to be met with in practice and there will be features not shown in this basic schematic. Integrated circuits are now used for all of the decoder functions but these are not suitable for illustrating the basic decoder operation.

MONOCHROME RECEIVER SCHEMATIC

A monochrome television receiver block schematic is given in Fig. 8.5.

The monochrome receiver may be regarded as a simplified version of the colour receiver where the natural tone colour picture is replaced by an unnatural, but acceptable, monochrome image. Thus the monochrome receiver does not require the colour decoder, luminance delay or the three stage output video amplifier and the three gun tricolour display tube is replaced by a single gun monochrome display c.r.t.

Apart from the above differences, it will be seen that schematic format is very similar to the colour receiver block diagram of Fig. 8.3; many of the stages are identical, *e.g.* tuner, vision i.fs., vision detector, sound section, sync. separator and timebases *etc.*

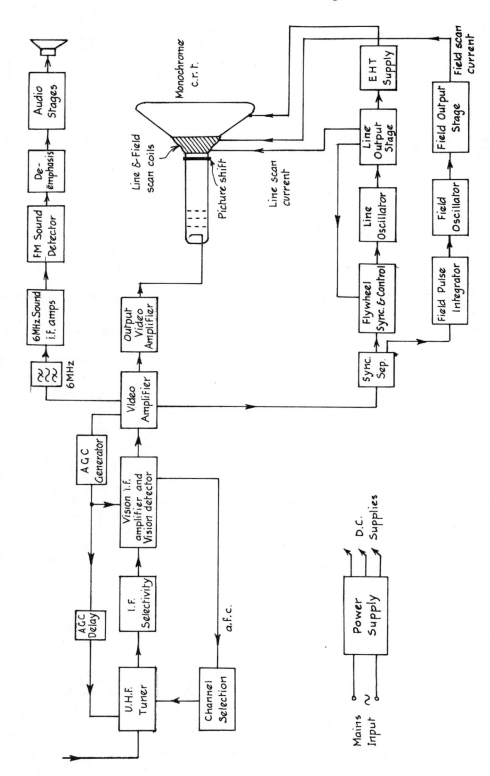

Fig. 8.5 Monochrome receiver block schematic.

CHAPTER NINE

THE U.H.F. TUNER

Objectives

1 Explain the purpose and arrangement of the u.h.f. tuner.
2 Describe Lecher line tuning and basic features of a typical tuner circuit.
3 Examine the tuning voltage supply and describe frequency synthesis tuning.

THE PURPOSE OF the u.h.f. tuner is to select and amplify the desired channel signal and to change its frequency to the receiver i.f. band following normal 'superhet' receiver principles. The tuner unit contains r.f. and frequency changer stages (see Fig. 9.1) and for operation over Bands 4 and 5 a coverage of 470–854 MHz is required.

An r.f. amplifying stage is needed to increase the signal at the mixer input above the critical noise level so as to maintain a high signal-to-noise ratio. This is important because noise generated in the early stages of the receiver may limit its useful gain. In addition, the r.f. stage must provide sufficient selectivity so that only the wanted channel signal is accepted. Any response to the **image signal**

must be low (approaching − 60 dB). The 3 dB bandwidth of the r.f. stage is normally around 10–20 MHz, see Fig. 9.2 and is the essential factor in determining a low response to the image signal and intermediate frequency rejection.

In the U.K. the intermediate frequencies are 39·5 MHz (vision) and 33·5 MHz (mono sound) and this is achieved by tuning the local oscillator to 39·5 MHz **above** the incoming vision carrier. Energy from the local oscillator must not reach the aerial, as aerial or direct radiation from the oscillator circuit may cause interference to other receivers. Thus the u.h.f. tuner must be adequately screened.

At one time v.h.f. tuners were used to receive television transmissions on Bands 1

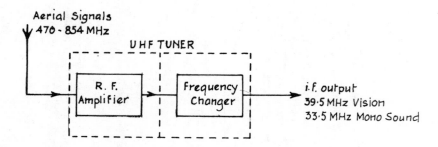

Fig. 9.1 The U.H.F tuner stages.

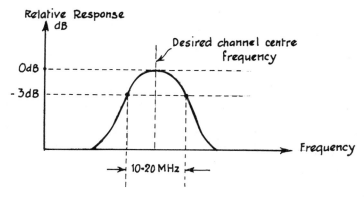

Fig. 9.2 U.H.F. tuner bandwidth.

and 3, but in the U.K. the v.h.f. television transmissions have ceased although they are still used in other countries. However, some television receivers may be equipped with a v.h.f. tuner for accepting 625-line colour signals from cable distribution systems.

Lecher Line Tuning

At Band 4 and 5 frequencies, conventional *L, C* tuned circuits are not practical owing to the very small values of inductance required. For example a 5 pF capacitor requires an

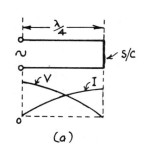

(a)

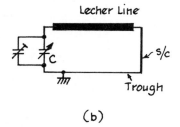

(b)

Fig. 9.3 Lecher line tuning.

inductance of $0.012\,\mu$H to resonate at 800 MHz. This is the approximate self-inductance of a 0·7 mm diameter wire about 1 cm long. Fortunately, where ordinary *L, C* tuning is not feasible, it is possible to use tuned transmission lines.

A pair of transmission lines $\lambda/4$ in length and short-circuited at the far end has ideal voltage and current standing waves as indicated in Fig. 9.3(a). This arrangement behaves in a similar way to a parallel tuned circuit at a resonant frequency *f* to which the lines are exactly $\lambda/4$ in length. To deal with signals in the range of 470–854 MHz it is necessary to tune the lines. It is not practical to vary the physical length of the lines, but their electrical length may be altered by placing a variable capacitor at one end of the line. This is shown in the practical arrangement of Fig. 9.3(b) where one of the lines is formed by the tuner chassis (called the 'trough'). The variable capacitor *C* alters the electrical length of the lecher line allowing it to achieve resonance anywhere within Bands 4 and 5. A trimming capacitor is often included to 'track' the line. Coupling to or from a tuning line may be via a small loop of wire running parallel to the line or by connection to a tap on the line.

U.H.F. Tuner Circuit

Figure 9.4 shows the circuit for a u.h.f. tuner of recent design. Signals from the 75 ohm aerial are coupled to *G*1 of the dual-gate mosfet *TR*1 via *C*1 from the input circuit having a high-pass characteristic. The diode *D*2 limits the amplitude of the input on very

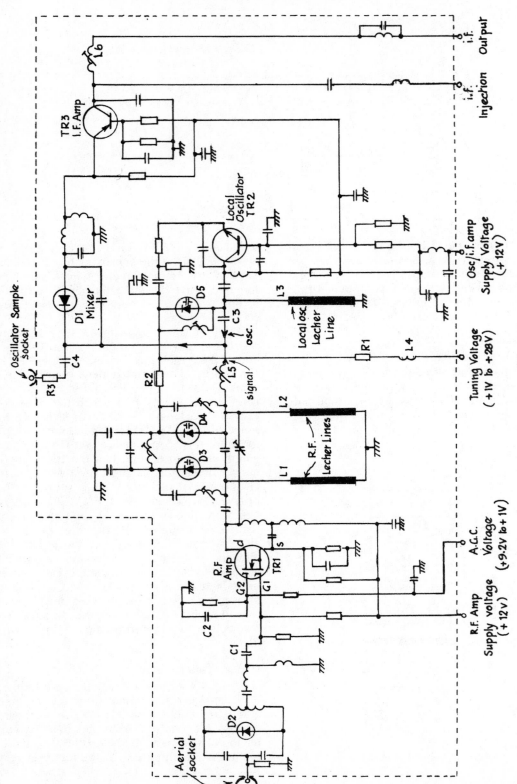

Fig. 9.4 U.H.F. tuner (Mullard) with electronic tuning.

strong signals to prevent overloading. An a.g.c. voltage applied to *G*2 of *TR*1 reduces the gain of *TR*1 on strong signals. Capacitor *C*2 'grounds' *G*2 to signal frequencies. The design of *TR*1 stage ensures a low noise performance.

Amplified signals from *TR*1 stage are developed across the tuned r.f. Lecher Lines *L*1 and *L*2 forming a band-pass circuit. This coupled circuit provides the essential selectivity to ensure good 'image signal' rejection. The lines are electronically tuned with *D*3 tuning *L*1 and *D*4 tuning *L*2, fed from a common tuning voltage supply via *L*4 (r.f. choke), *R*1 and *R*2.

*TR*2, operating in common base, forms a separate local oscillator stage with the oscillator line *L*3 tuned by *D*5 from the common tuning voltage supply. A diode mixer is used here with the oscillator signal fed to the mixer diode *D*1 (Schottky diode) via *C*3 and the r.f. signal applied to *D*1 via *L*5. 'Additive mixing' takes place in *D*1 producing at its output the intermediate frequencies which are amplified by the common base i.f. amplifier *TR*3. A sample of the oscillator signal is fed to a coaxial socket via *C*4 and *R*3 for use with frequency synthesis tuning systems.

The i.f. output is taken from *TR*3 via the i.f. coil *L*6 to be fed to the main vision i.f. strip of the receiver. An 'i.f. injection' input is provided to which the i.f. output of a switched v.h.f. tuner may be applied.

Other tuner designs may offer a grounded base r.f. amplifying transistor with a.g.c. applied to vary the signal applied to its emitter from a diode attenuator connected in the input circuit. In some cases instead of using a separate oscillator and diode mixer as featured above, a combined mixer/oscillator transistor stage is employed.

Tuning Voltage Supply

At one time mechanically variable tuning capacitors were used to tune the resonant lecher lines in the tuner by employing a push-button mechanism that set the tuning capacitor moving vanes to different positions. This type of tuning suffered from a poor reset facility and was later replaced by 'electronic tuning' using vari-cap diodes, like the tuner featured in Fig. 9.4.

It is clearly desireable to have a number of preset channels and when electronic tuning is employed this may be achieved using an arrangement similar to that shown in Fig. 9.5. The tuning voltage must be well stabilised otherwise changes in voltage will cause detuning of the u.h.f. tuner. In the above arrange-

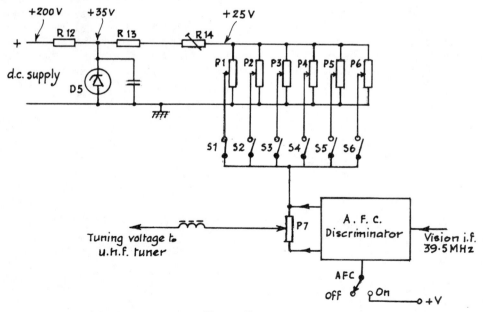

Fig. 9.5 Tuning voltage supply.

ment, the tuning voltage is derived from a 200 V d.c. supply using a zener diode to provide a basic 35 V stabilised supply. In place of D5 an **integrated circuit stabiliser** may be employed. P1–P6 are the tuning potentiometers and the voltage across each is set to 25 V by R14 which determines the tuning range. By pressing any of the six selector buttons which actuate the switches S1–S6, a tuning voltage may be supplied to the tuner from one of the potentiometers. It is therefore possible to select any of six preset channels.

Automatic frequency control (a.f.c.) is commonly used in colour television receivers to off-set frequency drift in the local oscillator due to supply or temperature variations. Changes in the local oscillator frequency are usually sensed by measuring the **frequency error of the vision i.f.** by means of a frequency sensitive circuit or discriminator.

The frequency sensitive circuit (*e.g.* a Foster-Seeley discriminator) produces at its output a d.c. voltage having a magnitude and polarity proportional to any frequency error in the vision i.f. This 'error voltage' may be added in series with the tuning voltage as in Fig. 9.5. The frequency range over which the a.f.c. will 'track' oscillator drift (the 'holding range') may be set by P7.

When tuning the receiver to a station the **a.f.c. switch** is set to the 'off' position which inhibits the a.f.c. circuit and prevents the generation of an error voltage. Once the station has been tuned in approximately, the a.f.c. switch is set to the 'on' position whereupon the a.f.c. circuit will correct any initial tuning error and subsequent drift in the local oscillator frequency.

The diagram of Fig. 9.6 shows the relationship between the magnitude of the tuning voltage and the u.h.f. channel selected. The slope of the tuning, which is dependent upon the characteristics of the vari-cap diodes, is about 22 MHz per volt (channels 21–50) reducing to about 10 MHz per volt (channels 50–68). Thus a tuning voltage variation of, say, 100 mV will cause a frequency variation of between 1 MHz and 2·2 MHz depending upon the channel in use.

Frequency Synthesis Tuning

The principles underlining frequency synthesis tuning for a radio receiver were explained in Chapter 1. Exactly the same principles apply when the tuning technique is adopted in a television receiver. A tuning scheme including 'sweep search' is illustrated in Fig. 9.7 where three main i.cs. are used.

The frequency of the local oscillator in the u.h.f. tuner is made vary accurate by comparing its output (using the 'osc sample') after suitable frequency division with the output of a stable crystal 'reference' oscillator forming part of a phase locked loop. The comparison takes place in a phase detector which generates an 'error voltage' output whenever there is a frequency or phase error between its two inputs. After amplification and filtering the error voltage appears as a tuning voltage and operates with a magnitude and direction so as to pull the local oscillator into step by varying

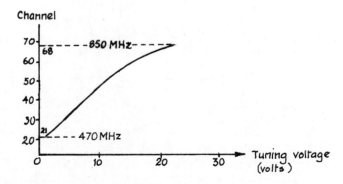

Fig. 9.6 *Relationship between tuning voltage and U.H.F. channel for an electronic tuner.*

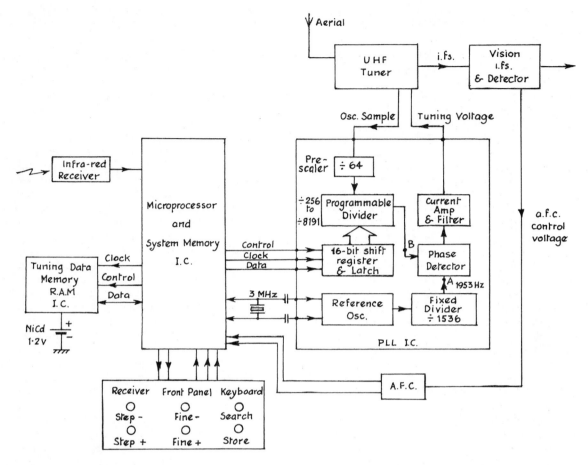

Fig. 9.7 Frequency synthesis tuning of U.H.F. tuner incorporating sweep search.

the d.c. potential on its vari-cap diode tuning circuit.

The reference input comes from a 3 MHz crystal oscillator which after passing through a fixed divider of 1536 provides a 1953 Hz signal at input A of the phase detector. The local oscillator in the tuner will become locked to a multiple of this frequency; the exact multiple being set by the division ratio of the programmable divider.

Consider, for example, the reception of Ch 50 which has a vision carrier of 703·25 MHz. The local oscillator should be set to 703·25 + 39·5 = 742·75 MHz. After frequency division by 64 in the 'pre-scaler' which may be internal or external to the tuner unit, the frequency of the signal input to the

programmable divider becomes 11·605 MHz. To produce a signal of 1953 Hz at input B of the phase detector, the programmable divider will be set to give a division of:

$$5942 \left(\frac{11 \cdot 605 \times 10^6}{1953} \right)$$

Thus to tune the u.h.f. tuner to a desired channel it is only necessary to set the programmable divider to the divisor required for that channel. This information is stored as a binary code in the system's programme memory. Whenever a particular channel number is selected on the infra-red remote hand unit, an address in the system's programme memory is accessed and the divisor binary number stored in that address is fed to the 16-bit register and latch to be loaded into the programmable divider. For example, when channel 50 is selected, address 50 is accessed and the binary code corresponding to the required divisor of 5942, *i.e.* 1011100110110 is loaded into the programmable divider. As a result a tuning voltage will be generated to shift the local oscillator to the precise frequency required for channel 50. The divisor of 5942 is just one of 48 divisors required to be stored in the system's programme memory to set the local oscillator accurately to any of the 48 television channels in Bands 4 and 5. If channel 66 is selected, address 66 is accessed and the binary equivalent of the divisor 6966 is fed to the programmable divider.

To initiate the **sweep search** facility the 'search' button is operated and this action causes the microprocessor to sequentially sweep through all of the 48 addresses in the system's programme memory thus presenting their contents in turn to the programmable divider. In consequence, the tuner is stepped through all the available television channels searching for a broadcast from a near transmitter. When a station of pre-determined characteristics is found, the line oscillator in the receiver quickly synchronises to it and 'signals' the microprocessor to instruct it to stop searching. If the viewer wishes to memorise that particular station, the 'store' button is operated which causes the divisor for that channel to be written into the 'tuning data memory' (RAM). By restoring the 'search' mode other stations may be found and the divisors required for the programmable divider stored in the tuning data memory, to be available for instant recall at a later time when required.

When frequency synthesis tuning is adopted, there is **no need for a.f.c.** since the action of the PLL will correct local oscillator frequency drift. This is true for broadcast transmissions where the frequency of the vision and sound carriers are held very accurately at the transmitter. However, the u.h.f. modulators fitted to home computers, television games and video recorders may drift in frequency causing errors in the i.f. output of the u.h.f. tuner. Thus a.f.c. may be incorporated as shown to 'fine tune' the local oscillator by incrementing the programmable divider in either direction in small steps. The minimum step is $64 \times 1953 \cdot 125\,\text{Hz} = 125\,\text{kHz}$ and corresponds to a change in the divisor ratio of one, *e.g.* 6966 to 6967. This frequency change will provide 64 separate tuning points across an 8 MHz wide television channel and approximates to continuous tuning.

In advanced television receivers having comprehensive control requirements, it would be inappropriate to use dedicated control i.cs. To embrace a wide range of control possibilities such as frequency synthesis tuning with sweep search, peritelevision socket switching and analogue control *etc*, a microcomputer system is adopted that is acceptable to a receiver manufacturer with a range of television models having different control requirements.

The microcomputer which interfaces the remote control or front panel data with the receiver's control system has a mask programmable memory which implements the receiver's unique operating system and it is in this memory space that the divisors for the programmable divider are stored. All of the receiver's controlled sub-systems are connected to the microcomputer by an advanced I^2C bus (asynchronous inter-i.c.). This is a bi-directional, two-line serial bus which allows i.cs. to pass control information and data from one to another.

CHAPTER TEN

I.F. AMPLIFIER STAGES

Objectives

1 To show the vision i.f. channel frequency response and explain how it eliminates adjacent channel interference.
2 Describe the main circuit techniques used in receivers to obtain the required i.f. response.
3 Give reasons for the use of inter-carrier sound and describe typical 6 MHz i.f. channel circuits.

THE VISION I.F. amplifying stages serve two principal functions:

(1) To increase the signal output of the u.h.f. tuner to an amplitude to operate the vision demodulator satisfactorily. When a diode demodulator is employed an i.f. gain of about 80 dB is typical, but is less (about 65 dB) when a synchronous demodulator is used.

(2) To provide sufficient bandwidth to accommodate the vision and sound i.fs. and their sidebands. Careful shaping of the i.f. response is required to correct for vestigial sideband working and to transmit the sound i.f. signal down the i.f. channel at a suitable level to create the inter-carrier sound i.f. of 6 MHz. In addition, the response must ensure adequate rejection of unwanted signals, *e.g.* the adjacent channel vision and adjacent channel sound i.f. carriers.

The gain of the i.f. channel is not fixed but made automatically variable to deal with variations in the received signal strength. This is achieved by the use of a.g.c. which operates on one or two of the i.f. amplifier stages (also the r.f. stage in the tuner).

I.F. RESPONSE

The intermediate frequencies used for the mono sound and luminance (vision) carriers are 33·5 MHz and 39·5 MHz respectively, *i.e.* the sound i.f. is 6 MHz **below** the vision i.f. On transmission, the sound carrier is 6 MHz **above** the vision carrier, thus the local oscillator in the tuner must be tuned **above** the frequency of the incoming u.h.f. carrier. This is shown in Fig. 10.1 taking channel 26 as an example.

A local oscillator frequency of 550·75 MHz will produce a difference-frequency of 39·5 MHz with a vision carrier of 511·25 MHz and a difference-frequency of 33·5 MHz with a sound carrier of 517·25 MHz. Thus the vision and sound i.f. carriers form a mirror image of the vision and sound u.h.f. carriers. The response must be so shaped that the vision i.f. sits 6 dB down from level response (0 dB) which is correct for vestigial sideband transmission. The response to the sound i.f. is depressed by about 26 dB and this is necessary to produce an optimum intercarrier sound signal.

The actual frequencies used for the i.fs. are chosen to prevent interference to the displayed picture and reproduced sound. The frequencies are not critical and small variations

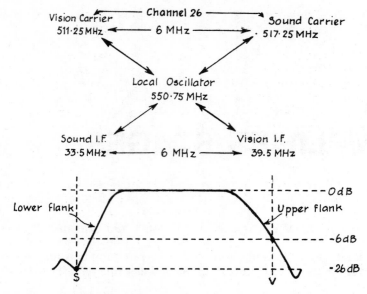

Fig. 10.1 *Response of the I.F. stages to the vision and sound I.F. signals.*

will be met with in practice, *e.g.* 33·4 MHz for sound and 39·4 MHz for vision.

Response to Adjacent Channel Signals

The response of the i.f. stages to the adjacent channel sound and vision carriers are shown in Fig. 10.2. This diagram illustrates how channels on either side of the one to which the receiver is tuned (Ch 26) can produce signals which lie close to the pass band of the i.f. channel.

The sound carrier of Ch 25 will give rise to a difference-frequency of 41·5 MHz with a local

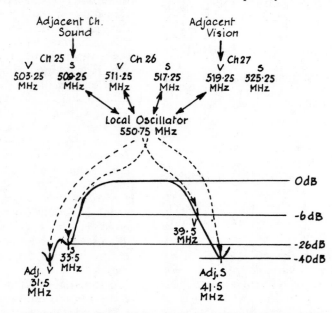

Fig. 10.2 *Typical I.F. response showing depression of adjacent channel vision and sound I.F. carriers of 41·5 MHz and 31·5 MHz.*

oscillator setting of 550·75 MHz (receiver tuned to Ch 26) and the vision carrier of Ch 27 will produce a difference-frequency of 31·5 MHz with this oscillator setting. Since these frequencies lie close to the i.f. passband they must be suppressed or interference may occur when a receiver picks-up the adjacent channel carriers from a transmitter different to the local one. Thus the response must be well depressed at the Adj.V and Adj.S frequencies of 31·5 MHz and 41·5 MHz respectively. Note that these frequencies are separated by 10 MHz and lie 2 MHz above and below the wanted i.fs. of 39·5 MHz and 33·5 MHz.

Position of Chrominance i.f.

In the baseband, the chrominance signal occupies the range of 4·43 ± 1 MHz but on transmission these frequencies are translated to 4·43 ± 1 MHz **above** the vision u.h.f. carrier. Thus in the i.f. stages the chrominance signals are 4·43 ± 1 MHz **below** the vision i.f. carrier, *i.e.* 39·5 − 4·43 MHz = 35·07 MHz. The position of the chrominance i.f. on the response is usually at level response, as in Fig. 10.3(a), or 6 dB down on level response, as in Fig. 10.3(b). The position on the i.f. response of the chrominance signal sometimes depends upon the type of vision demodulator used and the aims of the designer.

OBTAINING THE I.F. RESPONSE

There are three main techniques that will be found in receivers to obtain the required i.f. response and necessary i.f. signal gain.

(1) Bandpass LC Circuits with Discrete Transistor Stages

Prior to the introduction of integrated circuits the broad part of the vision i.f. response was obtained with the aid of staggered tuned bandpass coupled *LC* resonant circuits using either mutual inductance, top capacitance or bottom capacitance coupling methods. The degree of coupling was set to provide either an over-coupled, under-coupled or critically coupled response with resistive damping often used to broaden the response of a particular coupled circuit. To achieve adequate depression at the sound i.f. and to reject the Adj.V and Adj.S i.f. carriers, resonant circuit 'rejectors' or 'traps' were used to suck down the response at these frequencies by the required amount.

A representative example is given in Fig. 10.4 which incorporates many of the circuit techniques used during this era. The i.f. amplifier comprises four separate modules with module 1 containing a passive input selective filter and modules 2, 3 and 4 incorporating three discrete transistor amplifying stages.

Module 1 contains a bridged-T rejector *R*1, *C*2, *C*3 and *L*1 which is tuned to 41·5 MHz. This rejector is responsible for the depression in the i.f. response at the frequency corresponding to the Adj.S i.f. Also in this module are two series tuned rejectors *C*4, *L*2 and *C*6, *L*4 tuned to 33·5 MHz and 31·5 MHz respectively. These rejectors suck down the response at the sound i.f. and Adj.V i.f.

*L*3 is a bandpass coupling coil which is bottom capacitance coupled to the i.f. coil in

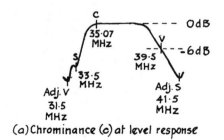

(a) Chrominance (c) at level response

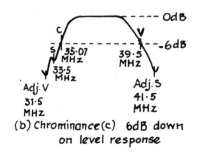

(b) Chrominance (c) 6dB down on level response

Fig. 10.3 Different positions for the chrominance I.F. (35·07 MHz) on the response curve.

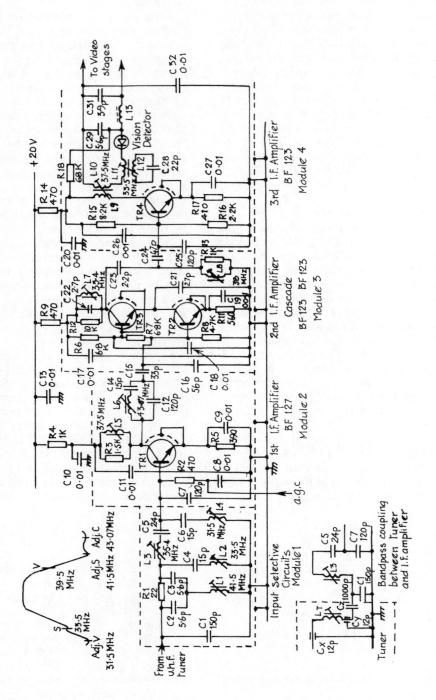

Fig. 10.4 I.F. stages (Bush-Murphy).

the tuner. This coupling arrangement is shown in the insert diagram where L_T is the i.f. output coil of the tuner which is tuned by C_x and C_y. The rejector circuits have been omitted from this diagram and it will be seen that the coupling between the two tuned circuits is via the common capacitance $C1$. This is a common method of coupling between the tuner and the i.f. amplifier. $C5$ and $C7$ which tune $L3$ form a capacitive divider to prevent undue damping of $L3$ by the input impedance of $TR1$.

The first i.f. amplifier $TR1$ uses a single tuned circuit in its collector consisting of $L5$ and its self-capacitance tuned to $37 \cdot 5\,MHz$ with $R3$ damping its response. Base bias for $TR1$ is supplied from the a.g.c. line via $R2$ and decoupled by $C8$. $R5$ is the emitter stabilising resistor decoupled by $C9$. With increasing signal strength the base bias of $TR1$ is increased thereby reducing the gain of the stage (forward gain control). $R4$, $C10$ and $C11$ provide a decoupling circuit in the line supply feed to $TR1$ stage. The output of $TR1$ is coupled to module 3 via the parallel tuned rejector $L6$, $C14$ and $C12$ which is tuned to $43 \cdot 07\,MHz$. This frequency corresponds to the adjacent channel chrominance i.f. which is close to the i.f. pass band and in some receivers (as in this one) is rejected. $C15$ and $C16$ form a capacitive divider to prevent undue damping of $L5$ by the input impedance of $TR2$.

The second i.f. amplifier consists of $TR2$ and $TR3$ connected in cascode. The upper transistor is connected in common base ($C18$ 'grounds' the base) and the lower transistor in common emitter. The cascode arrangement combines the advantage of the small signal feedback between input and output of the common base circuit with the higher input impedance (compared to common base) of the common emitter connection. The cascode pair thus provides high gain with stable amplification. Base bias is provided from across $R8$ for $TR2$ and from across $R7$, $R8$ for $TR3$. Line decoupling is provided by $R9$, $C17$. $R11$ is an emitter stabilising resistor and is suitably decoupled at the i.f. by $C19$. The output of $TR3$ feeds a band pass coupled circuit consisting of $L7$, $C22$ and $L8$, $C24$ and $C25$, top capacitance coupled by $C23$. $R12$ and $R13$

damp the response to broaden the bandwidth. $C24$ and $C25$ provide a capacitance divider to prevent excessive damping due to the input resistance of $TR4$.

The final i.f. amplifier $TR4$ contains a bifilar wound transformer $L9$, $L10$ (tuned to $37 \cdot 5\,MHz$) in the collector circuit which couples to the vision detector diode. Base bias for $TR4$ is provided by $R15$, $R16$ with line decoupling formed by $R14$, $C20$ and $C26$. $R17$ is the emitter stabilising resistor and is decoupled by $C27$. $L12$ and $C28$ form an absorption type rejector tuned to $33 \cdot 5\,MHz$. This trap assists $L2$, $C4$ in depressing the response at the sound i.f.

(2) LCR Filter with Integrated Circuit

In this arrangement a linear integrated circuit amplifier of wide bandwidth is used to provide the i.f. signal gain. Response shaping is carried out by a complex *LCR* network fitted usually prior to the i.c.

An example of an integrated circuit vision i.f. amplifying channel using a Motorola MC 1352 i.c. is shown in Fig. 10.5. Signals from the u.h.f. tuner are coupled to the i.c. on pin 1 via an *LCR* filter which performs the major part of the i.f. response shaping. The i.f. band pass is set by two *LC* band pass circuits. One band pass circuit is formed by the input coil $L3$ which is bottom impedance coupled to the i.f. coil in the tuner output. The other band pass circuit is connected at the output of the i.c. and is formed by $L5$, $C18$ and $L6$, $C20$. These resonant circuits are capacitively coupled by $C19$ and damped by $R6$.

The bridged-T network $C3$, $C4$, $L1$ and $R2$ provides rejection of the Adj.S i.f. of $41 \cdot 5\,MHz$. Depression at the Adj.V i.f. of $31 \cdot 5\,MHz$ is performed by the series resonant trap comprising $C6$, $L2$. Another series trap $C8$, $L4$ sucks down the response by the required amount at the sound i.f. of $33 \cdot 5\,MHz$.

Commonly the i.c. performs other functions as with the MC 1352. The i.c. provides a signal amplifying section with a power gain of 53 dB which is gain controlled, and also generates the a.g.c. voltage using a gated a.g.c. system (see Chapter 11); hence the reason for the video signal input on pin 6 and line gating pulses on pin 5 of the i.c.

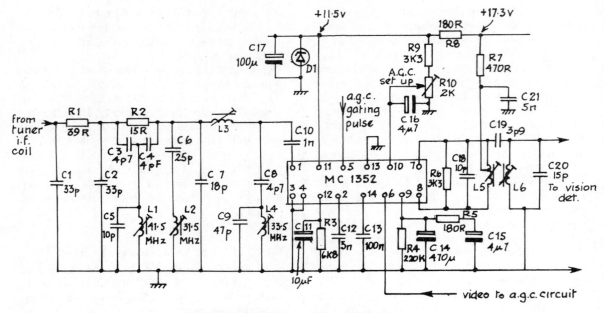

Fig. 10.5 Integrated circuit I.F. amplifier (Decca).

(3) Surface Acoustic Wave Filter with Integrated Circuit

When *LCR* filters are used for response shaping, the receiver performance depends to a large extent upon the careful adjustment during alignment of the bandpass and rejector circuits. With the advent of colour television, and later teletext, both of which rely on high frequency video signal components, greater accuracy and stability was sought for the response shaping components. An alternative to the *LCR* filter became available in the form of a surface acoustic wave filter (SAWF) and now is the acceptable method for shaping the i.f. response in modern receivers.

A simplified form of a SAWF is shown in Fig. 10.6. It consists of a piezo-electric substrate on which there are two transducers formed, a transmitter and a receiver. Each transducer consists of two combed-shaped electrodes with the fingers enmeshing one another (inter-digital electrodes). The electrodes are usually of gold or aluminium and are evaporated on to the surface of the substrate, usually made of lithium niobate but other materials may be used.

Electrical signals are fed to the input transducers (the transmitter) and this generates surface waves at the frequency of the input signal which travel in the surface

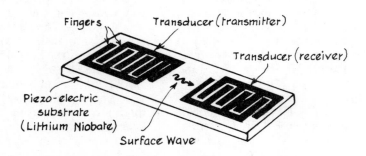

Fig. 10.6 Surface acoustic wave filter (simplified representation).

particles of the substrate. The surface waves on arrival at the other transducer (the receiver) are converted back into electrical signals. The term 'acoustic' is somewhat misleading as the surface waves are at the frequency of the electrical signal input, which in television terms means at the receiver intermediate frequencies (around 37 MHz). However, the surface waves are similar to sound waves in that they are propagated via oscillations in the surface particles.

Each finger of the transmitting transducer acts as a source of surface waves and the strength of each wave depends upon the length of the finger. The waves thus travelling over the surface of the substrate (with a velocity of about 1600 metres per second) can be considered as delayed replicas of the original input signal but of differing strengths. At a given point on the substrate the surface waves will be in phase to form a strong signal, whereas at the other frequencies the waves will be out of phase and thus cancel. By varying the form and dimensions of the transmitting and receiving transducer electrodes using computer aided design, bandpass characteristics may be obtained. The diagram of Fig. 10.7 shows the type of amplitude-frequency response that may be obtained with a SAWF for television applications.

As a circuit element measuring approximately $21 \times 4 \times 6$ mm, the basic encapsulated

filter is fitted with four pins and may be soldered on to a printed circuit board. The diagram of Fig. 10.8 shows the position of the filter in the i.f. amplifying chain. A SAWF suffers appreciable insertion loss in mid-band, which may be as high as 20 dB. Thus it is normal to place a broadband driver amplifier before it to make up the filter loss to ensure that the filter output signal significantly exceeds the noise generated in the input stage of the i.f. amplifier.

INTER-CARRIER SOUND

The reasons for the adoption of inter-carrier sound in 625-line television are:

(1) Because frequency modulation is used for television sound, the centre-frequency presented to the f.m. demodulator must remain constant otherwise the sound will be distorted, see Fig. 10.9. If 33·5 MHz sound signals were fed to the f.m. demodulator, severe distortion would result from drift in the u.h.f. tuner oscillator. For example with a local oscillator operating at 800 MHz, a frequency drift of 125 kHz represents a drift in local oscillator frequency of only:

$$\frac{0 \cdot 125}{800} \times 100\% = 0 \cdot 016\%$$

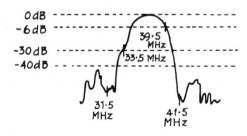

Fig. 10.7 Amplitude response of typical surface wave filter.

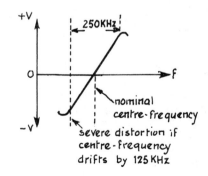

Fig. 10.9 F.M. demodulator response.

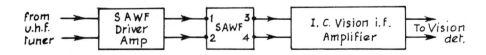

Fig. 10.8 Use of SAWF in colour or mono receiver.

(2) Also, there may be drift in the i.f. tuning which has similar results but not so serious as local oscillator drift. It is only likely to be a problem with *LCR* band pass tuning.

Inter-Carrier Sound Principle

In the inter-carrier sound system, see Fig. 10.10, both vision and sound i.f. carriers are passed through the vision i.f. stages to appear at the vision detector. As well as acting as a detector for vision signals, the diode detector (or synchronous detector) acts as a mixer to produce sum and difference frequencies from the vision and sound i.fs. The vision i.f. acts as a kind of 'local oscillator' and due to the non-linearity of the diode detector additive mixing takes place. As a result a difference frequency of 6 MHz is produced between the vision i.f. of 39·5 MHz and the sound i.f. of 33·5 MHz.

The 33·5 MHz input to the detector is frequency modulated thus all of its side-frequency components will beat with the vision i.f. to produce difference-frequencies on either side of the 6 MHz intercarrier, *i.e.* the frequency modulation is transferred to the intercarrier i.f.

Unfortunately, some of the amplitude modulation of the vision i.f. carrier is also transferred to the 6 MHz signal. This is responsible for the 'buzz' on sound heard in some receivers and is caused by the field sync. pulses (50 Hz) modulating the 6 MHz signal. However, effective a.m. limiting in the 6 MHz i.f. channel and accurate balancing of the f.m. detector will remove most of the buzz.

The main advantage of inter-carrier sound is that **the 6 MHz inter-carrier i.f. is accurately determined by the transmitted vision and sound carriers** and not by the stability of the u.h.f. tuner oscillator. If the tuner oscillator drifts causing the frequency of the vision and sound i.fs. to alter, the difference frequency remains constant at 6 MHz. The only effect will be that the sound i.f. carrier will vary in amplitude relative to the vision i.f. and unless the drift is large the effect on the sound will be negligible.

The same principle may be applied in advanced receivers to present to the NICAM decoder a **stereo sound inter-carrier i.f. of 6·552 MHz** by mixing together the vision i.f. of 39·5 MHz and the stereo sound i.f. carrier of 32·948 MHz.

6 MHz Sound I.F. Stages

The 6 MHz inter-carrier signal and its sidebands are extracted at the output of the vision detector (or video stage) by means of a bandpass tuned circuit which is resonant to 6 MHz. Examples of the methods used to extract the 6 MHz signal are considered in Chapter 11.

With a frequency deviation of ± 50 kHz and an upper audio frequency of 15 kHz, a bandwidth of 180–200 kHz is usually sufficient for the 6 MHz i.f. stages, thus the response will typically take the form shown in Fig. 10.11.

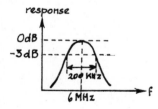

Fig. 10.11 Response of intercarrier sound I.F.S.

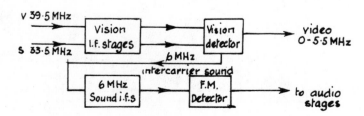

Fig. 10.10 The intercarrier sound system.

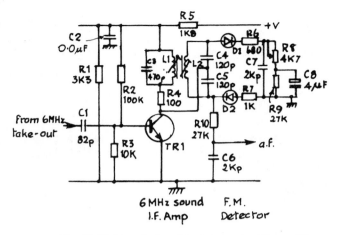

Fig. 10.12 Discrete transistor intercarrier I.F. amplifier.

When discrete transistors are used, a single stage of i.f. amplification is usually provided for the 6 MHz signal as shown in Fig. 10.12.

Here the 6 MHz f.m. signal is fed via C1 to the base of the i.f. amplifying transistor TR1. This stage is tuned to 6 MHz in its collector circuit by the tuned bandpass transformer comprising L1, C3 and L2, C4, C5.

In addition to amplifying the 6 MHz signal the stage also provides amplitude limiting to reduce the effects of 'inter-carrier buzz' or other unwanted amplitude modulation. The output from the secondary of the bandpass transformer is transferred to D1 and D2 operating in a ratio detector circuit (described

in Chapter 1), which demodulates the inter-carrier f.m. signal.

Another example of a 6 MHz i.f. channel is given in Fig. 10.13 where a ceramic filter (CF) is used in place of the conventional *LC* bandpass tuning circuit and an i.c. is used to provide the signal gain. R1 and R2 correctly match the ceramic filter at input and output. The high gain provided by the i.c. amplifier causes limiting of the inter-carrier signal thus removing amplitude modulation. Typically, an i.f. input to the i.c. of about $100 \mu V$ will cause amplitude limiting to occur. As in this case, the i.c. often contains a quadrature coincidence detector (which was described in Chapter 1) to demodulate the f.m. signal.

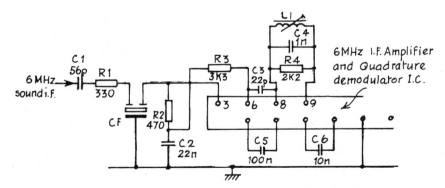

Fig. 10.13 Intercarrier I.F. amplifier using ceramic filter and I.C. amplifier.

CHAPTER ELEVEN

VISION DETECTOR, 6 MHZ TAKE-OUT AND A.G.C.

Objectives

1 To explain the principle of operation of diode envelope and synchronous vision demodulator circuits.
2 To study the circuit of a typical vision detector emitter-follower stage.
3 To show methods of extracting the 6 MHz inter-carrier sound i.f. from the video signal path.
4 To study the action of peak level and gated a.g.c. circuits and to give reasons for the use of black spot and white spot inverters.

VISION DETECTOR

THE PURPOSE OF the vision demodulator circuit is to extract the video signal information from the i.f. carrier and to filter out the i.f. component plus harmonics before passing the video signal to the video signal stages. Also, with an inter-carrier sound receiver the vision detector acts as a mixer to produce the inter-carrier sound i.f. of 6 MHz.

Diode Envelope Detector

The most common arrangement found in receivers prior to the introduction of i.c. demodulators has been the series connected diode envelope detector which is shown in basic form in Fig. 11.1.

$D1$ is the vision detector with $R1$, $C1$ providing the load time-constant. $D1$ rectifies the modulated i.f. carrier and the video signal is developed $R1$. Capacitor $C1$ operates as a reservoir capacitor and charges up through the diode during its conducting period. When the diode is 'off' (in this case during the positive

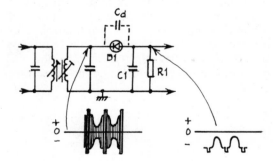

Fig. 11.1 Vision demodulator (basic circuit).

half-cycles of the i.f. carrier) $C1$ discharges through $R1$. To obtain a linear output the diode should receive a modulated i.f. input of about 3–5 V peak-to-peak so that operation is confined to the linear part A–B of the diode's characteristic as shown in Fig. 11.2. Small input signals will have some non-linear distortion due to the lower band of the diode's characteristic.

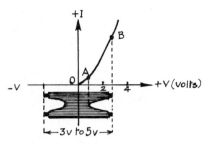

Fig. 11.2 Operation confined to linear portion of diode's characteristic.

Choice of *C*1, *R*1 Values

In arriving at suitable values for the detector load time-constant the following factors have to be considered:

(a) The capacitance of *C*1 should be large compared with the diode capacitance C_d. This is to prevent excessive i.f. signal appearing in the output when the diode is non-conducting due to the potential divider formed by $C1$, C_d across the detector input.

(b) The resistance *R*1 should be large compared with the forward resistance of the diode to provide high detector efficiency.

(c) The time constant must be long compared with the periodic time of the i.f. carrier to reduce the amount of i.f. ripple in the output.

(d) The time constant must be short compared with the periodic time of the highest modulating frequency (5·5 MHz) so that the output can follow the high frequency variations of the envelope.

(e) The detector load must provide a suitable impedance as seen by the final i.f. amplifier to give correct tuning and damping.

In view of the above factors, some of which are conflicting, the design of the detector tends to be complex but the main aim is to provide a video output with little distortion by sacrificing some detector efficiency. To give an idea of suitable values used consider the following:

The periodic time of one cycle of the vision i.f. of 39·5 MHz is:

$$\frac{1}{39\cdot5 \times 10^6} \simeq 0\cdot025\,\mu s$$

and the periodic time of one cycle of the highest video frequency of 5·5 MHz is:

$$\frac{1}{5\cdot5 \times 10^6} \simeq 0\cdot18\,\mu s$$

The time constant *C*1, *R*1 should be greater than $0\cdot025\,\mu s$ but less than $0\cdot18\,\mu s$. Suppose that a time of $0\cdot1\,\mu s$ is decided upon as a compromise value. If *C*1 is made $20 \times C_d$ and C_d is about 1 pF (typically), $C1 = 20\,pF$.

Therefore
$$R1 = \frac{\text{Time Constant}}{C1}$$

$$= \frac{0\cdot1 \times 10^{-6}}{20 \times 10^{-12}} = 5\,\text{k-ohm}$$

In a practical circuit the value of the physical *C*1 may be less than suggested due to stray capacitance across the circuit. In some cases *C*1 is omitted altogether, the capacitance being formed entirely by the stray capacitance.

I.F. Filter

The purpose of the i.f. filter is to remove the residual i.f. ripple plus harmonics at the detector output without unduly attenuating the video signal. The ratio of vision i.f./highest video frequency is only about 7:1 and calls for efficient filtering. The *RC* filter used in radio receivers is not suitable. If the value of the series resistor were high enough to attenuate the vision i.f. it would severely attenuate the video signal due to the low value of the detector load resistance used.

Thus the resistive element is replaced by an inductor as shown in Fig. 11.3. The value of the series inductor *L*1 is such that it has a much higher reactance than that of *C*2 at the i.f. but at video frequencies its reactance is much lower than that of *C*2. As a result most of the i.f. signal is 'dropped' across *L*1 and the video signal is developed across *C*2/*R*1. Sometimes

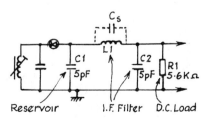

Fig. 11.3 I.F. filter.

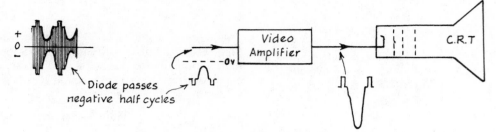

Fig. 11.4 Cathode modulation of monochrome C.R.T.

it is arranged that $L1$ and its self-capacitance C_s form a parallel tuned circuit resonant to the i.f. thereby providing additional rejection of the i.f. at the detector output.

Particular attention is given to effective filtering of the video signal because if the i.f. finds its way into the following video stages it may cause i.f. instability as a result of re-radiation. For this reason, the vision detector and the i.f. filter circuit are often fitted inside the final i.f. amplifier screening can. Sometimes a two-section LC filter is used to give more efficient filtering.

Polarity of Output

With the diode connected as in Fig. 11.1 the diode passes the negative half-cycles of the i.f. signal. Reversing the diode connections would cause it to pass the positive half-cycles with the result that the video signal would be inverted. Also a positive d.c. component would be obtained instead of a negative one, resulting in the monochrome image being reversed *i.e.* white would appear as black and vice-versa.

The polarity required at the diode output depends upon the type and number of video stages and the method used to modulate the c.r.t. With cathode modulation of the c.r.t., a negative going video content is required for modulation of the beam current as shown in

Fig. 11.4. Thus in a monochrome receiver which normally uses a single inverting video stage, the diode should be connected so that it will pass the negative half-cycles of the i.f.

D.C. Component

The diode vision detector being a rectifier produces at its output a **d.c. component** in addition to the video and i.f. components. For true picture fidelity the d.c. component should be retained as it represents the average scene brightness, see Fig. 11.5.

Figure 11.5(a) shows a line of video information of a particular scene where the studio lighting is assumed to be of high intensity producing an average or d.c. value for the waveform as shown. If the studio illumination is reduced to create the impression of a change from daylight to dusk, the video signal will reveal the same scene detail but the d.c. component will be smaller as shown in Fig. 11.5(b). Clearly, the d.c. component must be preserved if the impression of a change in scene illumination is to be conveyed to the viewer. To maintain the d.c. component, d.c. coupling should be used from the vision detector output right up to the modulating electrode of the c.r.t., *i.e.* no coupling capacitors will be fitted.

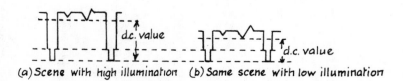

(a)*Scene with high illumination*   (b)*Same scene with low illumination*

Fig. 11.5 D.C. component.

Detector Emitter Follower

The output of the vision detector feeds the video amplifier stage. When a common emitter transistor video output stage is used it is normally fed from the detector via an emitter-follower stage. This is to prevent the low input impedance of the video amplifier from loading the vision detector.

An example of a detector emitter-follower stage (sometimes called the 'video driver') used in a discrete transistor monochrome receiver is given in Fig. 11.6. The emitter-follower stage $TR1$ will require forward biassing and if d.c. coupling is used, the base bias must be prevented from upsetting the operation of the vision detector. It is thus usual to find d.c. feeds to both sides of the detector diode which ensure that 'anode' and 'cathode' of the diode are at the same d.c. potential, or alternatively the 'anode' is made slightly positive to the 'cathode'. In this case the diode is given a small forward bias to reduce distortion on small signal inputs – the technique used in Fig. 11.6.

Forward bias for $TR1$ is supplied via $R2$, $L3$ and $R5$ to its base. The d.c. at the lower end of $R2$ is also fed to $D1$ 'cathode' via $R1$ and $L1$ whilst the diode 'anode' receives a d.c. potential via $R3$, $L2$. The resulting difference in potential across $D1$ gives the diode a small forward bias. $D1$ detects the negative half-cycles of the i.f. input and the output is filtered by the i.f. choke $L2$. The video signal is applied from the d.c. load resistance $R5$ to the base of $TR1$ via $R4$. Note that as the video signal goes towards sync. pulse level, the base bias of $TR1$ is reduced. Since $TR1$ acts as an emitter-follower for the video range of 0–5.5 MHz, the video signal at the emitter will follow the base signal but its amplitude will be slightly less (voltage gain of an emitter-follower about 0.95). The output signal is developed across $R8$, $R9$ and $R10$ and a portion of the video signal is fed to the a.g.c. circuit from across $R9$, $R10$ with $R9$ serving as a preset contrast control. The purpose of $L4$, $C6$ and $L5$, $C8$ is dealt with in the next section.

Inter-carrier Sound Take-Out

The inter-carrier f.m. sound signal of 6 MHz resulting from the mixing of the vision and sound i.fs. in the vision detector must be extracted and fed to the 6 MHz i.f. stages prior to detection. The 6 MHz signal may be taken out directly from the vision detector or from a suitable point in the video stages. The diagrams of Fig. 11.7 show some common 6 MHz take-out arrangements used.

In Fig. 11.7(a) the 6 MHz signal is extracted at the detector output using a parallel tuned circuit $L1$, $C1$ which is resonant at 6 MHz. At this frequency the tuned circuit is of high impedance and most of the 6 MHz signal will

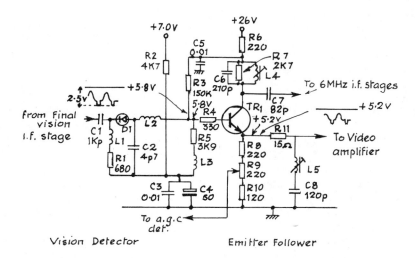

Fig. 11.6 Use of detector emitter follower.

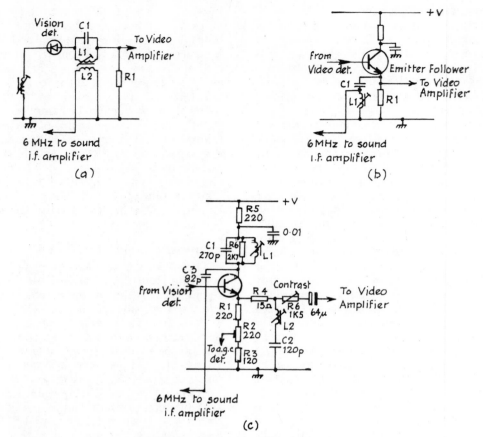

Fig. 11.7 6 MHz take-out circuits.

be developed across it with very little appearing across the detector load $R1$. At frequencies below 6 MHz the impedance of $L1$, $C1$ will be low and thus the tuned circuit does not interfere with the normal operation of the vision detector. Energy from $L1$ is transferred to the 6 MHz i.f. amplifying channel via the coupling winding $L2$.

The 6 MHZ signal may be extracted from the detector emitter-follower stage and in Fig. 11.7(b) is taken out from the emitter circuit using a series tuned circuit $L1$, $C1$ which is resonant to 6 MHz. The inter-carrier signal applied to the base of the transistor will also be present at its emitter. To 6 MHz, L, $C1$ behaves as a low impedance thus the signal will not be passed on to the video amplifier stage. This is important since any residual 6 MHz signal that finds its way to the PAL decoder may beat with the 4·43 MHz sub-carrier to

produce **an obtrusive 1·57 MHz pattern on vision**. However, the reactance of $L1$ will be high at the resonant frequency and the 6 MHz signal may be taken-out from across L. At frequencies below 6 MHz, $L1$, $C1$ will be of low impedance and the transistor operates as a normal emitter-follower stage to the video band of 0–5·5 MHz.

In Fig. 11.7(c) the 6 MHz signal is extracted from the collector circuit of the detector emitter-follower stage (this is the same circuit shown in Fig. 11.6). To 6 MHz signals the transistor as a common emitter amplifier and amplified 6 MHz signal is developed across the parallel tuned circuit $L1$, $C1$ in the collector circuit which is resonant to 6 MHz. These signals are transferred to the inter-carrier i.f. channel via $C3$. With this method the emitter-follower stage provides some useful gain so less gain may be required in the 6 MHz i.f.

stages. The series resonant circuit formed by *L2, C2* and tuned to 6 MHz prevents 6 MHz signals from reaching the video amplifier.

Synchronous Detectors

A diode envelope detector requires an i.f. input of several volts for linear detection. The high level signal must be provided by the final i.f. amplifier and due to the low input impedance of the vision detector appreciable power must be supplied from the final i.f. amplifier. This leads to difficulty in the design of consistently stable i.f. amplifiers when a diode demodulator is used because of the high level of signal present.

A 'synchronous' or 'switched' detector on the other hand is very linear in operation down to small input signals of the order of tens of millivolts. This allows the receiver vision gain to be shared between the i.f. stages and the video stages, which lends itself to a more stable design.

Another advantage of the synchronous detector is that there is less mixing of the luminance, chrominance and sound components of the signal which produce unwanted frequency components detrimental to the performance of the receiver.

Synchronous Detector Considered as a Switch

The synchronous demodulators found in receiver circuits function as switches and Fig. 11.8 shows the basic idea. Here the demodulator is considered as an ordinary electrical switch with the modulated vision i.f. carrier fed in at one side of the switch. The i.f. input is also fed to a selective and limiting amplifier which produces a square wave output at the vision i.f. of 39·5 MHz which is used to operate the switch.

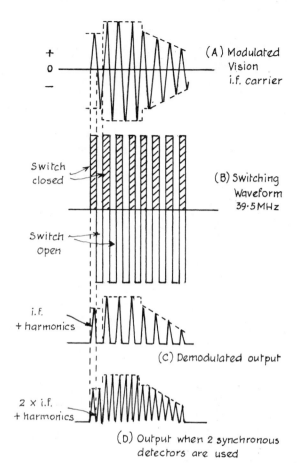

Fig. 11.9 Waveforms explaining action of synchronous detection.

It will be assumed that the switch is closed on positive half-cycles of the switching waveform **B** but open on the negative half-cycles as shown in Fig. 11.9. When the switch is closed, the signal at the detector input is passed to the output. Thus the switch passes only the positive half-cycles of the modulated i.f. input

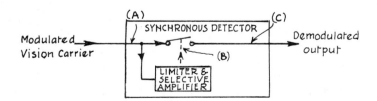

Fig. 11.8 Basic principle of synchronous detection.

to the output, thus the signal has been detected (waveform **C**). This demodulated output contains an appreciable amount of the i.f. component since half-wave rectification has been used. The fundamental component of the i.f. may be reduced at the detector output by employing two such switching demodulators with their outputs combined. These are operated by using opposite polarity switching waveforms and opposite polarity vision i.f. inputs, resulting in a full-wave output as shown in waveform **D**. There is now no output ripple at the fundamental i.f. frequency which assists in preventing instability. Thus a vision synchronous demodulator is a linear full-wave detector as opposed to the half-wave operation of the non-linear diode demodulator.

The synchronous demodulators used in the PAL decoder operate on similar principles but use a separate oscillator for the switching function. Synchronous detection was not available in discrete component form because of the prohibitive cost but is now available in integrated circuit form.

Synchronous Demodulator I.C.

The diagram of Fig. 11.10 shows the basic functions inside one type of synchronous demodulator i.c. The i.f. input is supplied to pin 7 at a peak-to-peak value of about 40 mV. A sample of this signal is amplitude limited in **A** and the output is used to develop a constant amplitude 39·5 MHz sine wave across the tuned circuit L1, C1 (fitted external to the i.c.).

The signal is squared in **F** and the antiphase outputs are fed to the two gates **D** and **E** which constitute the synchronous demodulators. The gates are formed by switching transistors inside the i.c. Gate 1 is supplied with the i.f. input direct from pin 7 but gate 2 is fed with antiphase i.f. input after inversion in **C**. The demodulated gate outputs are combined and fed to the video amplifiers **G** and **H**. The lower amplifier provides a video output of about 3 V peak-to-peak and the series rejector C2, L2 removes the inter-carrier signal from the video signal path. Pin 1 of the i.c. provides a constant amplitude 39·5 MHz output via the buffer stage **B** which may be used to operate the a.f.c. circuit.

A synchronous demodulator acts as a signal multiplier thus in the switching gates the 33·5 MHz sound i.f. carrier (which is also present at the gate inputs) is multiplied by the 39·5 MHz switching waveform. As a result a difference frequency of 6 MHz is produced which is the **inter-carrier sound i.f.** This signal

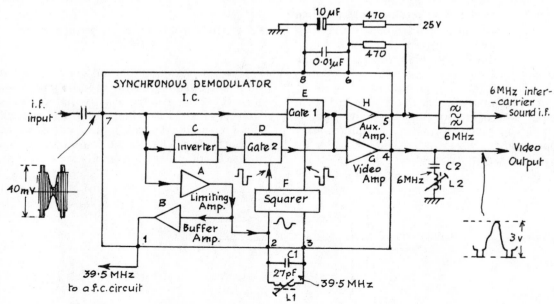

Fig. 11.10 Internal functions of I.C. synchronous demodulator.

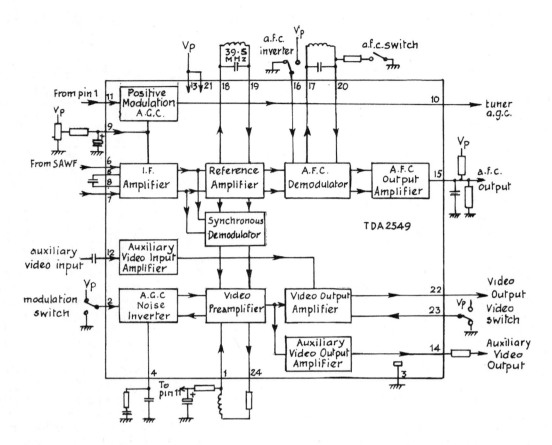

Fig. 11.11 TDA 2549 I.C. containing synchronous demodulator, vision I.F. amplification, A.F.C and A.G.C.

is readily available at both **G** and **H** outputs, as is the video signal. The inter-carrier signal is rejected from the video output signal path by *L2, C2* but passed on to the inter-carrier sound i.fs. via the 6 MHz band pass filter (a ceramic filter may be used).

It is now quite common to find the vision i.f. amplification and synchronous demodulator functions all included in one i.c. as with the TDA 2549 which also features a.f.c. and a.g.c. functions, see Fig. 11.11. This i.c. is capable of handling positive and negative modulated video signals in both colour and monochrome receivers. The 'reference amplifier' provides the 39·5 MHz switching waveform for the synchronous demodulator which supplies a demodulated video output at pin 22 of about 4 V for negatively modulated video signals.

A.G.C.

Automatic gain control of the vision signal of a receiver is necessary for the following reasons:

(a) To maintain a constant amplitude vision signal input to the vision detector so that the viewer does not have to readjust controls when switching between channels. Although the four programmes from the local transmitter are radiated with the same nominal power, the receiving aerial may not be sited in the maximum signal pattern for all four channels causing variations in input signal strength to the receiver. Also when a receiver is used in conjunction with aerials to receive the locally radiated programmes and programmes from a more distant transmitter

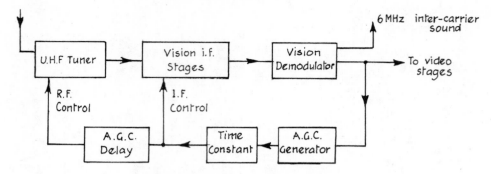

Fig. 11.12 Applying A.G.C. in a television receiver.

there may be considerable variations in received signal strength.

(b) To assist in preventing overloading of the receiver when switching from a weak distant signal to a strong local signal. Under high levels of input signal, cross modulation may occur between the vision and sound carriers, a condition that cannot be relieved by receiver selectivity.

Basic A.G.C. Arrangement

In applying a.g.c. in a television receiver, the aim is to maximise the range of received signal strengths over which the receiver will operate satisfactorily and the schematic of Fig. 11.12 illustrates the manner in which this is usually achieved.

The control voltage is produced at the output of the 'A.G.C. Generator' circuit which generates a gain control voltage that is proportional to the amplitude of the video signal in some way. The video signal input may come from the vision detector, the detector emitter-follower or a later video stage. Since an a.g.c. system is a feedback loop, a *CR* 'Time Constant' is required to stabilise the loop; the shorter the time constant the easier it is to follow rapid variations in signal strength.

For the best signal-to-noise ratio at low signal input levels, the tuner is held at maximum gain and control is exercised by varying the gain of the i.f. stages only. This is achieved by the use of the 'Tuner A.G.C. Delay' circuit which maintains a constant output voltage until a certain signal level is reached. When this level is reached on strong signals, the tuner gain is reduced to prevent overloading of the mixer and i.f. stages. I.F. control may still continue to be effective so that as the signal strength increases further, tuner and i.f. gain control will assist each other

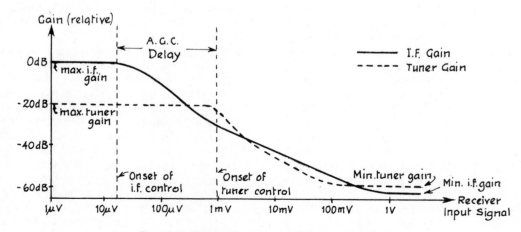

Fig. 11.13 Television receiver A.G.C. characteristics.

in attempting to maintain a constant amplitude vision signal at the input to the vision detector without overloading.

The characteristic of Fig. 11.13 shows the range of input signal levels that a television receiver may have to deal with, depending whether it is situated in the fringe reception area or close to the local transmitter. The difference in signal amplitude between the onset of i.f. and tuner control is the 'A.G.C. Delay' which is often adjustable in television receivers.

Two different methods of deriving the a.g.c. voltage from the video signal are commonly used in 625-line television receivers.

Peak Level A.G.C.

One way of obtaining an indication of received signal strength with the negatively modulated 625-line television signal is to measure its peak amplitude. The peak level corresponds to the sync. pulse tip which is set at 100% modulation and does not vary with the video content of the scene being televised. This level gives a true indication of the received signal strength as illustrated in the diagrams of Fig. 11.14 for strong and weak signals.

A representative peak level a.g.c. circuit of

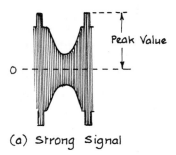

(a) Strong Signal

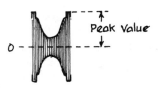

(b) Weak Signal

Fig. 11.14 Peak value of different signal strengths.

the type used in discrete component receivers providing i.f. and r.f. gain control is given in Fig. 11.15. The action of the circuit is as follows:

In the absence of a signal input to the receiver or when it is very weak, there is a standing voltage of $+3.5$ V d.c. on the emitter of the vision detector emitter-follower stage.

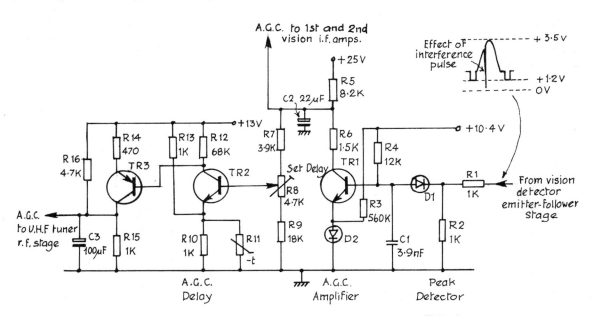

Fig. 11.15 Peak level A.G.C. with delayed voltage to tuner (Philips).

This voltage is divided down by the potential divider R1, R2 to give about 1·8 V on the cathode of the peak detector D1. The anode voltage of D1 is about 1·4 V (the forward voltage drop of D2 plus the base-emitter drop of the a.g.c. amplifier TR1). Thus D1 is in the non-conducting state. In consequence TR1 is biassed hard 'on' via R4 causing its collector voltage to bottom at about + 0·9 V. The voltage at the junction of R5, R6 is then about + 4·5 V. This voltage is applied to the first and second discrete transistor i.f. stages and the i.f. gain is then at a maximum.

When the amplitude of the signal input to the receiver increases, the amplitude of the video signal also increases, *i.e.* the sync. pulse tip moves closer to the zero voltage level (see input waveform to R1). At a certain level of the signal from the emitter-follower stage, D1 will conduct during the sync. pulse tip, *i.e.* at the peak level. This will cause the d.c. voltage across C1 to decrease thus taking TR1 out of saturation. As a result, the voltage at the junction of R5, R6 will rise which reduces the gain of the first and second i.f. amplifiers (forward gain control of n-p-n transistors). The larger is the input signal to the receiver, the more D1 conducts and the greater the rise of voltage at R5, R6 junction and the less the i.f. gain. In this way the amplitude of the video signal is stabilised.

The a.g.c. time constant for i.f. control is provided by C2 which charges via R5 and discharges via R6 and TR1. This sets the rate at which the i.f. control voltage can follow changes in signal strength.

To maintain a good signal-to-noise ratio, the gain of the tuner should be high when receiving weak and medium strength signals but reduced to prevent overloading when strong signals are received. To meet this requirement, the a.g.c. voltage across C2 is applied to the base of TR2 via the potential divider R7, R8 and R9. The emitter of TR2 obtains its voltage from R13, R10/R11. This standing emitter voltage ensures that TR2 will conduct only when there is a large a.g.c. voltage across C2 (corresponding to a strong signal input). The signal level at which TR2 comes into conduction is set by R8. When TR2 is 'off', TR3 is also 'off' and the voltage fed to the tuner r.f. stage is set by R16, R15 (about + 2·3 V). As soon as TR2 comes into conduc-

tion on strong signals, TR3 conducts causing the voltage across R15 to rise, thereby reducing the tuner gain (forward control of n-p-n r.f. stage).

This circuit arrangement **continuously** reads the peak value of the video signal input, thus if an interference spike is present and its amplitude exceeds the sync. pulse tips as shown, the effect will be to cause the receiver gain to momentarily decrease. The magnitude of the effect depends upon the a.g.c. time-constant; the longer the time-constant the greater the smoothing effect on the interference. However, the longer the time-constant the slower will be the response of the a.g.c. to normal changes in signal level.

Line Gated A.G.C.

In a 'gated' or 'keyed' a.g.c. system, the demodulated video signal is repetitively measured during **specific instants only** to obtain an indication of signal strength. Usually the signal is sampled at line rate (line gated a.g.c.) and the basic idea is shown in Fig. 11.16.

If the sampling occurs at instant x it is the peak level that is measured corresponding to the sync. pulse tips whereas if sampling occurs at instant y it is the back porch level that is measured. In either case amplitudes A or B provide a true indication of signal strength.

Line gated a.g.c. systems have the advantage that the a.g.c. time constant can be made short. This helps to minimise disturbance to

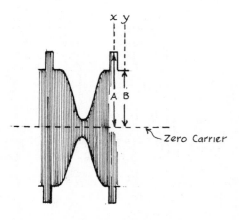

Fig. 11.16 Line gated A.G.C.

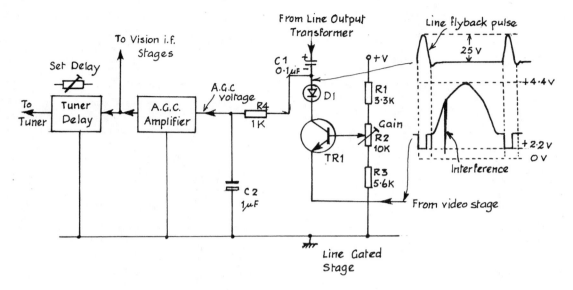

Fig. 11.17 Elements of line gated A.G.C.

the picture during rapid signal changes such as aircraft flutter and reduces the time taken for the picture to become stable after changing channels. Also there is less chance of interference pulses causing a reduction in receiver gain than with a continuous peak reading a.g.c. system.

The basic elements of a line gated a.g.c. system are shown in Fig. 11.17. $TR1$ is the gated stage which is fed with the video signal on its emitter from the detector emitter-follower stage of the receiver. Positive-going line flyback pulses from the line output stage are fed via $C1$ and $D1$ to $TR1$ collector. These pulses, which act like the collector supply voltage, cause $TR1$ to conduct during the period of each pulse charging $C1$ with the polarity shown.

The magnitude of $TR1$ current is determined by the base potential set by $R2$ and the emitter potential, *i.e.* the **peak level** of the sync. pulse tips. With increasing signal strength, the sync. pulse tips fall closer to the zero voltage level thus increasing $TR1$ current and the charge on $C1$. The d.c. at the junction of $C1$, $D1$ is smoothed by $R4$, $C2$ to produce a negative control potential across $C2$.

After amplification and inversion in the 'A.G.C. Amplifier' the control voltage is supplied to the vision i.f. stages to vary their gain. The 'Tuner Delay' maintains the gain of the tuner at maximum until strong signals are received at which point the gain of the tuner r.f. stage is reduced. Note that an interference spike occuring during the **picture period** will not affect the control voltage as the signal is sampled only during the line flyback pulse.

A.G.C. Function in I.Cs.

A.G.C. systems in current use are invariably fabricated in i.c. form but are usually included with other functions such as i.f. amplification, synchronous demodulation, a.f.c. *etc* as for the TDA 2541 i.c. shown in Fig. 11.18.

This i.c. features a line gated a.g.c. system with the sampling line flyback pulses supplied on pin 5 of the i.c. to the 'gated A.G.C.' block. An output from the 'Video Pre-Amp' provides the signal input to the gated a.g.c. stage. I.F. control is applied internally to the 'Gain Controlled I.F. Amplifier' and 'delayed' tuner control (set by $R1$) is fed out on pin 3 of the i.c.

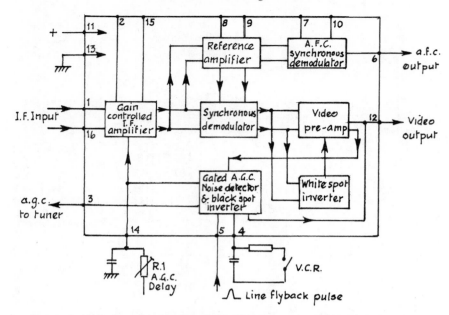

Fig. 11.18 TDA 2541 I.C. incorporating gated A.G.C. and Black/White Spot Invertors.

As is common, black spot and white spot inverters are included in the i.c. and reasons for these features will now be considered.

In the negatively modulated 625-line television system, bursts of r.f. interference received together with the signal have the effect of increasing the carrier amplitude during the interference period, see Fig. 11.19.

After demodulation assuming a diode envelope detector is used, the interference 'spike' acts in the direction of **black level** (or sync. pulses) regardless of the polarity of the half-cycles of the carrier passed by the demodulator to the output. This interference is known as **black spot interference** since its effect on the picture is to produce black spots. Should the amplitude of this black spot interference exceed the sync. pulse tips it is likely to upset the biassing of the sync. separator stage causing 'blocking' which can cause the picture to 'tear' or 'roll'. Thus it is usual to include circuitry to detect the interference and to invert it so as to cause cancellation of its effects. Usually the noise inverter is also made to mute the a.g.c. detector during the black spot interference to prevent the a.g.c. voltage level from being disturbed.

When a synchronous demodulator is used which is now the accepted demodulation method, it is possible for interference to appear in the 'white' direction. This is because, depending on the phase relationship between the r.f. interference cycles and the vision carrier, a synchronous demodulator will pass signals on either side of the zero carrier level when it is switched in an 'on' mode. Interference in the 'white' direction, see Fig. 11.20 is most visible on the reproduced picture since it causes overdriving of the c.r.t. resulting in white spots. Thus it is usual to include a white spot detector and inverter to nullify the effects of such interference.

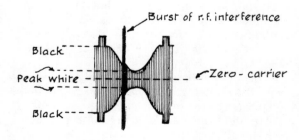

Fig. 11.19 Interference producing spike which acts in the direction of black level (Black spot interference).

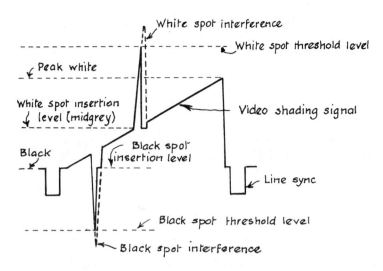

Fig. 11.20 Reducing effect of black and white spot interference.

The action of the black spot inverter inside the i.c. of Fig. 11.18 is to invert any interference pulses exceeding the inverter threshold level and to rapidly return the video signal to black level so that the output on pin 12 will not cause blocking of the sync. separator.

Similarly, the action of the white spot inverter is to invert any white spot interference above its threshold level and to rapidly return the video signal to mid-grey level at pin 12 output to make the interference less obtrusive. The increase in circuit complexity required for white spot inversion is more than justified by the high performance of a synchronous demodulator.

CHAPTER TWELVE

VIDEO AMPLIFIER STAGES

Objectives

1 To provide an understanding of the basic characteristics of video amplifiers and to show methods of h.f. compensation.
2 To study examples of the luminance signal amplifier stages in a monochrome receiver.
3 To show the luminance and colour-difference signal paths in a colour receiver and to give circuit examples including a luminance/colour-difference signal matrixing amplifier.
4 Give reasons for the use of the luminance signal delay.
5 To consider the use of i.c. video stages and RGB drive amplifiers.

THE STAGES IN the receiver that deal with either the detected luminance signal or the decoded colour information are **all** video stages, although in a colour receiver they are referred to as the luminance signal amplifiers and colour-difference signal amplifiers respectively.

VIDEO STAGES IN A MONOCHROME RECEIVER

The basic requirements of the video stages in a monochrome receiver which handle the luminance signal, see Fig. 12.1, will be considered first.

The output of a diode vision detector is usually fed to the video output stage via an emitter-follower for the reasons given in Chapter 11. The emitter-follower stage does not provide any voltage gain, therefore the output amplifier must develop sufficient video signal voltage to drive the c.r.t. The low output impedance of the emitter-follower stage is most suitable for driving the output amplifier as the input capacitance of the common emitter output amplifier is rather high. This capacitance arises mainly out of internal feedback within the transistor ('Miller effect'). In addition to driving the c.r.t., the video stages must also supply feeds to the

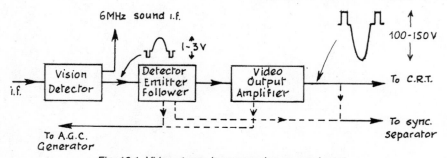

Fig. 12.1 Video stages in a monochrome receiver.

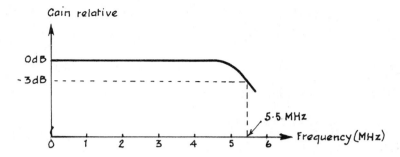

Fig. 12.2 Frequency response required to handle the luminance signal.

a.g.c. generator and the sync. separator stage.

Video stages handling the luminance signal must satisfy the following three requirements:

(1) Frequency Response

To preserve the fine picture detail conveyed by the 625-line luminance signal, the video stages should have a response that is substantially flat over the frequency range of 0Hz – 5·5MHz, as shown in Fig. 12.2. To maintain the gain down to 0Hz, a d.c. amplifier is required, *i.e.* d.c. coupling should be used from the vision detector right up to the modulating electrode (cathode) of the c.r.t. Sometimes a.c. coupling or partial d.c. coupling is used, in which case the d.c. component is removed or only partly retained.

(2) Phase Response

The relative phases of all frequency components present in the video signal must be preserved to avoid phase distortion of the video content. If an amplifier does not introduce phase shift this requirement is satisfied. Practical amplifiers, however, exhibit some phase shift particularly at high and low frequencies. To avoid phase distortion any phase shift introduced should be proportional to frequency, see Fig. 12.3, as this is the condition for constant delay at all frequencies. For example, a 3° phase shift of a 1MHz sine wave represents a timing error of approximately 8·34 ns relative to a 1MHz sine wave with zero phase shift. To produce the same timing error of 8·34 ns for a 2MHz sine wave, a phase shift of 6° is required.

(3) Gain

A peak-to-peak video drive of about 60 V on average is required to drive a monochrome c.r.t. (depending upon d.c. operating conditions) from black to peak white. The vision detector normally gives out a video signal of

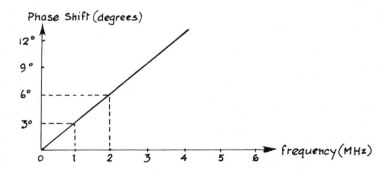

Fig. 12.3 Phase shift proportional to frequency.

1–2 V, thus the video amplification required is of the order of 30–60. This voltage gain may be obtained from a single transistor stage.

Basic Video Output Stage

A basic circuit of a common emitter video output stage is shown in Fig. 12.4 and is essentially a resistance loaded amplifier where the collector load R_L is used to couple the amplified video signal to the c.r.t.

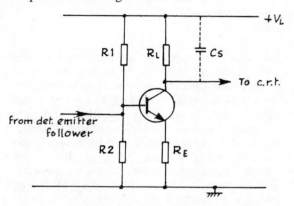

Fig. 12.4 Basic transistor video amplifier.

Only a small power is needed to drive the c.r.t. thus the video output stage acts primarily as a voltage rather than a power amplifier. The voltage gain must be maintained up to 5·5 MHz so an r.f. type transistor is used. Commonly, video output transistors have a cut-off frequency above 100 MHz so that the intrinsic bandwidth of the transistor does not impose a limit on the upper video frequency gain of the stage. An undecoupled emitter

resistor R_E is used which provides negative feedback to stabilise the parameters of the transistor. Base bias is provided by the potential divider R1, R2 but the d.c. bias may be obtained directly from the emitter-follower stage.

The volatge gain (A_v) of the ampliier at low frequencies is approximately given by:

$$A_v = \frac{R_L}{R_E} \text{ when } h_{fe} \text{ is large.}$$

Therefore, with constant values for R_L and R_E it would be expected that the gain would remain uniform over the video frequency range. Unfortunately, the gain falls at high video frequencies due to stray capacitance across R_L, see Fig. 12.5. The stray capacitance C_s is made up by the c.r.t. capacitance, wiring capacitance and the output capacitance of the transistor.

At high video frequencies, the falling reactance of C_s shunts R_L thereby reducing the effective load and causing the gain to fall. Because C_s is in parallel with R_L, when the reactance of C_s falls to a value such that it equals the value of R_L the gain of the stage will fall to:

$$0{\cdot}707\,\frac{R_L}{R_E}$$

i.e. the gain will be 3 dB down. To give some idea of the frequency at which this would occur, assume the following practical values: $R_L = 5\,\text{k}\Omega$, $R_E = 100\,\Omega$ and $C_s = 10\,\text{pF}$.

The gain at low frequencies will be:

$$\frac{R_L}{R_E} = \frac{5000}{100} = 50.$$

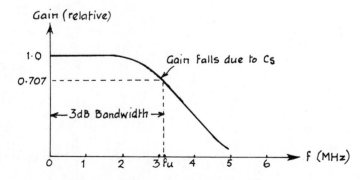

Fig. 12.5 Response on non compensated video amplifier.

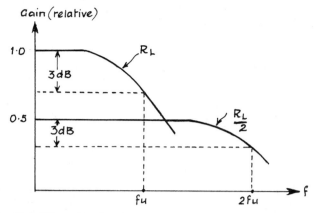

Fig. 12.6 Effect of load resistance value on frequency response.

At a particular frequency f_u the gain will be $0.707 \times 50 = 35.35$ (3 dB down) when $X_{C_s} = R_L$.

Now $X_{C_s} = \dfrac{1}{2\pi f C}$ or $5000 = \dfrac{1}{2\pi f C}$

$\therefore f = \dfrac{1}{2\pi C \times 5000}$

or $f = \dfrac{10^{12}}{6\cdot284 \times 10 \times 5000}$

thus $f \simeq 3\cdot2\,\text{MHz}$.

Thus in this case the 3 dB bandwidth would be 0–3·2 MHz which is insufficient to meet the requirement of 0–5·5 MHz. One way of increasing the 3 dB bandwidth is to reduce the value of R_L. If a collector load of 2·5 kΩ is used the 3 dB bandwidth would be doubled to 6·4 MHz but the gain would be halved to 25,

see Fig. 12.6. Since the reactance of C_s must fall to 2·5 kΩ to cause a 3 dB gain reduction.

The reduced stage gain may still be sufficient, but the smaller value of collector load resistance may cause the maximum power rating of the transistor to be exceeded unless a comparitively large power transistor is used which will now be considered.

Assume that the transistor is operating in class A (this is used in an a.c. coupled stage) and that a peak-to-peak signal output of 120 V is required. It should be noted that the **signal output voltage excursion** sets the **minimum value of the d.c. supply** that may be used. In this case a d.c. supply of, say, 160 V would be used. These conditions are shown in Fig. 12.7.

Now the **minimum value** of R_L may be found from:

$$R_L = \frac{(V_L)^2}{4\,P_{\text{max}}},$$

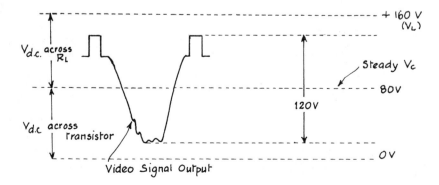

Fig. 12.7 Class-A operation.

where V_L is the d.c. supply and P_{max} is the maximum power rating of the transistor.

With a P_{max} of 1 W (typically) and a V_L of 160 V

$$R_L = \frac{(160)^2}{4} = 6.4 \text{ k}\Omega.$$

For a 3 dB bandwidth of 0–5.5 MHz and with a C_s of 10 pF, the **maximum value** of R_L that can be used is:

$$X_c = \frac{1}{2\pi f C}$$

$$= \frac{10^{12}}{6.284 \times 5.5 \times 10^6 \times 10} = 2.91 \text{ k}\Omega.$$

It is clear, therefore, that an R_L value of 2.9 kΩ which satisfies the frequency requirement cannot be used without exceeding the power rating of the transistor. To avoid exceeding P_{max} the value of R_L must be higher than 6.4 kΩ. Suppose a value of 7 kΩ is chosen to allow for circuit tolerances. The collector current of the transistor is given by:

$$\frac{V_L}{2R_L} = \frac{160}{2 \times 7000} \simeq 11.5 \text{ mA}$$

If the peak-to-peak input signal is, say, 2 V, the required voltage gain is 120/2 = 60.

Since

$$A_v = \frac{R_L}{R_E},$$

the value of R_E will be:

$$\frac{7000}{60} \simeq 117 \,\Omega.$$

The upper video frequency f_u will be:

$$f_u = \frac{1}{2\pi C \, X_{c_s}}$$

$$= \frac{10^{12}}{6.284 \times 10 \times 7000}$$

$$\simeq 2.28 \text{ MHz.}$$

Various h.f. compensating techniques may be used to improve the response at high frequencies.

Inductance Compensation

(1) Shunt Peaking Coil

Here a small inductor L is placed in series with the load resistor R_L as shown in Fig. 12.8(a). The presence of L in series with R_L causes a rise in the effective collector load impedance at the h.f. end of the video band thereby increasing the amplifier gain and partly compensating for the falling reactance of C_s. To establish a suitable value for L the following design formula is often used:

$$L = p \cdot R_L^2 \cdot C_s \text{ Henry}$$

(where p is a number usually between 0.3 and 0.7).

The effect on the amplifier response of varying p is shown in Fig. 12.8(b) using 'generalised' curves that can be applied to any amplifier. On the logarithmic horizontal axis is the ratio f/f_o, where f_o is the frequency at which the gain has fallen to 0.707 of the low frequency gain in an uncompensated amplifier and f is the frequency under consideration.

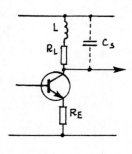

(a) Shunt peaking coil circuit

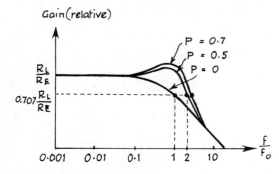

(b) Effect of peaking coil on frequency response

Fig. 12.8 Inductance compensation (shunt peaking coil).

When $p = 0$, L is zero and we have a curve for an uncompensated amplifier. At 3 dB down on this curve $f/f_o = 1$. If a value of $p = 0.5$ is taken it will be seen that at 3 dB down, $f/f_o = 2$, *i.e.* the -3 dB video frequency will be twice that of an uncompensated amplifier.

With an upper -3 dB frequency of 2·28 MHz (using the example of the previous section) and a p value of 0·5, the -3 dB video frequency will be increased to 4·56 MHz which is a useful improvement. Taking the previous values of $R = 7$ kΩ and $C_s = 10$ pF with a p value of 0·5, the approximate value of L will be:

$$L = p R^2_L C_s$$
$$= 0.5 \times (7000)^2 \times 10 \times 10^{-12} \text{H}$$
$$= 245 \, \mu\text{H}.$$

Values for L are commonly of the order of 50–300 μH. Once the approximate value of L has been established using the design formula, various values of the calculated L are experimented with using pulse test signals until the desired video response is achieved.

(2) Series Peaking Coil

Here a small inductance L is placed in series with the output signal path, see Fig. 12.9, as opposed to being in shunt with it as in the shunt peaking coil circuit. If the inductance is fitted close to the collector connection, it splits the stray capacitance into two parts: $C1$ the output capacitance of the transistor, and $C2$ the input capacitance of the c.r.t. plus wiring capacitance. L and $C2$ now take the form of a low pass filter. The value of L is chosen so that the filter passes all frequency components up to the desired upper video frequency with minimum attenuation but provides increasing attenuation above the upper limit of the video band.

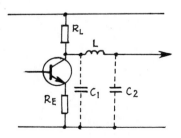

Fig. 12.9 Series peaking coil circuit.

As with the shunt peaking circuit, 'generalised' curves may be used to establish the required amount of compensation needed but the design is usually more complex. For best performance $C1$ and $C2$ must be in a definite ratio and in practice the final value of L is arrived at by using pulse testing methods.

Compensation Using N.F.B.

Compensation for the fall in gain at high video frequencies due to the effects of C_s may be achieved using frequency selective n.f.b. In the uncompensated circuit, R_E is undecoupled and introduces n.f.b. for d.c. and a.c. and the degree of feedback is the same for all video frequencies. The voltage gain is then settled by the ratio of R_L to R_E. If the capacitor (C_E) of suitable value is placed across R_E as in Fig. 12.10 it is possible to arrange that the amount of feedback at h.f. is small compared with the degree of feedback at the l.f. and m.f. video ranges.

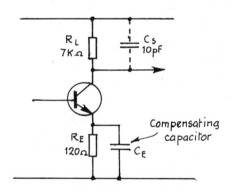

Fig. 12.10 Compensating using frequency dependent negative feedback.

The value of C_E must be such that at l.f. and m.f. its reactance is high compared with R_E so that the effective emitter load for signals is R_E. Whereas at the h.f. end of the video band (due to the falling reactance of C_E) the effective emitter impedance is reduced causing a reduction in the amount of n.f.b. and a rise in voltage gain. The idea is shown in Fig. 12.11 where at the h.f. end of the video band, the reduced feedback just compensates for the falling gain due to C_s thereby giving a level response up to a higher video frequency.

As a guide to the required value of C_E,

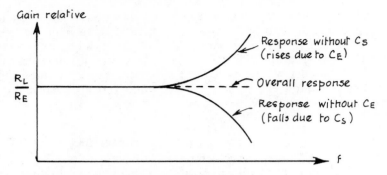

Fig. 12.11 *Showing the effect of C_E on frequency response.*

generally the time constant of R_E, C_E is made the same as the time constant R_L, C_s. For the values given in Fig. 12.10, the value of C_s is about 580 pF. Usually, the value of C_E will lie in the range of 300–5000 pF.

Typical Circuit Examples

Example 1

One example of a video amplifying channel is given in Fig. 12.12. This uses a driver stage $TR1$ and a video output amplifier $TR2$ with a.c. coupling between stages. The maximum peak-to-peak video voltage at $TR2$ collector is 110 V and this requires about 2 V of video signal from the detector.

The video signal at $TR1$ emitter is coupled via $R7$, $R8$ and $C5$ to $TR2$ base. $L2$, $C4$ which is series tuned to 6 MHz rejects the intercarrier sound signal from the output stage thereby preventing a 6 MHz fine dot pattern from being displayed. $R8$ serves as the manual contrast control by forming one arm of an attenuator with the input impedance of $TR2$; as the resistance of $R8$ is reduced the contrast is increased. $C5$ couples the video signal to $TR2$ base but blocks its d.c. component. Although theoretically the d.c. component should be retained, its omission is a matter of opinion as in practice the results on the picture are not so detrimental.

$TR2$ is biassed to class-A by the potential

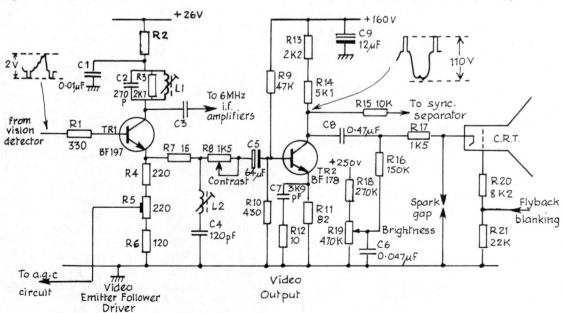

Fig. 12.12 *Emitter-follower and video output stage using A.C. coupling (monochrome receiver).*

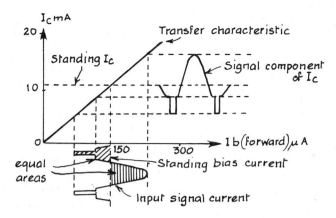

Fig. 12.13 Class-A operation of video output amplifier.

divider $R9$, $R10$. The collector load is formed by $R13$, $R14$ and $R11$ is the emitter resistor. High frequency compenation is provided by $C7$ in the emitter circuit. Resistor $R12$, which is part of the compensating network, sets a limit on the minimum emitter impedance and hence the maximum gain at high video frequencies.

Class-A operation of the output stage is shown in Fig. 12.13. For the circuit values given, a standing collector current slightly in excess of $10\,mA$ is indicated which requires a standing base current of about $150\,\mu A$ for the BF 178 transistor. Note that due to the a.c. coupling (via $C5$), the input current will be balanced about the standing base current as shown. Thus on the excursions towards the sync. pulse tips the collector current will reduce, whereas when the input goes towards peak video, the collector current will increase. A peak-to-peak collector current of about $15\,mA$ will be needed to develop $110\,V$ of signal at the collector. Note also that as the collector current increases, the collector voltage reduces, thus the output voltage is negative-going on the video content as is required for cathode modulation of the c.r.t.

Consider now the video output to the c.r.t. This is fed to the tube cathode via $C8$ and $R17$. $C8$ blocks the d.c. component and $R17$ helps to prevent voltage spikes from entering $TR2$ stage (where they may cause damage) in the event of an e.h.t. flash-over within the c.r.t. In this receiver brightness control is introduced

by varying the steady voltage at the c.r.t. cathode, the grid being connected to chassis potential via $R20$ and $R21$. The brightness voltage is supplied from $R19$ which varies the d.c. at the slider connection over the range of about $0\,V$ to $+160\,V$. As the brightness voltage is made more positive, the c.r.t. beam current is reduced and the picture brightness is decreased. $R16$ stands off the brightness control from the video signal thereby preventing $R19$ (or $C6$) from shorting out the video signal. At the minimum setting of $R19$, the c.r.t. cathode voltage will not be zero due to the beam current (high) which flows in $R16$. $C6$ decouples $R19$ to signal.

The a.c. coupled video signal 'sits' about the brightness potential from $R19$ and the correct setting for the brightness control is shown in Fig. 12.14 (upper waveform). The brightness control is adjusted so that blanking level on the video drive corresponds to zero beam current, *i.e.* black is represented by zero beam current. If the brightness control is increased or decreased from this ideal setting, the video drive waveform and its mean level will move bodily to the right or left on the diagram. If moved to the left, zero beam current will correspondingly move to a grey level on the video drive waveform and the peak white level will result in less beam current, *i.e.* the picture will be too dark overall. Conversely, if moved to the right, black level on the video drive will produce a grey in the picture, *i.e.* the picture will be too light overall. Although the bright-

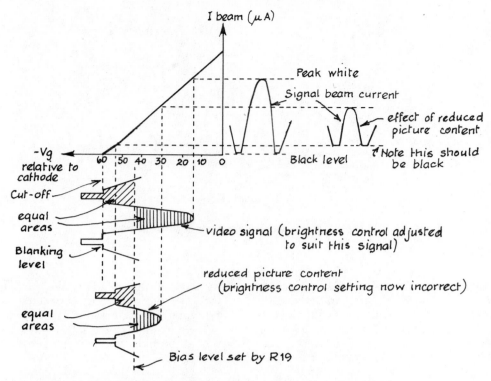

Fig. 12.14 Setting of brightness control potential for A.C. coupled video signal.

ness setting shown in the diagram is technically the correct one, the contrast range on the screen is a matter of individual preference and is affected by the ambient lighting in the room.

Altering the contrast setting will cause either a larger or smaller amplitude video signal to be applied to the c.r.t. If larger (increased contrast) the beam current will increase on the peaks of the video signal; if smaller (reduced contrast) the beam current peaks will be less. With a.c. coupling, however, alteration of the contrast setting or the picture content (see lower waveform will require an adjustment of the brightness setting to ensure that blanking level on the video drive corresponds to zero beam current.

Example 2

In this example, see Fig. 12.15, d.c. coupling is used throughout the video amplifying channel.

Detected video and 6 MHz intercarrier sound from the vision detector $D1$ are developed across the load $R4$ and fed to the base of the emitter-follower stage $TR1$. $C3$, $L1$ in $TR1$ emitter circuit form a series tuned circuit resonant to 6 MHz. Due to the low resonant impedance of this circuit very little intercarrier sound signal is passed on to $TR2$ stage. However, because of the relatively high reactance of $L1$ at 6 MHz, appreciable 6 MHz signal is developed across $L1$ which thus provides the take-out point for the intercarrier sound.

Video signal from across $R5$ is coupled to $TR2$ base via the contrast control $R7$. As $R7$ slider is moved to the right a smaller video signal is applied to $TR2$ and the picture contrast is lowered. $R8$, $R9$ are used to minimise the change in d.c. at $TR2$ base with variations in the setting of $R7$, thereby ensuring a constant black level.

$TR2$ is the video output stage providing a peak-to-peak output of about 70 V. $R12$ is the collector load and $R10$ the emitter resistor. H.F. compensation is provided by the shunt peaking coil $L2$ in the collector circuit and by $C4$ in the emitter circuit. The negative-going

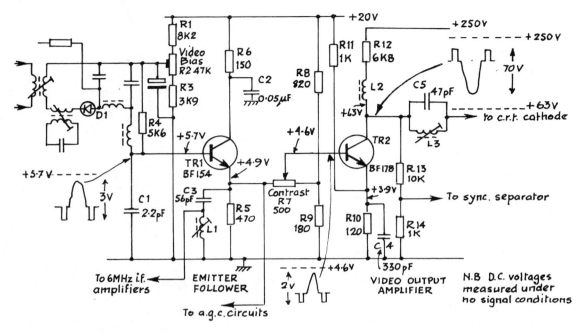

Fig. 12.15 Emitter-follower and video output amplifier using D.C. coupling (monochrome receiver).

video signal is applied to the c.r.t. cathode via the parallel rejector *L3*, *C5*. This circuit is tuned to 6 MHz and rejects any residual intercarrier sound signal.

As d.c. coupling is used in the video stages we will now consider the effect of the d.c. component of the video signal, see Fig. 12.16. In Fig. 12.16(a) we have the modulated i.f. waveform which is normally shown with a zero reference level. If the negative half-cycles are detected and the detector load resistor is connected on one side to chassis potential (as is often shown in basic detector circuits), the video output will be as in Fig. 12.16(b). Note here that the d.c. component or mean value of the signal is negative with respect to the zero line. When the video output is d.c. coupled to the emitter-follower stage, the video is no longer referenced to zero but to the base potential of the emitter follower stage. Thus in Fig. 12.16(c) the reference line is the base potential of *TR*1 which in Fig. 12.15 is +5·7 V. The d.c. component is, therefore, negative with respect to this potential. If the positive half-cycles of the input had been detected, the d.c. component would have been positive to the standing base potential.

Returning now to the circuit of Fig. 12.15 the standing bias on *TR*1 stage must be set high so that the input signal excursions towards the sync. pulse tips reduce the bias. Note that the d.c. measurements, if taken under signal conditions, will be less than the 'no signal'

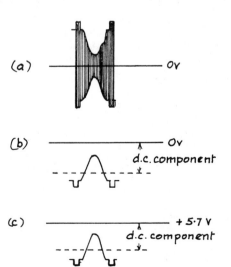

Fig. 12.16 Effect of D.C. component.

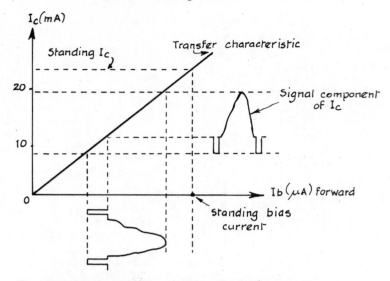

Fig. 12.17 Operation of video output amplifier (D.C. coupled).

values given on the diagram as the meter will indicate the average value of the signal waveforms.

Since the signal at *TR*1 emitter follows the signal at its base and the emitter output is directly coupled to *TR*2 base, the d.c. component of the signal at *TR*2 base will be negative with respect to the standing base potential of *TR*2. Thus the forward bias for *TR*2 stage is initially set high as shown in Fig. 12.17. The high standing bias current will, therefore, give rise to a high standing collector current of about 20 mA in this case (compare with Fig. 12.13). As the signal input progresses towards the sync. pulse tips the current in *TR*2

is reduced. The designer has to ensure linear operation for the video content without limiting the signal on peak white. Also, as the input signal takes the operation towards the lower bend of the input characteristic, excessive 'crushing' of the sync. pulses should not occur. The video bias control (*R*2) is used to set the forward bias of *TR*2 for optimum operating conditions. Note that *R*2 adjusts *TR*1 base potential and due to the d.c. coupling it also sets *TR*2 base bias.

The circuit arrangement for coupling the video output of *TR*2 stage to the c.r.t. is shown in Fig. 12.18. D.C. coupling is used via *L*3 and the **beam current limiting diode D2**. Under

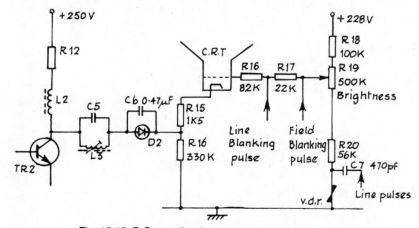

Fig. 12.18 D.C. coupling between video output and C.R.T.

normal conditions, *D2* is forward biased and the video signal at the c.r.t. cathode is clamped to the output at *TR2* collector. During high drive conditions when the c.r.t. beam current exceeds a predetermined value, *D2* becomes reverse biased due to the rise at its cathode as a result of the c.r.t. beam current flowing in *R16*. The video signal is then a.c. coupled to the cathode via *C6* thereby limiting the beam current to a safe level.

A different arrangement is used for brightness variation in this circuit. Here the brightness voltage is applied to the c.r.t. grid instead of the cathode (as with the previous circuit). The brightness voltage from *R19* is set so that the grid potential is negative with respect to the positive potential applied to the cathode from *TR2* collector. Increasing the voltage setting of *R19* reduces the grid-to-cathode bias, thereby increasing the beam current and so increasing the picture brightness. Negative-going pulses of suitable duration and amplitude are fed to the grid to black out the effects of the line and field flyback.

The correct setting of the brightness control potential is shown in Fig. 12.19. Here the brightness potential is set so that the video signal excursions are always to the right of this voltage level in the diagram and the sync. pulses take the operation beyond beam cut-off. With d.c. coupling, when the picture content alters the black level of the picture remains constant (compare with Fig. 12.14).

VIDEO STAGES IN A COLOUR RECEIVER

One arrangement of the video stages for providing primary signal (RGB) drive to the three guns of the colour display tube is shown in Fig. 12.20, and this diagram will be used to give a basic understanding of the video signal paths in a colour television receiver.

All of the stages represented in block form are video stages but are usually given the designations as shown. Any video stage that handles the luminance signal information should have a frequency bandwidth of 0–5·5 MHz, *i.e.* blocks 1, 2, 3, 4, 8, 9 and 10.

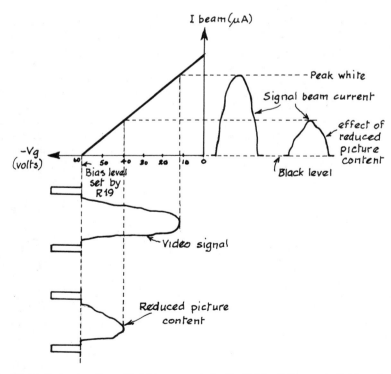

Fig. 12.19 Correct setting of brightness control potential for D.C. coupled video signal.

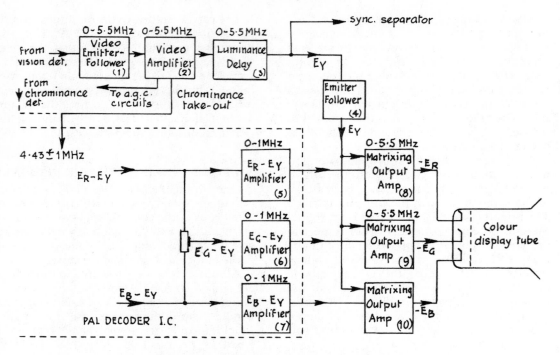

Fig. 12.20 The video stages in a colour receiver (R.G.B. drive).

Stages such as blocks 5, 6 and 7 which deal with the colour-difference signals, require a response of 0–1 MHz only, since the colour difference signals are restricted in bandwidth compared with the luminance signal.

The video stages found in a colour receiver use the same basic circuit techniques as in a monochrome receiver. However, the high frequency requirement of the luminance stages does not apply to the colour-difference signal stages and usually no h.f. compensation is necessary in these 0–1 MHz stages.

Luminance Signal Path

The luminance signal amplifying channel is formed by blocks 1, 2, 3, 4 and the matrixing amplifiers 8, 9 and 10. As with the monochrome receiver, outputs are required to feed the sync. separator and the a.g.c. circuits and although these may be taken from the points indicated, variations will be met with in practice. In addition to these outputs, the chrominance signal must be filtered out from the composite signal and fed to the PAL decoder as indicated. In some receivers the

chrominance signal is extracted from a video stage following the vision detector or from a separate chrominance detector fed by way of a stage of chrominance i.f. amplification from one of the vision i.f. stages.

One method of extracting the chrominance signal is shown in Fig. 12.21(a). $TR1$ is a video stage in the luminance channel with $R1$ serving as its collector load and $R3$ its emitter resistor. No special h.f. compensation is used in this stage since its gain requirement is modest so a small value of collector load resistance may be used.

$L1$, $C1$ in the emitter circuit is parallel tuned to 4·43 MHz and acts as a **notch filter**. At 4·43 MHz its impedance will be high causing a large amount of negative feedback. In consequence the gain of $TR1$ is reduced at the chrominance signal frequencies which, therefore, do not appear to any large extent across $R1$. Due to the high impedance of the filter at resonance it provides a suitable take-out point for the chrominance signals which are then fed to the PAL decoder.

The effect of the notch filter on the response of the luminance channel is shown in

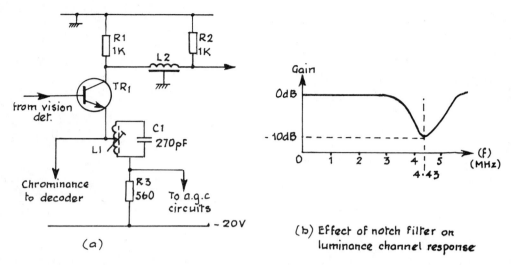

(a)

(b) Effect of notch filter on luminance channel response

Fig. 12.21 Luminance channel video amplifier with notch filter and luminance delay line.

Fig. 12.21(b). It will be seen that luminance signals around 4·43 MHz are removed from the luminance channel which degrades its high frequency response to some extent, but is necessary to prevent the chrominance signals from modulating the raster via the luminance channel. The Q of $L1$, $C1$ is maintained by the tap on $L1$ and the bandwidth of the filter is ± 1 MHz centred on 4·43 MHz.

Luminance Delay

Any signal passing through a circuit with restricted bandwidth is delayed. Because the luminance and colour-difference signals pass through video stages with different bandwidths they will, without any special compensation, arrive at the c.r.t. at different times. Owing to the narrower bandwidth of the colour-difference signal amplifiers, the colour-difference signal is delayed more than the luminance signal. The practical effect of

this is that the colour information would be displayed slightly to the right of the luminance information on the screen (about 5 mm on a 20 inch screen). This tends to cause vertical transitions in the picture to be blurred. To prevent misregistration of the colour and luminance content of the picture, the luminance signal is given a small delay of about 600 ns.

One way of delaying a signal is to send it along a transmission line. The amount of delay for a given length depends upon the distributed inductance and capacitance of the line. Most forms of transmission line, *e.g.* coaxial cable have a small inductance and capacitance per unit length. To reduce the length of cable needed for a specific delay, special forms of construction may be used which increase the distributed inductance and capacitance. The form of construction used for the luminance delay line is shown in Fig. 12.22.

Here a single layer of wire is wound over a

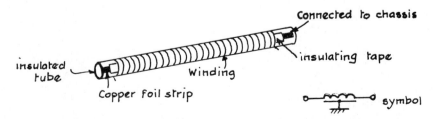

Fig. 12.22 Construction of luminance delay line.

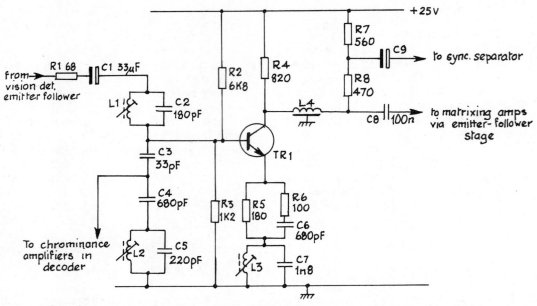

Fig. 12.23 Luminance channel video amplifier with bandpass filter and luminance delay line.

copper foil strip which is laid on the outer surface of an insulating tube. The inductance of the winding and its relatively high capacitance to the metal foil provide the necessary delay while at the same time keeping the overall dimensions to reasonable proportions (about 9 cm in length by 1 cm diameter). The delay line must be correctly terminated at either end to match its characteristic impedance which usually lies in the region of about $1 \cdot 2 \, k\Omega$ (see $R1$ and $R2$ of Fig. 12.21).

A different arrangement for extracting the chrominance signal is shown in Fig. 12.23. The composite signal from the vision detector emitter-follower stage is fed through $R1$, $C1$ to a bandpass filter comprising $L1$, $C2$–$C3$–$C4$–$L2$, $C5$. The response of the filter is given in Fig. 12.24.

$L1$, $C2$ is parallel resonant to 6 MHz and rejects the intercarrier sound signal from the luminance stage $TR1$ and from the chrominance signal take-out point. $L1$ also resonates with $C3$ as a series acceptor circuit providing a lift in gain at $5 \cdot 4$ MHz. $L2$, $C5$ form a parallel resonant circuit giving a rise in gain at $3 \cdot 4$ MHz. Also, together with $C4$, $L2$ forms a series acceptor circuit to attenuate luminance signals around $2 \cdot 5$ MHz from the chrominance take-out point. The overall response is double

peaked with almost a flat top, symmetrical about $4 \cdot 43$ MHz and high rejection at $2 \cdot 5$ MHz and 6 MHz. Thus the filtered signal available at the junction of $C3$, $C4$ contains the chrominance signal sidebands and the colour burst which are fed to the PAL decoder.

The input to $TR1$ comprises the full luminance signal bandwidth with its d.c. component blocked by $C1$ and the intercarrier signal rejected by $L1$, $C2$. The luminance signal is amplified and inverted by $TR1$ and the output is developed across the low value collector load $R4$. $TR1$ gain is set by $R4/R5$ and h.f. compensation is provided by $R6$, $C6$ which reduces the degree of n.f.b. towards the higher

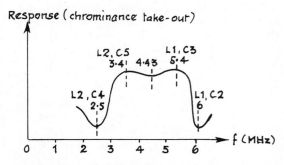

Fig. 12.24 Response of bandpass filter used in Fig. 12.23.

video frequencies. Chrominance signal information is rejected from the luminance channel by the parallel tuned circuit $L3$, $C7$ in the emitter circuit. This resonant circuit is tuned to 4·43 MHz and due to its high impedance at resonance, it introduces a large amount of n.f.b. thereby reducing the gain of $TR1$ to chrominance signals. $L4$ is the luminance delay line which equalises the mean delay of the luminance channel with that of the chrominance channel. The input of the delay line is terminated by $R4$ and the output by $R7$, $R8$. A suitable level of signal from across $R7$ is fed to the sync. separator stage via $C9$. Delayed luminance signal is supplied to the matrixing amplifiers via $C8$ and an emitter-follower stage.

Colour-Difference Amplifiers and Output Matrix

An example of an amplifying channel for one of the colour-difference signals (E_B–E_Y) is given in Fig. 12.25. As the circuits for the E_R–E_Y and E_G–E_Y channels are similar they need not be considered.

The output of the U synchronous demodulator in the PAL decoder, which detects the E_B–E_Y signal, is fed to $TR1$ base via $C1$ and $R2$. $TR1$ is a common emitter amplifier with $R4$ serving as its collector load. As the upper video frequency is only 1 MHz, no special h.f. compensation is used. $R4/R3$ set the gain of the stage and a suitable portion of the E_B–E_Y signal is fed to the E_G–E_Y amplifier via $R5$, $C2$ for matrixing with an appropriate amount of the E_R–E_Y signal.

Amplified and inverted blue-difference signal from $TR1$ collector is fed to an emitter-follower stage $TR2$. This stage drives $TR6$ on its emitter with a $-(E_B$–$E_Y)$ signal via the blue gain preset $R9$.

$TR6$, $TR5$ constitute the output matrixing amplifier. These transistors are connected in series to share the high d.c. supply voltage that is necessary to provide a signal of about 150 V

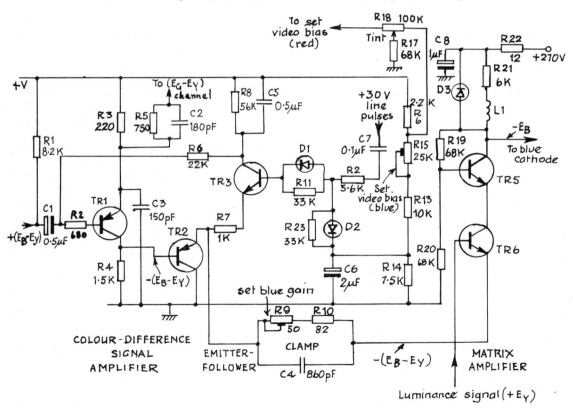

Fig. 12.25 Colour-difference amplifier and output matrixing amplifier.

peak-to-peak at the c.r.t. cathode. $R21$ is the load resistor and $L1$ (shunt peaking coil) provides h.f. compensation to maintain the response for video frequencies up to 5·5 MHz. $D3$ prevents the collector of $TR5$ from rising above the line supply voltage in the event of 'ringing' in $L1$. Base bias for $TR5$ is from the potential divider $R19$ and $R20$ and $TR6$ receives its base bias from the source of the luminance signal input.

A $+E_Y$ signal is fed to $TR6$ base and a $-(E_B-E_Y)$ signal is fed to the emitter. Since a $-(E_B-E_Y)$ signal at the emitter is equivalent to a $+(E_B-E_Y)$ signal at the base, the effective base drive is $E_Y+(E_B-E_Y) = +E_B$. Now a $+E_B$ signal on $TR6$ base will produce a $-E_B$ signal at $TR5$ collector which is of the right sign (polarity) to drive the c.r.t. on its cathode. On monochrome, when the colour-difference signals disappear, a $+E_Y$ signal at $TR6$ base will give rise to a $-E_Y$ signal at $TR5$ collector with the result that the c.r.t. is driven by the luminance signal only as is required.

The clamp transistor $TR3$ is used to eliminate d.c. drift in the video stages and the a.c. couplings ($C1$ for example) which otherwise might cause colour tint changes in the picture. Note that $TR6$ emitter is d.c. coupled via $R10$ and $R9$ to $TR2$ and this stage is d.c. coupled to $TR1$. Any change in $TR2$ emitter potential as a result of d.c. variations in $TR1$ or $TR2$ stages will alter $TR6$ emitter potential and hence the steady potential at $TR5$ collector which will affect the bias on the blue gun of the c.r.t. The luminance signal fed to $TR6$ is d.c. restored to a level set by the brightness control and this is stabilised so preventing drift at $TR6$ base.

$TR2$ and $TR6$ emitters are clamped to a preset level during the line blanking period by line pulses applied via $C7$ to $D1$ and $D2$. These 30 V pulses cause $D1$ and $D2$ to conduct, thereby connecting $TR3$ base to the positive potential present at the junction of $R13$, $R14$. When $TR3$ comes 'on' the current flowing is determined by the voltage across $C6$ (set by the video bias control $R15$) and the d.c. potential at $TR2$ emitter (decided by the d.c. drift). Suppose that $TR2$ emitter has drifted in the negative direction. This will cause $TR3$ to conduct more and its collector potential to fall to a lower voltage (as $C5$ charges). Due to the d.c. coupling from $TR3$ collector to $TR1$ base, $TR1$ will conduct harder causing its collector

voltage to rise (with respect to chassis). $TR2$ base and hence $TR2$ emitter follow this rise which tends to counteract the original fall thus stabilising $TR2$ and $TR6$ emitter potentials. Should $TR2$ emitter drift in the positive direction, $TR3$ will conduct less during the line pulse period and $C5$ will discharge via $R8$. The rise at $TR3$ collector is fed back to $TR1$ causing $TR1$ to conduct less. As a result, $TR1$ collector potential falls so $TR2$ emitter potential also falls which cancels the original rise.

I.C. Matrixing with Discrete Transistor RGB Drive

It is now common practice in receivers for the low level video circuit functions to be performed by integrated circuits. Designers of integrated circuits have their own ideas as to what video operations may be packaged into a particular i.c. which has led to a variety of designs during the development of receivers with i.cs. used exclusively for low level signal functions.

For medium gain video amplifier applications, single common emitter amplifiers with resistive loads and incorporating n.f.b. are fabricated into the i.c. using emitter-follower amplifiers for coupling between stages. When high gain is required, differential amplifiers are fabricated into the i.c. with emitter-follower stages used to couple the signal out of the i.c. Sometimes n.f.b. is incorporated into these amplifiers when a provision for adding extra feedback externally is required.

Matrixing of the luminance signal with the colour-difference signals is normally carried out in the PAL decoder i.c. such as with the TDA 3560, providing at its output low level primary signals which are raised to a sufficiently high level to drive the c.r.t. by discrete transistor video amplifiers.

A simplified diagram of one such arrangement is given in Fig. 12.26. The i.c. contains a low level luminance amplifier, V and U synchronous detectors, E_G-E_Y matrix and the luminance/colour-difference signal matrix. Low level primary signals are available at the i.c. output on pins 2, 3 and 4 which are then amplified and inverted by external discrete transistor drive amplifiers.

The schematic of Fig. 12.27 shows the essential processes within the i.c. for the

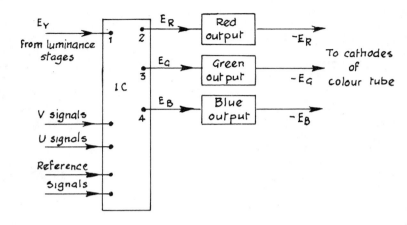

Fig. 12.26 Use of I.C. for luminance colour-difference signal matrixing (simplified diagram).

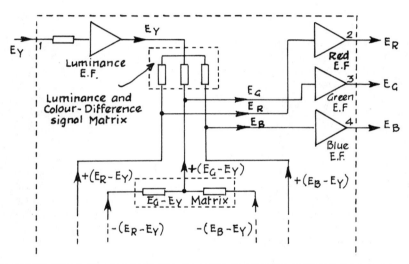

Fig. 12.27 Schematic of part I.C. showing video signal paths and matrixing network.

luminance/colour-difference signal matrix. Here the three colour difference signals and the luminance signal are fed to a resistive matrix which provides the required primary signals at its output. These are fed out of the i.c. via emitter-follower stages. The diagram also shows a resistive matrix for developing the green difference signal from the red and blue difference signals.

One of the primary signal output stages of Fig. 12.26 is given in Fig. 12.28. As the circuit is the same for the E_R, E_G and E_B outputs only the E_R amplifier has been shown.

The $+E_R$ output from pin 2 of the i.c. is developed across $R1$ which is the emitter load for the emitter-follower stage **inside** the i.c. The signal is d.c. coupled to the base of the video output transistor $TR1$ with $R2$, $C1$ forming a filter to remove unwanted harmonics. Amplified and inverted signal is developed across the collector load $R3$ and fed to the 'red' gun cathode via the series peaking coil $L1$ (damped by $R11$) the $R12$ (flash-over protection). In addition to the h.f. compensation provided by $L1$, extra boost for the high frequencies is given by $R6$, $C2$ (using n.f.b.) to

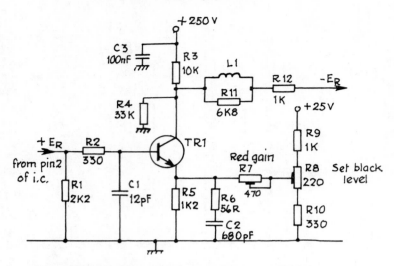

Fig. 12.28 Red output (repeated for blue and green outputs).

maintain the gain of the stage up to 5·5 MHz. During monochrome reception, the output of the luminance/colour-difference signal matrix will be the luminance signal only and this will drive all three output stages. R4 divides down the h.t. supply to the stage so that *TR*1 'sees' an effective voltage of 190 V.

The emitter circuit of *TR*1 is in the form of a bridge circuit, operating in an almost balanced condition. R9, R8 and R10 form one side of the bridge with *TR*1 and R5 forming the other side. R7 (the 'red' gain control) is connected between the two mid-points which are balanced. Thus very little current flows in R7 and in consequence adjustment of the control has

little effect on the d.c. conditions of *TR*1. When the video signal swings towards peak white (on monochrome) the emitter voltage of *TR*1 rises. This causes the bridge to go out of balance and R7 varies the load 'seen' by the emitter and hence the gain of the stage. With this arrangement, R7 may be adjusted to give the correct signal drive to the c.r.t. (when setting the 'grey-scale') with very little effect on the d.c. conditions and so little change in background colour. R8 adjusts the balance of the bridge to accommodate component tolerances and sets the collector voltage of *TR*1 to the required d.c. condition at black level.

CHAPTER THIRTEEN

DISPLAY TUBES

Objectives

1 To show the basic principles of the beam forming, focusing and deflection sections of display tubes.
2 To show the important tube dimensions and to explain how picture shift, pin-cushion distortion correction and flash-over protection is achieved.
3 Describe a typical monochrome c.r.t. and its supplies.
4 To outline the principle of operation and the 'colour alignment' difficulties of the delta gun colour c.r.t.
5 State how the above difficulties are overcome with in-line tubes.
6 To give reasons for auto-degaussing and grey scale tracking in a colour receiver.
7 To explain the basic ideas of scan velocity modulation.

ALL DISPLAY TUBES in current use are cathode ray tubes (c.r.t.). The c.r.t. converts the video signal back into light information, thus reversing the process which takes place in the television camera. The monochrome c.r.t. will be considered first as the beam forming, focusing and deflection sections are common to colour display tubes.

MONOCHROME C.R.T.

In a c.r.t. a beam of electrons is directed at high velocity towards a glass faceplate, the inside of which is coated with a layer of electroluminescent material that emits light on being struck by the electrons, Fig. 13.1. This layer is called the screen phosphor and the colour of the light emitted depends upon the chemical composition of the layer. To produce white light, a mixture of zinc sulphide (emitting blue light) and zinc cadmium sulphide (emitting yellow light) are used together with a silver activator. The particular proportions used in the mixture determine the type of white light that is emitted. Emission of light from the screen is due to both fluorescence and phosphorescence. Fluorescence occurs when the screen phosphor is excited by the electrons whilst phosphorescence occurs after the excitation has ceased producing an 'afterglow'. In television picture reproduction the afterglow is useful as it aids the persistence of vision. It would, however, degrade the picture image if it exceeded the picture period of 40 ms. A typical afterglow for a receiver c.r.t. is of the order of 0·1 ms.

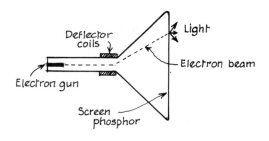

Fig. 13.1 Basic idea of display tube.

The construction and operation of the c.r.t. may be considered under four headings:

(1) The electron gun assembly which produces the beam of electrons.
(2) A focusing system to produce a fine electron beam.
(3) The viewing area of the screen which emits light on being excited by the electron beam.
(4) A deflection system to move the electron beam vertically and horizontally over the screen face to produce the raster.

(1) The Electron Gun

The function of the gun assembly is to produce a finely pointed beam of electrons to strike the c.r.t. screen. The electrons must have high velocity and the intensity of the beam must be controllable so that the luminance output from the screen can be varied. The gun assembly employs the same basic principles as a thermionic valve with the gun mounted in a glass envelope of high vacuum.

Figure 13.2(a) shows a complete 4-anode assembly (a heptode tube) which is the most common gun assembly, but guns employing five electrodes (pentode) or seven electrodes (hexode) may be used. The production of the electron beam may be explained by considering Fig. 13.2(b). An indirectly heated cathode is used but the oxide emitting area is of different form to an ordinary valve. In a c.r.t. only a small beam current is required and the emitting area is made smaller. Preferably, the emission should come from a point source to keep the beam dimensions small. One method of construction uses a small cylindrical tube which serves as the cathode but with the oxide emitter placed at one end as shown, and not all over the cylinder surface as in a valve. A heater is passed down the centre of the tube and when fed with a current raises the oxide to a sufficiently high temperature. for emission to take place.

To get the electrons moving towards the c.r.t. screen the first anode is placed at a potential of about 400–600 V positive with respect to the cathode. The resulting electric

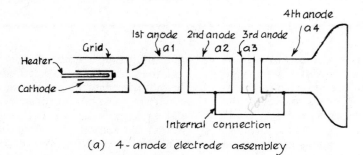

(a) 4-anode electrode assembley

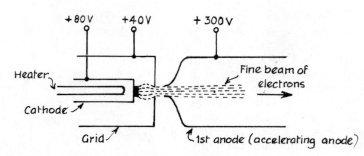

(b) Producing a fine beam of electrons

Fig. 13.2 The electron gun.

field that is set up between the first anode and the cathode provides the initial acceleration of the electrons on their way to the screen.

Surrounding the cathode is the control grid which is constructed differently to the control grid in an ordinary valve. It consists of a cylinder which is open at one end and has a fine aperture at the other end. The grid cylinder is normally held at a potential which is negative with respect to the cathode. The electric field set up between grid and cathode is in such a direction as to return electrons back towards the cathode. However, electrons of high energy overcome the retarding field and converge on the aperture at the end of the grid cylinder. On entering the aperture the electrons come under the influence of the first anode potential and begin to accelerate, and the resulting beam leaving the aperture is very narrow.

The intensity of the electron beam and hence the light output from the screen may be controlled by adjustment of the p.d. between grid and cathode. As the grid is made more negative to the cathode, fewer electrons have sufficient energy to reach the grid aperture. This results in a beam of lower intensity and a reduction of light output. Conversely, reducing the grid-to-cathode p.d. permits a greater number of electrons to reach the aperture with a resulting increase in beam intensity and increase in light output. If the grid-to-cathode bias is sufficiently large, none of the electrons will have sufficient energy to overcome the intense retarding field. In consequence there is no beam current and no light output from the screen. The value of bias which produces beam cut-off is called the cut-off voltage.

When viewing the screen, light of high intensity is interpreted as 'white', light of medium intensity as 'grey' and no light as 'black'. The actual colour of the unactivated screen appears a greyish colour, thus 'black' is the sensation of viewing the natural screen colour in contrast to the brighter energised areas.

Although the beam leaving the aperture in the grid cylinder is very narrow, the electrons tend to diverge due to the natural repulsion they have for one another. It is therefore necessary to focus the beam in some way so that on arrival at the screen a sharply converging beam is obtained.

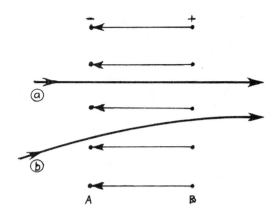

Fig. 13.3 Deflection of an electron beam due to electrostatic field.

(2) The Focusing Lens

In all modern c.r.ts. the beam is focused using an electrostatic lens. When an electron enters an electrostatic field it tends to travel in a direction opposite to the lines of force, which by convention are shown existing from positive to negative sources of potential. Suppose that we have two fine mesh wires A and B with a potential between them as shown in Fig. 13.3. If an electron arrives in the direction shown at (a) then the electrostatic field will accelerate it to a higher velocity but will not alter its direction of travel as it was initially travelling parallel to the lines of electrostatic force. On the other hand if an electron enters the field at an angle as shown at (b), the force acting on the electron in the direction A to B will accelerate it in this direction and, therefore, alter its direction of travel. When it leaves the electrostatic field it will again travel in a straight line; not in the direction that it entered the field, but in a direction more nearly that of the electrostatic lines. This principle is made use of in an electrostatic lens.

Figure 13.4 shows the basic action of a 3-anode electrostatic lens. The final anode potential is fed to a_2 and a_4; these anodes are commoned by an internal connection. A much lower potential is supplied to a_3 to set up the electrostatic fields shown between the three electrodes. Electrons entering these fields are subjected to forces urging them to travel in paths exactly opposite to the direction of the lines of force. When an electron enters the

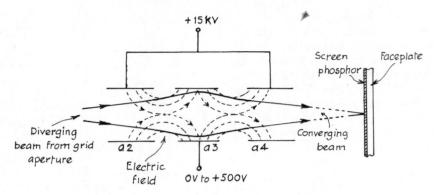

+15 KV

Screen phosphor

Faceplate

Diverging beam from grid aperture

Electric field

OV to +500V

Converging beam

a2 a3 a4

Fig. 13.4 An electrostatic lens.

fields at an angle its direction will therefore be changed. Due to the shape of the anodes and the resulting electric field patterns, the electrons are brought to a focus at the screen of the c.r.t. Whilst within the electrostatic fields the electrons may take curved paths but on leaving the fields they travel in straight line paths. To ensure that the point of focus coincides with the screen phosphor, the contour of the electrostatic field is altered by adjusting the potential fed to a_3. This potential is supplied from the 'focus potentiometer' and a_3 is referred to as the focusing anode. In some designs, another anode is used between the first and second anodes and is connected to a_3 (the focusing anode).

(3) The Viewing Area

As was mentioned earlier, the screen is made of an electroluminescent material which fluoresces on being bombarded by the electron stream. As the electrons approach a_2 they accelerate under the influence of the high a_2 potential. On entering the focusing field they at first decelerate and then accelerate once more on their way to the screen. Once past a_4 the electrons coast along (but with high speed) as the screen is at the same potential as a_4. The velocity attained by the electrons is given by $v = \sqrt{2e/m\,V}$ metres per second, where e/m is the ratio of electric charge to electron mass = $1 \cdot 759 \times 10^{11}$ coulombs/kg and V is the accelerating voltage in volts. With a final anode voltage of 18 kV, the velocity is approximately 8×10^7 metres per second! The kinetic energy acquired by the electrons

during motion is given to the screen coating on impact causing it to fluoresce.

The screen phosphor is deposited on the faceplate of the tube which is made from heavy reinforced plate glass. The faceplate protects the viewer from flying glass in the unlikely event of the tube imploding. In a 20″ tube, the total pressure on the faceplate is in the region of about 2300 kg (1·5 tons) and extreme care should be exercised in handling a c.r.t. A careless blow may fracture the glass envelope and a serious implosion could result.

On the back of the screen phosphor is deposited a very thin coating of aluminium which serves three purposes:

(a) Prevention of Ion Burn

Negative ions generated in the region of the electron gun travel towards the screen along with the electron beam. The mass of an ion may be several thousand times greater than that of an electron and if allowed to strike the screen coating may result in permanent damage to the screen. When an ion collision has occurred, the light output of the screen phosphor at that point may be severely reduced or even non-existent; this results in darkened areas on the picture referred to as ion burns. When a coating of aluminium is used, the kinetic energy of the ion is given up to the aluminium on colliding with the aluminium atoms. Electrons, however, due to their smaller mass pass through the atomic spaces of the aluminium and strike the screen coating. Electron-aluminium collisions will occur but with e.h.t. values over about 10 kV the loss is small.

(b) Increased Light Output

In a c.r.t. without an aluminium coating about 50% of the light emitted from the screen phosphor is directed away from the viewer, back down the c.r.t. With an aluminised screen, the coating is deposited in such a way that it forms a high reflective backing for the screen phosphor. This results in the rearward light being reflected towards the viewer giving a greater light output from the tube.

(c) Beam Current Return Path

Electrons which strike the screen phosphor must return to the e.h.t. supply to complete the beam current circuit. In non-aluminised tubes this was achieved by secondary emission. Each arriving electron caused secondary emission and the secondary emitted electrons were attracted to the internal graphite coating leaving the screen coating positively charged. In this way the potential of the screen phosphor increased until it reached the final anode potential. In an aluminised c.r.t. however the aluminium coating is connected to the e.h.t. supply thereby providing the electrons with a return path.

Aquadag Coating

The inside and outside of the tube flare are coated with a layer of graphite (applied in the form of a colloidial solution). The outer coating is connected to chassis and the inner coating is connected to e.h.t. supply and via spring clips to the second and fourth anodes. These two coatings separated by the thick glass of the tube form the e.h.t. reservoir capacitor (see Fig. 13.5). Typical values for the capacitance between a_2, a_4 and the external coating are 1750–2500 pF. It is important to ensure that the tube capacitance is discharged before handling the c.r.t. otherwise a very nasty 'kick' may be received and one is liable to drop the tube.

(4) Deflecting the Beam

Now that a sharply focused beam has been obtained it is necessary to deflect the beam in order to obtain a raster. All display tubes in current use employ magnetic deflection and this is achieved by feeding the scanning currents into two sets of scan coils disposed at

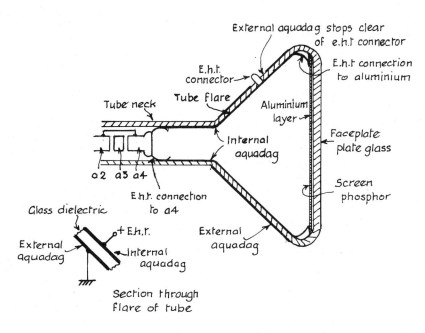

Fig. 13.5 Details of the screen section of the tube.

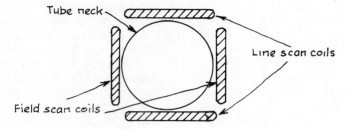

Fig. 13.6 Disposition of vertical and horizontal scan coils.

right angles to one another and fitted close to the tube neck as in Fig. 13.6.

When an electron enters a field of constant magnetic flux it experiences a force acting in a direction at right angles to both the direction of the field and the direction of motion of the beam, see Fig. 13.7. This force deflects the beam away from its original path with the result that the beam emerges from the field along a path at an angle to its original direction. Whilst in the deflecting field, the electron travels in a curved path, which is part of the circumference of a circle of radius r. On leaving the deflecting field, the beam path is tangential to the deflection curvature. The magnitude of the angle through which the beam is deflected depends upon the strength of the magnetic field, the time spent by the electrons in the field and the mass of the electron. With an 18 kV final anode potential

and with the deflecting field extending over a distance of, say, 5 cm the time spent in the field is only about 0·6 nano seconds. Although the mass of the electron is very small, strong deflecting fields are required with m.m.f.s. of the order of 400–500 ampere-turns.

If the deflecting field is perfectly uniform and all electrons have the same velocity, the electrons appear to have been deflected from a point D called the deflection centre. If the field is non-uniform as in Fig. 13.8(b), the electrons will be deflected through different angles and an elliptical spot will be produced on the screen. This defect is called astigmatism.

Figure 13.9 and 13.10 show the magnetic fields set up by the vertical and horizontal scanning currents fed to the scan coils. The direction of the resulting force acting on the beam may be found by applying Fleming's left-hand rule, but note that electron motion is

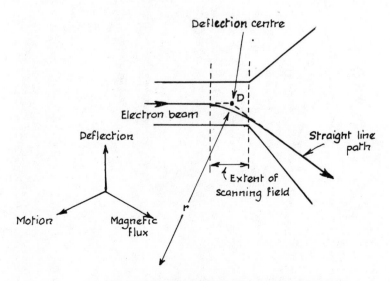

Fig. 13.7 Deflecting the beam (magnetic deflection).

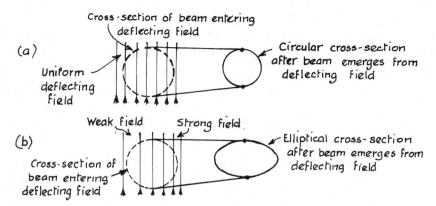

Fig. 13.8 Astigmatism due to non-linear deflecting field.

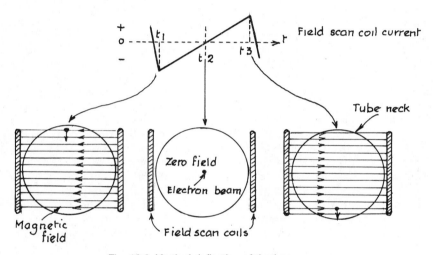

Fig. 13.9 Vertical deflection of the beam.

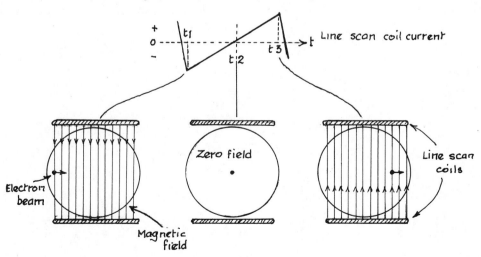

Fig. 13.10 Horizontal deflection of the beam.

opposite to conventional current flow. In both diagrams the electron beam is assumed to be moving out of the paper. Quite clearly, in order to produce deflection left or right and up or down from the screen centre, the deflection currents must be a.c. type waveforms.

As the only useful flux produced by the scan coils is that which passes through the tube neck, the coils are bent round the neck as in Fig. 13.11(a) which shows one set of coils only. At one time the coils were arranged in a castellated ferroxcube core to reduce the reluctance of the magnetic circuit and decrease the losses thereby enabling a stronger magnetic field to be obtained for a given scanning current. With modern wide-angle tubes, the castellated core is not used; the coils tend to be flatter and bent round the tube neck more as in Fig. 13.11(b). Also, to reduce the possibility of corner-cutting, *i.e.* darkening in the corners due to beam striking the tube neck at the extremities of deflection, the coils are taken up the tube flare as in Fig. 13.11(c). The line deflector coils are placed nearest the tube neck and extend further up the flare since the line scan coils must produce the greatest amount of deflection (aspect ratio 4:3). Note that if the deflector coil assembly is not pushed home against the flare of the tube then corner-cutting may occur. Also, if the coils are rotated away from their correct orientation, the raster will not be square with the sides of the tube.

The two halves of the scan coils may be arranged in series or in parallel with one another. The arrangement used depends upon the aims of the designer and the type of drive amplifier used. Parallel connected coils provide a high current, low impedance configuration whereas series connected coils provide a low current, high impedance arrangement. Field deflector coils used in transistor receivers generally have an inductance in the range 20–100 mH and a d.c. resistance of up to about 30 ohms. Line scan coils have a smaller inductance in the range of 50–100 μH and a d.c. resistance which is usually less than one ohm. These values depend on the line supply voltage, c.r.t. voltages and the deflection angle required. With a field deflection coil of inductance 100 mH and resistance 20 ohms, the ratio of reactance/resistance at field frequency is approximately 3:2 but with an inductance of 20 mH the ratio is 0·3:1. Thus with field coils, the inductive reactance or the resistance may be predominant depending upon the particular design. With line coils having an inductance of 50 μH and a d.c. resistance of 0·5 ohm, the ratio is approximately 10:1 (at line frequency) and with an inductance of 200 μH (same resistance) approximately 40:1. Thus the line coils are usually predominantly inductive.

Let us now consider the voltage waveform across the scanning coils when a linear sawtooth current flows in them. The line coils will be considered first and it will be assumed that the current passing through them is 1 A peak-to-peak (values up to several amperes peak-to-peak are common) and that the

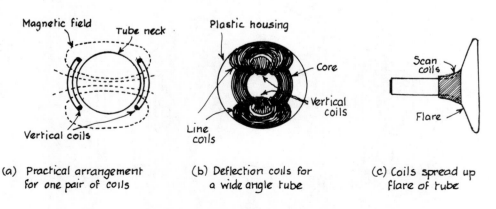

(a) Practical arrangement for one pair of coils

(b) Deflection coils for a wide angle tube

(c) Coils spread up flare of tube

Fig. 13.11 Practical scan coils.

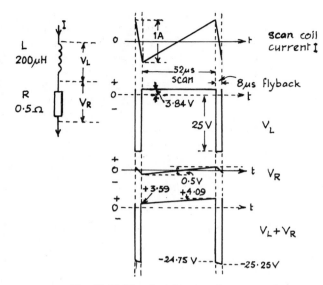

Fig. 13.12 Waveforms across line scan coils.

inductive and resistive components are as given in Fig. 13.12.

The voltage across an inductor is given by $E = -L \, di/dt$ where L is the inductance (H) and di/dt is the rate of change of current (A/s).

During the scan period ($52 \, \mu s$):

$$E = \frac{200}{10^6} \times \frac{10^6}{52} \text{ volts}$$

$$= 3 \cdot 84 \text{ V}.$$

Since di/dt is constant over this period, the induced voltage will be constant at $3 \cdot 84$ V.

For the flyback period (say $8 \, \mu s$):

$$E = \frac{200}{10^6} \times \frac{10^6}{8} \text{ volts}$$

$$= 25 \text{ V}.$$

Again, as di/dt is constant the voltage across L will also be constant at 25 V.

Now the voltage across $R = 0 \cdot 5 \times 1$ volts $= 0 \cdot 5$ V and the voltage will be sawtooth shape.

It should be appreciated, of course, that we cannot measure the voltage across R as the resistance is distributed throughout the inductor and not 'lumped' as shown. The actual waveform across the line scan coils will therefore be $V_L + V_R$ as shown in the diagram. It will be seen that the ratio of flyback voltage scan voltage is approximately $6 \cdot 5 : 1$. The

actual voltage across the coils during flyback may be greater than that calculated as the flyback may not be linear. Thus, over some parts of the flyback di/dt will be greater. Also, due to the self-capacitance of the coils, the flyback pulse will be half-sine and not rectangular as indicated.

Corresponding waveforms for the field coils are given in Fig. 13.13. The voltage values indicated are calculated for a coil inductance of 100 mH and a d.c. resistance of 20 ohms with a peak-to-peak current of 800 mA. A scanning time of $18 \cdot 7$ ms has been used and a flyback time of 1 ms which is about the maximum time for the average receiver. The resultant waveform $V_L + V_R$ shows the predominating influence of the resistive component, whereas for the line coils it is the

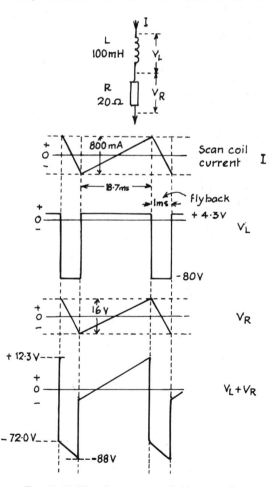

Fig. 13.13 Waveforms across field scan coils.

inductive component that determines the actual voltage waveshape.

Tube Dimensions

The important dimensions that are often quoted in technical literature are shown in Fig. 13.14.

Screen Size

The screen size is measured diagonally and is given in inches or millimetres. Common screen sizes are 12″ and 14″ in portable receivers and 20″, 22″ and 26″ in table receivers. The choice of screen size determines the maximum viewable distance at which important scene detail may be clearly discerned, *e.g.* written text. The larger the screen size the greater the maximum viewable distance, also close up shots of people appear more life size.

Deflection Angle

The deflection angle, *e.g.* 70°, 90° and 110° of a c.r.t. is normally quoted for the diagonal angle. With modern c.r.ts. deflection angles of 90° and 110°; are the most common. A 110° tube, for example, may have a vertical deflection angle of 81° and a horizontal deflection angle of 98°.

With, say, a 20″ tube using a 90° deflection angle a certain amount of power is fed into the scan coils. If the tube size is increased to 22″ but the deflection angle kept the same, the distance from the deflection centre to the screen must be increased. If the e.h.t. is kept the same there is no need to supply the scan coils with extra power. In practice the e.h.t. would be increased since the spot brightness is spread over a larger screen area hence the picture would appear dimmer with the larger screen size (although the light output is the same as the smaller screen). An increase in e.h.t. increases the speed of the electrons hence they spend less time in the scanning field. Thus a larger power must be supplied to the scan coils to maintain the same actual deflection angle and hence picture size.

Neck Diameter

As the deflection angle increases a greater amount of power must be supplied to the scan coils. However, with careful design it is possible to achieve large deflection angles without a great increase in scanning power by reducing the c.r.t. neck diameter (and by minimising losses in the scan coils).

A decrease in neck diameter allows the scan coils to be brought closer to the electron beam and a more intense field is produced for a given scanning current. With a small neck diameter the length of the scan coils must be kept short to prevent the beam striking the tube neck and causing 'corner-cutting'. As a short coil requires a stronger magnetic field, the coil is taken up the flare of the tube thereby eliminating the corner-cutting problem. The design of the neck flaring helps in this respect.

Some typical dimensions for a 20″, 110° tube are given in Fig. 13.15.

Rim Band

A metal band is fitted around the edge of modern tubes to prevent implosion. The band prevents expansion or deformation of the tube should a crack occur, hence preventing the crack from opening or spreading. The band comprises a cadmium plated ring of mild steel and is sealed by a polyester resin to the periphery of the tube face-plate, which is the region having the highest stress. Four lugs on the ring facilitate fixing of the tube. It is possible for the metal rim band to acquire a high static potential via capacitive coupling through the glass cone from the internal coating which is at e.h.t. potential. Although the rim band is not normally accessible to the

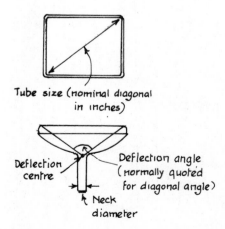

Fig. 13.14 Significant dimensions of television tube.

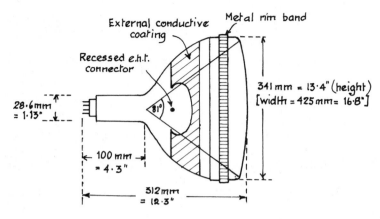

Fig. 13.15 20" rectangular tube (110°).

viewer, accidental contact may occur. For this reason any static charge that builds up on the rim band must be discharged to chassis. A direct connection to chassis cannot be used because of the danger of a lethal shock in the event of the chassis being live. The rim band is therefore connected to chassis via a high value resistor, *e.g.* $2\,M\Omega$.

'S' Correction

When a tube with a round screen area is used as in Fig. 13.16(a) where the distance between any point on the tube face to the deflection centre is the radius for the circumference of the tube face, a linear picture will result when the scan coils are fed with linear increasing current waveforms. This is because a linear, increasing current produces equal increments θ in the deflection angle, thus the distances a–b, b–c, c–d *etc* on the screen are equal. The modern rectangular tube has a much 'flatter' face thus the distance between the deflection centre and the tube face increases with the deflection angle as in Fig. 13.16(b) where the effect has been exaggerated for clarity. Therefore, with equal increments in the deflection angle the distances a–b, b–c and c–d *etc* are no longer equal and the display will be non-linear. As the effect becomes more pronounced as the deflection angle is increased it is necessary to provide some form of correction with wide-angle tubes.

Correction is achieved by modifying the scanning current waveform and Fig. 13.17

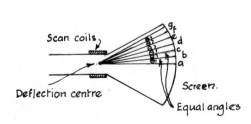

(a) Small deflection angle (round tube)
Linear display

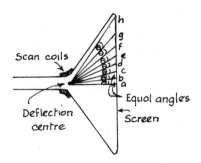

(b) Large deflection angle (flat tube face) Non-linear display

Fig. 13.16 Distortion of picture image on flat screen with large deflection angle.

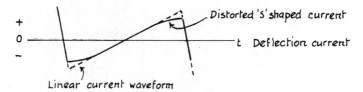

Fig. 13.17 'S' correcting waveform.

shows the waveform required. Clearly, the deflection angle increments must be progressively reduced as the deflection angle increases. Thus the rate of change of current is progressively reduced towards the start and end of scan producing an 'S' shaped waveform as shown. To achieve this result, a capacitor of suitable value is placed in series with the scan coils. 'S' correction operates by resonance between the correcting capacitor and the scan coil inductance, the circuit being shocked into oscillation by the flyback. By arranging that the resonance is between one-third and one-half of the scanning frequency, a suitable portion of the sine-curve may be used. 'S' correction may be used in the vertical and horizontal scanning circuits but usually is only applied to the horizontal scanning current since non-linearity of display is more apparent with the larger deflection angle used for the horizontal deflection.

Centralising the Raster (Picture shift)

Some means must be employed to centralise the picture on the screen due to manufacturing tolerances in the alignment of the gun assembly in the tube neck and in the production of the scan coil assembly. Picture centering is achieved by applying weak magnetic fields from permanent magnets fitted outside the tube neck. Commonly the magnets are made in the form of magnetised annular rings as shown in Fig. 13.18(a). The rings are magnetised in such a way as to set up a magnetic field across the tube neck. Two rings are used which can be rotated independently of one another as in Fig. 13.18(b). The resultant magnetic field of the two rings can be moved radially by moving the two rings together in the same direction and the strength of the field may be adjusted by moving the rings in opposite directions. Movement of the rings thus allows the electron beam to be deflected in any radial direction by a controlled amount causing an appropriate shift in the raster on the screen. The shift magnets are mounted immediately behind the scan coil assembly, see Fig. 13.18(c), and so correct the beam position prior to its being deflected by the scanning fields.

Raster Correction Magnets

Shape distortion of the raster may occur due to non-uniformity of the scanning field. One

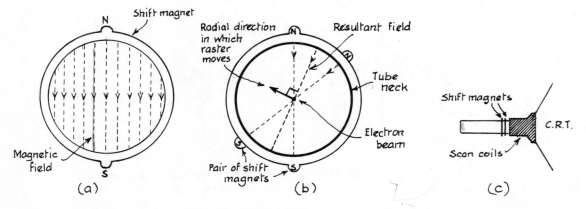

Fig. 13.18 Picture shift magnets for centralising the picture.

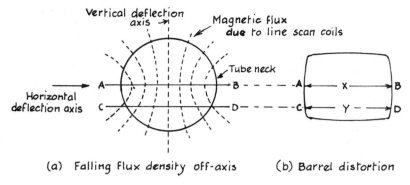

(a) Falling flux density off-axis   (b) Barrel distortion

Fig. 13.19 Barrel distortion caused by non-uniform deflecting field.

form of shape distortion arises when the magnetic field density falls off away from the deflection axis as illustrated in Fig. 13.19(a). Here the flux density is greater along a line a–b (zero vertical deflection) than along a line such as c–d (vertical deflection now applied). Hence the line trace amplitude (x) at the screen centre will be larger than the trace amplitude (y) away from the screen centre. If both sets of scan coils produce flux distributions similar to that of Fig. 13.19(a), the raster will exhibit outward curvature called 'barrel distortion' as in Fig. 13.19(b).

Inward curvature of the raster is common with flat screens particularly when a large deflection angle is used. The reason for this may be explained by reference to Fig. 13.20(a). Consider that vertical deflection only is applied to the beam so that it traces out the vertical line a–b. If the beam is now moved left and right of the screen centre as it is

scanning vertically, it will trace out vertical lines e–f and c–d at the screen edges. These lines are longer than at the screen centre because with a flat screen the distance between deflection centre and the screen is greater at the edges than in the centre. Similarly, by considering the beam scanning a horizontal line only and then moving the beam up and down from centre, it may be shown that the vertical sides of the raster will also exhibit inward curvature. This form of picture shape distortion is called **pin-cushion distortion**, see Fig. 13.20(b).

Pin-cushion distortion may offset barrel distortion (if any) produced by the deflecting field. However, either form of distortion or their combined result may be corrected by external magnetic fields applied via small permanent magnets mounted on the scan coil assembly as in Fig. 13.21(a).

Figure 13.21(b) shows the effect of one pair

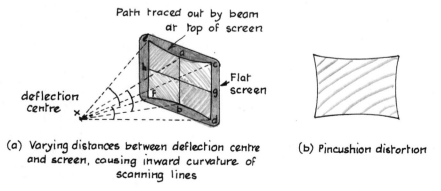

(a) Varying distances between deflection centre and screen, causing inward curvature of scanning lines

(b) Pincushion distortion

Fig. 13.20 Pin-cushion distortion caused by employment of flat C.R.T. screen.

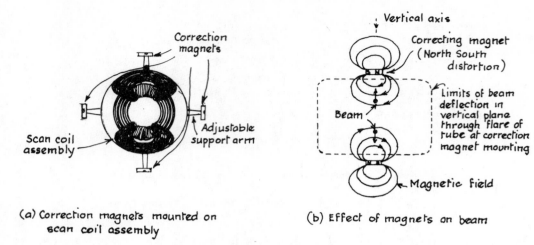

(a) Correction magnets mounted on
scan coil assembly

(b) Effect of magnets on beam

Fig. 13.21 Raster correction magnets.

of magnets on the electron beam assuming that the raster is exhibiting pin-cushion distortion. As the beam is traversing the screen at the top, the effect of the field due to the upper magnet is to exert a force on the beam deflecting it upwards. At the bottom of the screen the field due to the lower magnet produces a force deflecting the beam downwards. The deflection forces due to the magnets are greatest around the extremities of the vertical axis of the tube but diminish towards the screen centre as is required. The two magnets will thus correct for north-south distortion of the raster. If both magnets are rotated through 180° to reverse the direction of their fields, they will correct for barrel distortion. The same principle applies to the other pair of magnets which are used to correct for east-west distortion. As the magnets are mounted on soft metal flanges they can be positioned to give the correct strength of field or twisted to reverse the direction of the field.

Modulating the Raster

To produce an image on the face of the display tube, the light output from the screen phosphor must vary from instant to instant as the beam scans the screen. This is achieved by varying the intensity of the beam with the video signal from the final video amplifier in the receiver.

The video signal is applied to the c.r.t. (normally to the cathode) so that the bias between grid and cathode is varied as in Fig. 13.22. With no picture information the brightness control is set so that cut-off voltage is applied to the gun resulting in zero beam current. The video signal excursions commencing at blanking level progressively reduce the bias causing the beam current to increase. Thus a high beam current corresponds to peak white, medium beam current to grey and zero beam current to black. The relationship between the grid drive voltage V_D and the light output L is not linear but follows the law $L = k\,V_D^y$ where y is the gamma of the tube, but this is corrected for at the transmitter.

If the contrast is set too low resulting in a small amplitude signal being applied to the c.r.t., there will be insufficient beam current on the peaks of the signal and the picture will appear pale or 'thin'. The **contrast control thus sets the white level** of the picture.

The effect of maladjustment of the brightness control is shown in Fig. 13.23. In Fig. 13.23(a) the brightness setting is too high causing a reduction in the standing bias. In consequence there is some beam current under no signal conditions. This beam current level corresponds to black level as far as the video signal is concerned. Thus black on the video signal is reproduced as a grey on the screen and the picture will be overall too light or lacking in blacks.

If the brightness control is set too low as in Fig. 13.23(b), the video signal excursions beyond cut-off will not produce any beam

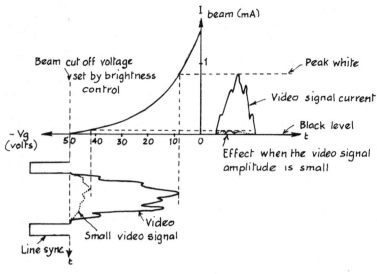

Fig. 13.22 Modulating the beam current.

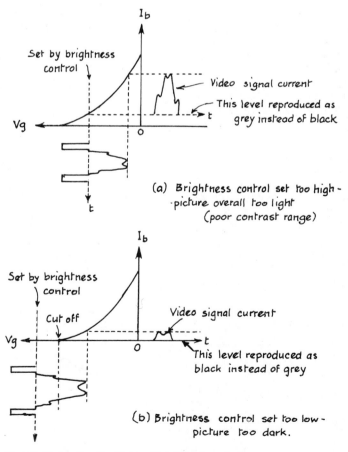

Fig. 13.23 Incorrect settings of brightness control.

current. Thus grey level on the video signal is now reproduced as black on the picture and the picture will be too dark overall. The setting of the **brightness control thus determines the black level** of the picture.

C.R.T. Flashover

In spite of adequate clearance given between the electrodes carrying e.h.t. potential and the lower potential electrodes of the c.r.t., occasionally the energy stored in the tube e.h.t. smoothing capacitance is released via an arc to one of the lower potential electrodes. It is generally believed that flashover is initiated by small particles which are stripped off the electrodes by the intense electrostatic fields that are present in the gun assembly. No matter how well a high voltage television tube (mono or colour) is made and designed, sooner or later one of the electrodes (grid, cathode, heater, a_1 etc.) will receive a flashover discharge.

If no protection is provided, the current that flows in the external circuit connected to the electrode which receives the discharge will cause extensive damage to transistors, diodes and integrated circuits, *etc*. Fig. 13.24(a) shows the flashover current path in an unpro-

tected circuit when a discharge to the grid electrode takes place. The component parts of the flashover current path may be represented by an equivalent circuit as shown in Fig. 13.24(b) where C is the tube capacitance (2000 pF), R is the series resistance made up primarily by the internal and outer c.r.t. coatings (20 Ω) and L is the series inductance made up primarily by the external connecting leads and gun electrodes (1 μH). During flashover when the circuit is completed, the energy stored in the tube capacitance is released in the form of a damped oscillation. The flashover current thus takes the form shown in Fig. 13.24(c). The frequency of the oscillation is of the order of 3 MHz and the peak current in the region of 600 A!

To prevent extensive damage from this high current, spark-gaps are used to by-pass the flashover currents from the external circuits, see Fig. 13.25. A spark-gap is required at each electrode which is not directly connected to chassis from the a.c. or d.c. point of view. Each spark-gap is fitted close to the electrode on one side and to chassis via the shortest possible path on the other side with all spark-gaps connected to a common point. The spark-gaps may be formed in the printed circuit of the p.c. board fitted on the c.r.t.

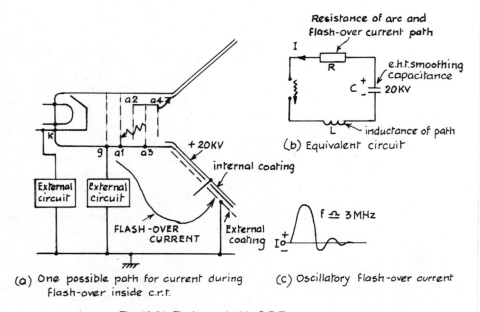

(a) One possible path for current during flash-over inside c.r.t.

(b) Equivalent circuit

(c) Oscillatory flash-over current

Fig. 13.24 Flash-over inside C.R.T.

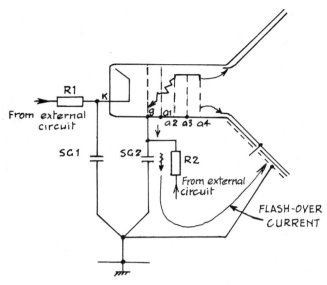

Fig. 13.25 Use of spark gaps and protection resistors.

base. In some c.r.ts. parallel spark-gaps are fitted to all the base pins inside the c.r.t. with one pin serving as a common connection. This pin is directly connected to the external coating of the tube (and to chassis).

The length of the lead from the spark-gaps to the tube coating is important. During flashover the rate of change of current is high and quite high voltages (a few kV) may be induced in the inductance of a lead of modest length. The lead should not be coiled up to make it look neater nor should its length or position be altered in any way as voltages may be induced into circuits far removed from the tube, *e.g.* the u.h.f. tuner. The e.h.t. should not be tested by allowing it to arc over to a screwdriver as large voltages may be induced into surrounding circuits causing damage to semiconductor devices, *etc*.

Protection resistors such as $R1$ and $R2$ of Fig. 13.25 are placed in series with the external crcuits to assist in the build-up of the firing voltage across the spark-gaps. This technique makes the spark-gaps break down more quickly and protects the external circuits from the firing voltage of the spark-gaps. Any electrode which is supplied from a high voltage line, *i.e.* an h.t. line should be protected by a series resistor otherwise the line may be short circuited via the arc during breakdown of the spark-gap.

During a flashover some of the transient energy inside the tube neck may be transferred to the deflector coils via capacitive coupling. As this can lead to the failure of scan rectification diodes, boost diodes and the line output transformer, spark-gaps should be fitted to each side of the deflector coils.

Soft-Flash Tubes (Mullard In-Line Colour tubes)

The soft-flash tube is a more recent development to reduce the amount of transient energy which by-passes the normal protective measures and is injected into the receiver circuitry during a flashover. This is achieved by the provision of a built-in resistor inside the tube. The resistor is formed by the internal coating of the c.r.t. which is a specially developed layer containing iron oxide. During an e.h.t. flashover the effective resistance to currents flowing in the gun structure is increased to about $400 \, \Omega$ by the internal coating. The value of R in the equivalent circuit of Fig. 13.24(b) is now increased to $400 \, \Omega$ as opposed to $20 \, \Omega$ for the standard tube. The increase in resistance thus severely damps the oscillatory flashover current, see Fig. 13.26

During a flashover the peak current flowing is reduced by a factor of 10 and the rate of change of current by a factor of about 100. The

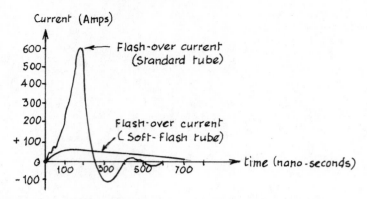

Fig. 13.26 Comparison of flash-over currents in standard and soft-flash colour tubes.

reduction in the rate of change of current considerably reduces the amount of transient energy that will be transferred to the receiver circuits. Also, the major resistive component in the flashover path is inside the picture tube. Thus the voltage drop across the external aquadag coating is reduced which further reduces the transient coupling problem. Since the magnitude of the flashover current has been considerably reduced there will be less deterioration of the external coating chassis contact.

Receivers fitted with soft-flash tubes still require the normal spark-gap and resistor protective measures and a standard tube may be replaced by a soft-flash tube. The inside coating of a soft-flash tube may be recognised by its reddish colour.

The Monochrome Tube Supplies

Typical supply circuits immediately around a monochrome c.r.t. are shown in Fig. 13.27. All c.r.t. electrode connections are bought out

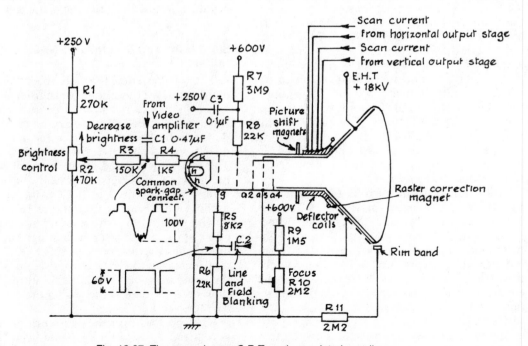

Fig. 13.27 The monochrome C.R.T. and associated supplies.

to the base of the tube except for the second and fourth anodes which are internally connected to the e.h.t. connector on the tube flare. Internal spark-gaps are fitted in the base of the tube for all electrodes and the common connection is taken to the outer coating of the c.r.t. These spark-gaps together with the series resistors $R4$, $R5$ and $R8$ provide a system of full flashover protection for the external circuits.

Cathode modulation of the c.r.t. is used with the negative going video signal a.c. coupled to the tube cathode via $C1$ and $R4$. Brightness control voltage is also applied to the cathode from $R2$ which forms a potential divider with $R1$ across the h.t. supply. As the brightness voltage from $R2$ is increased, the bias is increased and the beam current decreased. $R3$ is a stand-off resistor to prevent the video signal being shorted out via the brightness control when the slider is set at high brightness (low voltage) level. The grid electrode which is normally held at chassis potential via $R5$ and $R6$ is supplied with negative-going line and field blanking pulses via $C2$. These pulses cut off the tube during the line and field flyback periods thus suppressing the beam retrace.

The accelerating anode (a_1) is supplied with a fixed potential via $R7$ and $R8$ from a 600 V supply which is derived from the line output transformer. $C3$ maintains the first anode potential for a short period at switch-off to ensure that the e.h.t. smoothing capacitor is discharged before the scanning fields fully collapse. This prevents a spot burn on the tube face at switch-off. The focusing anode (a_3) is fed with a variable voltage from the preset potentiometer $R10$ which serves as the focus control. This potentiometer varies the focus voltage over the approximate range of 0–350 V. $R11$ discharges any static built up on the rim band which may be transferred via the glass section of the tube from the internal coating.

COLOUR C.R.T

Since the commencement of colour television transmissions, the only colour display tubes to have been produced in large quantities are those using some form of shadow-mask, *e.g.* **Delta Gun**, **Trinitron** and **P.I.L.** tubes. The delta gun assembly was the first colour tube to be adopted and although it is no longer fitted in modern domestic receivers, a knowledge of its operation is important in the understanding of other types of shadow mask tubes and how the practical 'colour alignment' difficulties of the delta gun system have been overcome. The delta gun tube is important for another reason as it is still used in high resolution graphic monitors where its high definition, refined over some twenty years of development, is not easily matched by other forms of colour tube.

Delta Gun Shadow-Mask Tube

The basic principle of operation is shown in Fig. 13.28. Three phosphors which emit light in the primary colours of red, green and blue are deposited on the screen tube. The phosphors are applied to the screen face in the form

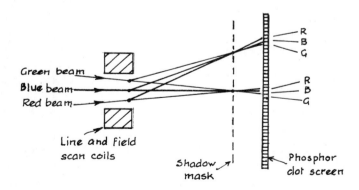

Fig. 13.28 Basic principle of delta-gun shadow mask C.R.T.

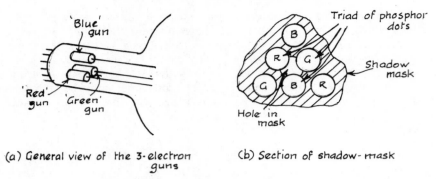

(a) General view of the 3-electron guns

(b) Section of shadow-mask

Fig. 13.29 Delta-gun arrangement and shadow-mask.

of small dots in such a way as to constitute a regular system of triangular groups called **triads**. Behind the phosphor dot screen is placed the shadow-mask, a thin steel plate with holes in it. Three separate electron guns, one for each primary colour, are arranged in triangular formation within the tube neck. A common deflection coil assembly is used for the three beams.

The holes in the shadow-mask, see Fig. 13.29(b) are so arranged that the electron beam from the blue gun always falls on the blue phosphor dots. Also, the red and green beams fall on their respective red and green dots. The geometry of the system is such that when the beams are deflected, they still fall on their respective phosphor dots. On a 25″ tube there are about 1,300,000 phosphor dots or

approximately 430,000 triads. As each hole in the shadow-mask is associated with one triad, there are also about 430,000 holes in the shadow-mask. **Since the phosphor dots are extremely small, the eye does not resolve the individual coloured dots but only the additive mixture of their light outputs**; this is the essential feature of all colour tubes.

Each of the electron guns may be switched 'on' or 'off' by applying appropriate signals to its cathode. Consider the conducting state of the three guns to produce the following hues by checking Table 13.1.

The Shadow-Mask

The purpose of the shadow-mask may be understood by reference to Fig. 13.30 which

Table 13.1 State of three guns for reproduction of hues.

Hue	Red gun	Green gun	Blue gun
(1) High luminance, saturated red	ON	OFF	OFF
(2) Lower luminance, saturated red	ON (but less than in 1.	OFF	OFF
(3) High luminance white	ON	ON	ON
(4) Low luminance white (grey)	ON	ON	ON
	(all guns less hard ON than in (3))		
(5) Saturated yellow	ON	ON	OFF
(6) Desaturated yellow	ON	ON	ON
	(red and green guns harder ON than blue)		
(7) Saturated magenta	ON	OFF	ON
(8) Saturated cyan	OFF	ON	ON
(9) Black	OFF	OFF	OFF

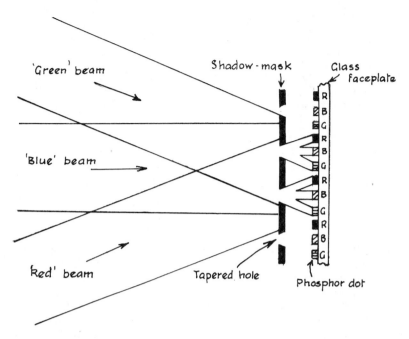

Fig. 13.30 Diagram showing action of shadow-mask.

shows the three electron beams arriving at a single position on the screen. Each beam has a diameter such that it embraces several holes of the shadow-mask. It will be seen that, for example, the part of the green beam passing through the holes of the shadow-mask only fall on the green phosphor dots, *i.e.* the mask 'shadows' the green beam from the blue and red phosphor dots. Similarly the mask allows the red and blue beams to strike only the red and blue phosphor dots.

The mask made from mild steel, is about 0·2 mm thick and is placed about 1·25 cm from the screen. A photo-etching process from a master negative is used for producing the holes in the mask which have a diameter of about 0.25 mm with a spacing of 0·6 mm between holes. The holes are tapered as shown to prevent reflections of the electrons off the sides of the holes so that they are not scattered as this would result in a loss of saturation and definition. To allow a margin for beams that land slightly off-centre the diameter of the phosphor dots is about 0·4 mm (slightly larger than the holes in the mask).

The holes in the shadow-mask constitute only about 15% of the total mask area, thus 85% of the electrons emitted by the three guns do not strike the screen phosphors and are intercepted by the mask. As only 15% of the electrons give up their energy to produce light output, the beam current and e.h.t. are higher in a colour tube than in a monochrome one. Electrons which are intercepted by the mask are absorbed to produce heat. Since the mask is at the final anode potential the heat production is considerable, *e.g.* with a final anode potential of 25 kV and a mean beam current of 1 mA (for three beams) the power dissipated in the mask $= 25 \times 10^3 \times 1 \times 10^{-3} \times 0·85\,\mathrm{W} = 21·25\,\mathrm{W}$. The heat generated causes the mask to expand outwards and if no compensation is made for this effect, then the holes will no longer line-up correctly with their associated triads.

This is shown in Fig. 13.31 using the red beam as an example. Due to the radial movement of the holes in the shadow-mask as the mask heats up, the red beam lands partly on a red dot and partly on a green dot. If,

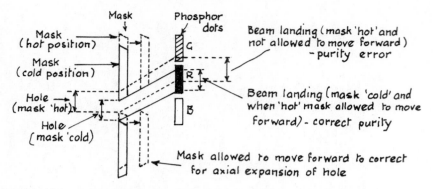

Fig. 13.31 *Diagram showing effect of temperature rise in shadow-mask on beam landing and compensation required.*

however, the mask is allowed to move forward as its temperature rises the correct beam landing can be maintained as shown. This is achieved by using a mounting system consisting of springs and bimetallic clips. Heat is conducted from the mask to the bimetallic clips which bend and cause the mask to move forward.

Typical Delta Gun C.R.T.

The three guns are identical in construction and are spaced 120° apart, see Fig. 13.32, with their axes tilted towards the tube axis by 1° so that the three beams land on their respective phosphor dots in the same part of the screen.

As with modern monochrome tubes, electrostatic focusing and electromagnetic deflection is used. Pentode guns are usually employed: cathode – grid – accelerating anode-focusing anode, and final anode. The internal conductive coating which conveys the e.h.t. to the final anode is usually referred to as a_4 (the ultor). The blue gun is uppermost with the red and green guns orientated as in Fig. 13.32.

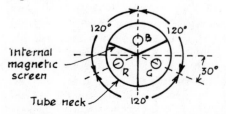

Fig. 13.32 *Disposition of the guns in a delta tube (viewed from the screen).*

The supplies associated with a delta gun c.r.t. are shown in Fig. 13.33. Voltages given on this diagram are the steady (no signal) voltages. Spark-gaps are provided together with associated series resistors *e.g. R1, R5, R7 etc* to keep the flashover current out of the supply circuits as is common with normal monochrome practice. The first anode potential to each gun is supplied from a preset (background control). This is to permit all three guns to be set to cut off with identical grid-to-cathode potentials during the 'grey scale' adjustments. During colour transmissions, the three primary signal drives are applied to the cathodes of the c.r.t. (or luminance signal on monochrome). The brightness voltage may be applied to the grid or brightness may be varied by altering the black level of the signal applied to the cathodes. A higher a_2 potential is required than for a monochrome tube and this is supplied from the focus potentiometer which varies the voltage over the range of about 4–5 kV. The heater requirement is 6·3 V at 900 mA with the three heaters arranged in parallel.

Beam Currents

The beam currents of the three guns in a colour tube are not normally equal because the efficiency of the red, blue and green phosphors are different. To produce the standard white illuminant 'D', the proportions of the total tube currents (the e.h.t. current) for each beam are typically:

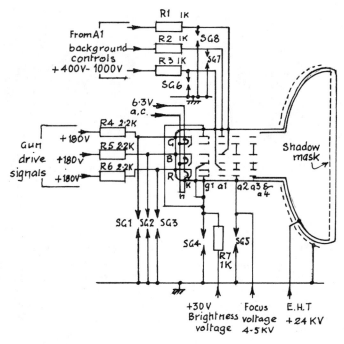

Fig. 13.33 Typical delta gun C.R.T. and supplies.

RED : 43% GREEN : 32% BLUE : 25%

Small variations from these values will be found with tubes of different manufacture as slightly different phosphors may be used.

The main significance of the dissimilar beam currents is that in order to produce the standard white, **unequal amplitude video drive voltages** are required on the three cathodes of the display tube. For the above proportions, the ratio of:

$$\frac{\text{Red Drive}}{\text{Green Drive}} = \frac{43}{32} = 1\cdot34 : 1$$

and the ratio of:

$$\frac{\text{Red Drive}}{\text{Blue Drive}} = \frac{43}{25} = 1\cdot72 : 1$$

These are average figures as there is some spread in beam current characteristics and will vary as the tube ages. Unequal beam currents also mean that the size of the beams and hence their focused spots will be unequal.

Colour Alignment Difficulties

In order to obtain a colour image on the c.r.t. that is free from unwanted patches of colour or colour fringing, a number of critical adjustments are required to the three beams.

Purity

The 'purity' of a raster depends upon how accurately the three electron beams fall on their respective phosphor dots. During manufacture the holes in the shadow mask are used to position the phosphor dots by placing a point u/v light source at the points where theoretical deflection will take place for the three beams (these points are known as the 'colour centres'). The light from the point light source which passes through the holes in the shadow mask photo-chemically fixes the position of the phosphor dots. Thus if during operation the three beams appear to originate from their respective colour centres, the beams will strike their respective coloured dots.

When the electron beams land centrally on their respective phosphor dots, the raster is said to have 100% purity as in Fig. 13.34(a). Under this condition **the actual deflection centre of each beam coincides with its colour centre**. In practice, due to manufacturing tolerances in the mechanical alignment of the

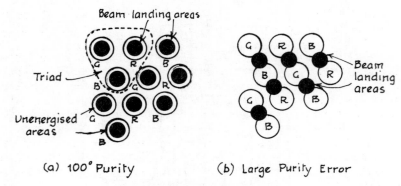

Fig. 13.34 Purity of raster.

three guns and the positioning of the deflector coils on the tube neck, correct purity may not be achieved and a particular beam may straddle two phosphor dots as shown in Fig. 13.34(b) (here the beam is striking one dot of its own colour and one of the wrong colour). This will result in patches of colour in the picture and also shows up on an unmodulated raster.

To adjust for 100% purity of the three coloured rasters, a pair of magnetised rings (purity magnets) are fitted on the tube neck as shown in Fig. 13.35. The resulting magnetic field from the purity magnets which may be adjusted in strength and radial direction, corrects the angle of approach of the three beams to the scan coil fields. Also, to ensure correct purity all over the screen the scan coils are mounted so that they may be moved along the tube neck.

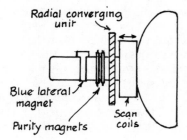

Fig. 13.35 Colour alignment components used with delta gun tube.

Static Convergence

The ideal condition for the reproduction of colour is that all three beams **converge at a single point lying in the plane of the shadow-mask**. The electron guns are aligned such that the undeflected beams converge at the screen centre as shown in Fig. 13.36. However, in spite of careful alignment during manufacture small discrepancies occur which are best corrected with the aid of weak magnetic fields applied externally.

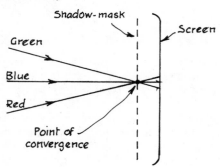

Fig. 13.36 Static convergence.

To achieve correct convergence at the screen centre (static convergence) it is necessary to be able to move all three beams radially and one of the beams laterally (the blue beam). This is carried out with the aid of three adjustable permanent magnets located on the **radial converging unit**, see Fig. 13.35, and the blue lateral magnet. The magnetic fields from the permanent magnets couple through the glass of the tube neck to internal pole pieces.

Convergence errors whether static or dynamic (see next section) show up as 'colour fringing' and is evident only on a modulated raster; usually a cross-hatch pattern generator is used during convergence adjustments.

Dynamic Convergence

It would be possible to obtain uniform convergence of the three beams over the entire screen using the static adjustments only if the shadow mask and screen formed part of a sphere with its centre located at the deflection centre of the beams. However, the colour tube like its monochrome counterpart has a relatively flat screen or small curvature and causes distortion of the individual rasters.

With a small curvature of screen, the point of convergence progressively falls short of the shadow mask with increasing deflection angle as illustrated in Fig. 13.37. Because of the longer path lengths at the sides and corners of the screen compared to the centre, the three beams will be more divergent in these areas producing severe convergence errors. The increase in path length towards the sides of the screen is essentially of parabolic form. Thus to correct for this error it is necessary to 'push' the point of convergence progressively forward as the deflection (left and right or up and down) increases. This can be achieved by applying **parabolic** correcting fields through the radial converging assembly, see Fig. 13.35, via the line and field dynamic coils wound on the limbs of the assembly.

In addition to the convergence error arising out of the varying path length at the sides of the screen compared to the centre, there is a second error as the three beams lie off the axis of the tube and are inclined towards this axis. This causes the three rasters to exhibit trapesium (keystone) distortion which is corrected by applying sawtooth correcting fields to the electron beams via the radial converging assembly.

For a typical receiver using a delta gun c.r.t. about **fourteen separate adjustments are required to correct the dynamic convergence errors**. These adjustments are time consuming and require considerable skill and patience if good results are to be achieved.

Due to the use of a flat screen, the individual rasters will also exhibit pin-cushion distortion. In a colour receiver, the raster correction magnets used in a monochrome receiver cannot be used as their magnetic fields would upset purity and convergence. Instead a 'transductor' is employed connected between the line and field scan coils so as to cause some cross modulation.

In-Line Gun Tubes

With a delta gun c.r.t. there are about twenty preset adjustments to be made to ensure that a well converged and pure colour image is produced on the screen and these adjustments are required to be stable over long periods. The introduction of the in-line gun c.r.t. in recent years has been one of the most important developments towards the simplification of the colour television receiver.

Precision In-Line Tube

Instead of placing the electron guns in triangular formation, they are arranged in a horizontal line. The basic arrangement used in

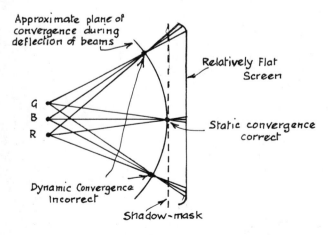

Fig. 13.37 Dynamic convergence errors due to use of flat screen (plan view of guns).

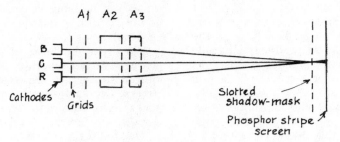

Fig. 13.38 Basic arrangement of in-line gun tube (RCA and Thorn).

the RCA and Thorn precision in-line tubes is shown in Fig. 13.38.

The three guns have electrically separate cathodes but the grids are connected together as they are formed from a single piece of metal. Video drive signals can thus only be applied to the cathodes; the grids are held at a common potential which may be variable to achieve brightness control. A one-piece metal construction is also used for the three anodes with A_1 accelerating anode, A_2 focus anode and A_3 final anode. The single electrode construction for the grids and anodes (unitised gun assembly) results in a shorter gun assembly with the beams closer together than in a delta gun arrangement. Mainly, because of the one-piece grid, the accuracy of the spacing between the three guns can be held to 0·25 per cent. The three beams start off parallel to one another but the outer beams are bent slightly by off-setting the apertures in the final anode, so that the beams meet at a single point on the screen. The green beam is normally the centre one but in early production tubes the red beam was in the centre. This does not alter the principle of operation (in fact both types are interchangeable) but with the green beam in the centre any small residual convergence errors are less noticeable.

Shadow-Mask

With in-line tubes, the screen phosphors are laid in the form of vertical stripes as shown in Fig. 13.39. The shadow-mask is slotted with the slots bridged at regular intervals to accommodate the spherical contour shape required by the mask. Each slot is thus associated with a triad of blue, green and red energised areas of the vertical stripes. Because

each beam is vertically aligned with its particular coloured stripe, beam landing errors in the vertical direction have no effect on colour purity. This simplifies the purity adjustments. To obtain the same apparent fineness of colour picture as with a delta gun tube, the width of the stripes must be about half the diameter of a conventional phosphor dot which means that there is less tolerance in horizontal beam landing errors. This disadvantage must be

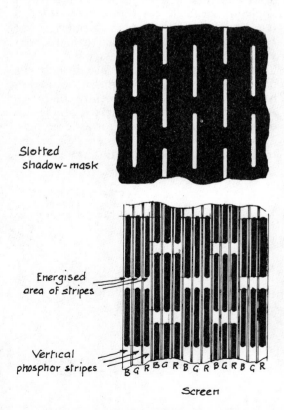

Fig. 13.39 Mask and screen of in-line tube.

weighed against the unlimited landing tolerance in the vertical direction.

Purity and Static Convergence

Since phosphor stripes are used instead of dots, only horizontal purity adjustment is required. Any error in vertical landing will, of course, result in the beam falling on the same colour phosphor stripe and hence is of no importance. Purity adjustment is carried out with a pair of conventional two-pole ring magnets mounted on the tube neck, see Fig. 13.40.

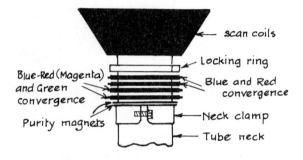

Fig. 13.40 Purity and static convergence ring magnets used with P.I.L. tube.

To take up tolerances in the alignment of the three beams, static convergence adjustments are provided so that the beams converge accurately at the screen centre. The diameter of each beam is such that it embraces two or three slots of the shadow-mask and for correct reproduction the outer beams must cross over accurately in the plane of the shadow-mask. Thus the positions of the red and blue phosphor stripes are interchanged with the positions of the red and blue guns with respect to the green.

A different method for adjusting static convergence is used as the tube neck is made shorter. Two pairs of barium ferrite ring magnets are used. One pair is magnetised to give four-pole fields as in Fig. 13.41(a) and the other pair gives six-pole fields as in Fig. 13.41(b). Barium ferrite is used since it has a permeability of approximately unity and thus reduces interaction from the scanning fields. These magnets are mounted on the tube neck in front of the purity rings and act on the outer beams only. The four-pole magnets of (a) move outer beams in opposite horizontal and vertical directions and those at (b) move the outer beams in the same horizontal and vertical directions. Thus, by adjustment of the

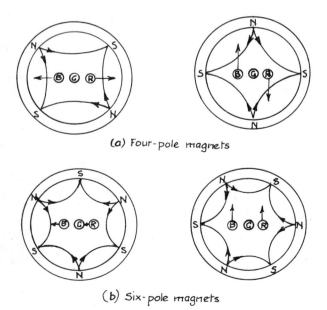

(a) Four-pole magnets

(b) Six-pole magnets

Fig. 13.41 Barium ferrite magnetic rings used for static convergence.

four ring magnets, the blue and red beams can be made to converge with the green beam at the screen centre.

Dynamic Convergence

Without any compensation, the convergence will not be maintained out to the edges of the screen since the beams are deflected through an arc, and the screen has a large radius of curvature, *i.e.* is nearly flat. During deflection the beams will cross over behind the mask and become divergent upon reaching it. As the guns are in-line the outer beams will produce rasters with keystone distortion in one direction only (north-south) whilst the centre beam will produce a rectangular raster. Also, because of the flat screen each raster will exhibit some pin-cushion shape distortion. With in-line tubes the problem of dynamic convergence has been solved in an ingenious way and for small screen sizes (up to 19″) and deflection angles of 90°, there are no extra adjustments to the static ones. The automatic convergence action of the in-line tube depends primarily upon the use of **non-linear** or **astigmatic deflecting fields**. How this affects convergence will now be explained.

Consider first a conical pencil of electron beams emanating from a larger beam and in particular the individual beams 1–5 as shown in Fig. 13.42. In the absence of a deflecting field, the beams will converge at the screen centre O in the plane of the mask. With a linear deflecting field applied in the horizontal direction the beams will all meet or converge

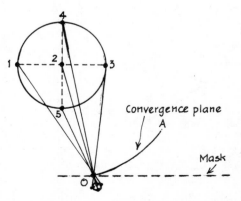

Fig. 13.42 Pencil beams converging at O around the screen centre.

along the arc OA behind the mask. If, instead of using a linear deflecting field one with the right amount of astigmatism is employed, the beams will converge as shown in Fig. 13.43.

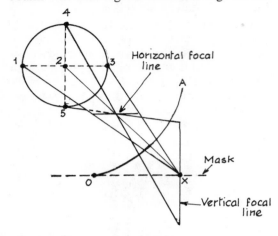

Fig. 13.43 Pencil beams deflected by an astigmatic deflection field producing two focal lines.

The astigmatic deflection field causes the convergence point to separate into two focal lines, one parallel to and one perpendicular to the direction of deflection (assumed to be horizontal). One of these lines lies behind the arc OA and one in front of it (the same effect occurs with optical lenses when light strikes the lens obliquely). Note that with the correct amount of astigmatism the vertical focal line lies in the plane of the shadow-mask. If we now consider the electron beams of an in-line tube as elements 1, 2 and 3 of the pencil beams, the vertical focal line degenerates to a point as shown in Fig. 13.44 (since there are no beams emanating from points 4 and 5) resulting in perfect convergence at all positions on the screen.

To ensure the automatic convergence action occurs for both horizontal and vertical deflection of the beams, the horizontal and vertical deflection fields must have opposite astigmatism. The horizontal deflection field is thus made pin-cushion shape and the vertical deflection field barrel-shape, see Fig. 13.45. If the vertical deflection field was pin-cushion shape (the same as the horizontal field), the horizontal focal line would coincide with the mask and not the vertical one (which degenerates to a point) as is required.

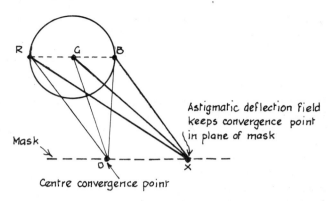

Fig. 13.44 *In-line guns placed at points 1, 2 and 3 of Fig. 13.43 resulting in automatic dynamic convergence.*

Fig. 13.45 *Types of astigmatic deflection fields required for automatic convergence of in-line beams.*

In the RCA and Thorn P.I.L. tubes the required deflection field distribution is achieved by employing a special deflection coil assembly known as a precision static toroid (PST), the principle of which is shown in Fig. 13.46.

Each turn of wire is precisely placed in position in winding grooves in plastic rings which are cemented to each end of the

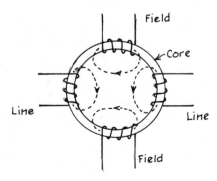

Fig. 13.46 *Toroidal deflecting coils.*

deflection yoke. By this means a very precise field distribution with the required amount of astigmatism is produced. Using this system, tolerances between individual scan assemblies becomes very small. For correct performance, the deflection coils must be carefully positioned with respect to the beams. During assembly by the manufacturer, the deflection coils are moved radially about the tube neck until optimum convergence is obtained. The deflection coil assembly is then cemented to the tube and no further adjustment is necessary. After convergence has been obtained any remaining raster shape distortion *e.g.* pin-cushion may be corrected by conventional deflection current modulating circuitry (see Chapter 16). In-line gun systems give greater E–W pin cushion raster distortion but less N–S distortion as compared with delta gun tubes.

An additional feature used to reduce convergence errors is provided by four magnetic rings built into the final anode attachment called the shield cup see Fig. 13.47. The rings round the outer beams shunt part of the

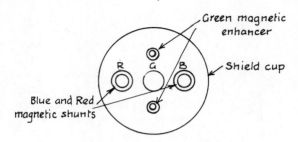

Fig. 13.47 Magnetic shunts and enhancers.

deflecting field from the scan coils to slightly reduce the width of the green raster provided by the centre beam. By this means the green beam lands centrally between the others at all points on the screen.

20 AX System

The Mullard 20 AX system comprises an in-line colour tube, deflection yoke and static convergence/purity/N–S symmetry assembly. The three electron guns of the c.r.t. are mounted side by side with two outer guns (red and blue) slightly inclined towards the centre gun (green). All three cathodes are of the quick-vision type enabling a picture to be obtained within five seconds from switch-on. The cathodes, control grids and first anode electrodes are electrically separate. Because the first anodes are electrically separate, background controls may be used to supply these electrodes to set the lowlights during grey scale adjustments. In common with other 110° tubes the magnetic shield is fitted inside the glass cone. Advantage is taken of the unlimited landing tolerance in the vertical direction of the beams by rotating the degaussing coils through 90° as for the P.I.L. tube.

In addition to deflecting the beams over the face of the screen, the complex field of the scanning assembly ensures that the three beams remain converged out to the screen edges (as previously outlined). Thus the normal complex dynamic convergence adjustments are not required. To produce the complex astigmatic deflecting fields the 20 AX uses a saddle-type deflector coil assembly in preference to the toroidal deflector assembly used with the P.I.L. tube.

The static correction units contains two pairs of rings providing 4-pole and 6-pole fields

for static convergence adjustment and one pair of rings (2-pole field) for purity adjustment. In addition there is another pair of rings which are magnetised as a 2-pole magnet in the horizontal direction. These magnets (N–S symmetry or Raster shape) correct for any vertical misalignment of the three beams and the axis of the deflection yoke. Such misalignment would cause curvature of the horizontal axis of the raster.

The 20 AX is essentially a self-converging system but due to small manufacturing tolerances some dynamic correction may be necessary; for the 22″ version there are six corrections required.

30 AX System

The Mullard 30 AX in-line 110° colour display system, developed from the design experience gained with the 20 AX, eliminates the need for purity, static convergence, dynamic convergence and raster orientation adjustments by the servicing technician. Unlike the in-line systems described earlier, the display tube and deflector coil assembly are fully interchangeable. The 30 AX is a truely self-aligning and self-converging colour display system.

It was found that the only way to eliminate dynamic convergence errors was to reduce manufacturing tolerances. With the 30 AX system, the alignment of the tube and deflector coil assembly has been improved by providing a reference system. This consists of three bosses fitted on the cone of the tube, see Fig. 13.48, which mate with the inside of the deflector coil assembly. The three bosses define three reference points, the centre of which together with a clamping ring on the deflector coil assembly determine a common axis for the tube and deflector coil assembly.

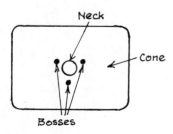

Fig. 13.48 30AX alignment bosses on C.R.T. cone.

Throughout the manufacturing process care is taken to ensure that this axis coincides with the screen axis. Other special measures taken include tight tolerance control of the neck-to-cone sealing, screen-to-cone sealing and gun sealing. An important manufacturing step is making sure that the cone edge is perpendicular to the tube axis. In addition, the design of a new deflector coil assembly with a one-piece ferrite ring contributes to the reduction of tolerances. The extra attention given to manufacturing tolerances permits any combination of tube and deflector coil assembly of the same size to be used without introducing dynamic convergence errors.

Purity and static convergence adjustments are eliminated by a thin magnetic wire ring incorporated in the gun assembly. This ring is magnetised with 2, 4 and 6-pole fields of the required strength and direction during a late stage of manufacture, so that no further purity and static adjustments are necessary.

A typical 30 AX in-line gun c.r.t. with its supplies is shown in Fig. 13.49. From the circuit point of view it is very similar to that for a delta gun tube.

Each electron gun utilises a 3-anode assembly: $A1$ accelerating anode; $A2$ focusing anode; $A3$ final anode. Primary signal drive from the RGB video output amplifiers is applied to the three cathodes via the flash-over protection resistors $R1$, $R2$ and $R3$. The grids of the three guns are all connected to chassis and brightness control is introduced by varying the black level of the video drive signals. The first anodes are fed with a variable voltage via $R4$ (flash-over protection) from a common $A1$ preset which is adjusted for raster cut-off during the 'grey scale' adjustments. $C1$ smoothes or decouples the $A1$ supply voltage. Variable focus voltage is fed to the second anodes from a focus potentiometer which is supplied from the receiver e.h.t. transformer. The final anodes are supplied with e.h.t. via

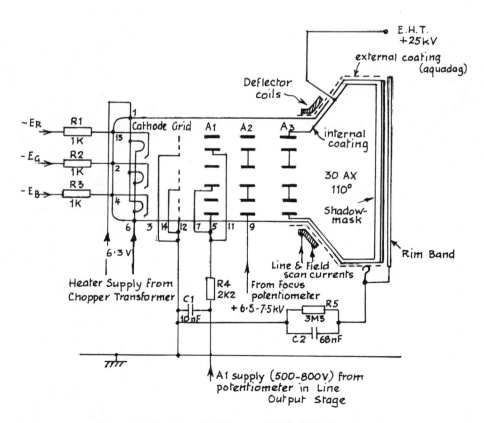

Fig. 13.49 Typical 110° in-line gun C.R.T. (30AX) and supplies.

the internal coating of the tube from the e.h.t. connector. *R5* discharges any static built-up on the rim band which may be transferred from the internal coating via the glass section of the tube.

45 AX FST

The 45 AX FST is the latest in-line 110° colour tube and uses the 'flatter squarer tube' format which suits the recent trend in rectangular cabinet styling along the lines of professional video monitors. The picture is presented on an almost flat screen having square corners instead of round ones. As a result, the picture appears larger for the same tube size and a wider viewing angle is achieved. Also there is less picture distortion and a reduction in the amount of external light that is reflected off the screen.

The new shaped flat screen tends to accentuate the problems of focus, convergence, purity and scan geometry for the tube manufacturer. Thus in the 45 AX FST a redesigned in-line gun assembly is employed with the guns brought closer together and the neck diameter reduced. Also, a higher focus voltage is required. Like the 30 AX, the new tube is a self-converging system.

A particular problem is heating of the shadow-mask on picture highlights which causes localised heating of the mask and purity errors. This problem is present in other colour tubes but is accentuated in the FST format. In the 45 AX FST the shadow-mask is mounted on hinges at its corners. As the mask expands on heating, the pressure on the hinges moves the mask closer to the screen to compensate and maintain purity. The bi-metallic strip used in other colour tubes is not used as its response time is too slow for FSTs. In order to assist in removing heat quickly from the shadow mask, the back of the screen is sprayed with graphite which absorbs heat from the mask.

Trinitron Tube

The principle of operation of the Trinitron tube developed by the Sony Corporation and used in their receivers is shown in Fig. 13.50. A single gun assembly which emits three beams simultaneously from separate cathodes lying in an horizontal plane is used. The beams are pre-focused by an electrostatic lens formed by Grid 2 and the first anode. After passing through the first anode the beams cross over one another in the centre of the main focusing lens formed by the anodes. Since the beams pass through the centre of a large lens, good focusing is achieved.

The outside beams diverging from the centre beam are deflected by two sets of electrostatic deflector plates *D1*, *D2* and *D3*, *D4* so that the three beams converge accurately at one point. This point should lie in the plane of the aperture grille which serves the same purpose as a shadow-mask. It consists of a large number of vertical slits and associated with each slit is a triad of red, blue and green phosphor stripes. When the beams pass through the grille they fall on their respective phosphor stripes. The brightness of the picture is about twice that of a delta gun c.r.t. owing to the high electron transparency of the aperture grille and the larger beam current that can be obtained for a given spot size. The use of vertical slits and phosphor stripes makes it easier to obtain good purity as small beam

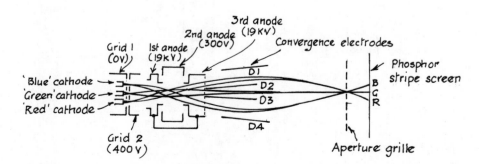

Fig. 13.50 Principle of trinitron tube (90°).

landing errors in the vertical direction do not produce a detrimental effect as the beam will still fall on its associated phosphor stripe.

Convergence problems are eased with the Trinitron and only horizontal correction is required, see Fig. 13.51(a). The convergence plates $D2$ and $D3$ are at e.h.t. potential thus the centre beam (green) passes through the plates unaffected. The outer beams (red and blue) are deflected towards the tube axis by the electric field between the outer and inner plates since $D1$ and $D4$ are held about 400–1 kV below $D2$ and $D3$. Thus the potential on $D1$ and $D4$ sets the static convergence of the three beams. Dynamic correction is effected by applying a parabolic voltage waveform to the outer deflecting plates as shown in Fig. 13.51(b). Ring magnets, mounted on the tube neck, are provided for purity and vertical static adjustments. Also the deflector coil assembly must be moved during purity settings as for the delta gun tube.

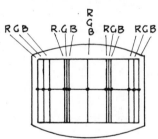

(a) Convergence errors on 90° Trinitron

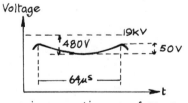

(b) Dynamic correction waveform applied to convergence electrodes

Fig. 13.51 Dynamic convergence.

The Trinitron is also available in 20″ and 22″ screen sizes with 114° deflection angle. Extra adjustments are provided with these tubes to give correct convergence in the corners of the picture. The number of adjustments required

with a Trinitron tube is less than with a delta gun of comparable size.

DEGAUSSING

Stray magnetic fields that change in the vicinity of a colour tube deflect the electron beams away from their proper paths causing purity errors. These stray fields come from the earth's magnetic field, magnetised objects close to the receiver and fields from electrical appliances, *e.g.* vacuum cleaners, *etc.* It is essential that the shadow-mask, rim band or any other tube supports do not possess any residual magnetism.

During initial installation of a colour receiver it is standard practice to use an external degaussing coil to demagnetise the mask and tube supports and nearby objects which may contain some permanent magnetism. This type of degaussing coil is about 1′ in diameter and is fed from the mains supply. There should be sufficient turns to establish a field of about 1000 ampere-turns. The coil is moved around the tube supports and face of the tube (but not too close) and gradually withdrawn until it is, say, about 10′ away then rotated through 90° and switched off. In this way any magnetic materials are taken through many cycles of decreasing magnetisation as illustrated in Fig. 13.52.

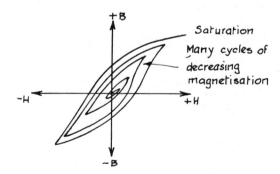

Fig. 13.52 Principle of degaussing.

If after carrying out external degaussing and purity adjustments the receiver is moved there may be a change in purity as a result of a variation in the earth's magnetic field. With modern receivers, however, the effects on purity are small when the orientation of the receiver is altered.

To take care of accidental magnetisation of the shadow-mask and tube supports which may occur if a vacuum cleaner or electric drill is brought near to the receiver, receivers are fitted with auto-degaussing coils which are brought into operation **each time the receiver is switched on**.

With the delta gun tube, see Fig. 13.53(a), there are two coils fitted on each side of the tube flare and disposed as shown. Each coil is arranged so that it is partly outside and partly inside a magnetic shield fitted over the tube flare. A similar arrangement is used for an in-line c.r.t., see Fig. 13.53(b), except that the degaussing coils are rotated through 90° (because of the unlimited tolerance in beam landing in the vertical direction) and the magnetic shield is fitted inside the glass cone as

is common with other 110° tubes. As the coil is fixed, it is arranged that at switch-on a large current flows which after a short period gradually reduces to a small value. In this way the shadow-mask, rim band and tube supports are taken through many cycles of diminishing magnetisation thereby removing most of any accidental magnetisation.

A common type of auto-degaussing circuit for a delta gun tube is shown in Fig. 13.54(a). $R1$ is a thermistor with a positive temperature coefficient, $R2$ is a voltage dependent resistor and $R3$ an ordinary linear resistor. At switch-on, $R1$ is of low resistance and a large voltage is developed across A–B. With a large voltage applied to $R2$ its resistance will be low and thus a large current flows in $R2$ and the degaussing coil (also $R1$). This current must be sufficiently large to saturate the magnetic materials of the tube and supports (about 500 ampere-turns are required). As $R1$ warms up its resistance increases and the current falls. There is thus less voltage across A–B and the effective resistance of $R2$ is increased. Most of the current then flows in $R3$ which maintains $R1$ hot. The current in the coil gradually decreases as shown in Fig. 13.54(b) and the final ATs are reduced to 0·03.

With an in-line tube the m.m.f. can be made smaller (about 300 AT) since the mask material is not interrupted by holes in the

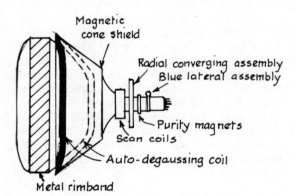

(a) Delta-Gun c.r.t.

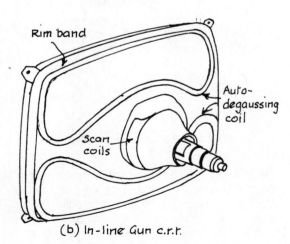

(b) In-line Gun c.r.t.

Fig. 13.53 Auto-degaussing coil.

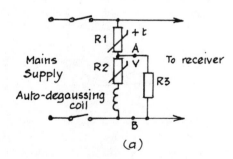

(a)

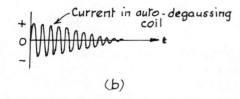

(b)

Fig. 13.54 Auto-degaussing circuit.

direction of the degaussing field. The degaussing circuits are similar to those used with delta gun tubes except for a $0.1\,\mu\mathrm{F}$ capacitor placed in shunt with the degaussing coils. This capacitor has a low reactance at the horizontal scan frequency and eliminates the risk of beam landing errors by currents induced in the degaussing coils from the line scanning field.

GREY-SCALE ADJUSTMENTS

The purpose of the grey-scale adjustments is to produce the standard white (illuminant 'D') at all drive levels from the picture lowlights to the picture highlights. This ensures that:

(1) On a monochrome picture there is no colour tinting.
(2) On a colour picture, the flesh tones are correctly reproduced and that coloured objects do not change colour when moving out of the shade into the light.

To carry out the adjustments, a grey-scale test signal such as that shown in Fig. 13.55 is required or a well graduated monochrome picture. Before adjusting the grey-scale, the brightness and contrast controls should be set to give a normal picture.

Lowlight adjustment

In spite of the fact that the three guns are identical in construction their Ib/Vg characteristics do not have precisely the same cut-off

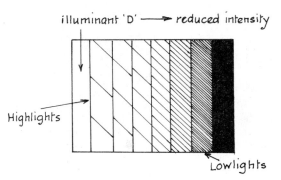

Fig. 13.55 Grey-scale test signal.

points nor do their characteristics have the same slope. The effect of non-identical cut-off points is illustrated in Fig. 13.56. Here, a larger grid voltage is required to cut-off the red gun than for the blue and green guns (which are assumed to have identical cut-offs).

If a video shading signal is applied as shown (which in a well adjusted receiver would produce a shaded picture going from black on the left-hand side to white on the right-hand side), between instant t_1 and t_2 only the red gun will be ON resulting in a red cast in the lowlights of the picture. Between instants t_2 and t_3, all three guns will be ON producing a 'kind of white'. Now the object of the lowlight adjustments is to ensure that all three guns cut-off with identical grid-to-cathode potentials. This is achieved by adjusting the a_1 voltages using the background controls (P_4, P_5 and P_6 of Fig. 13.57) until all traces of colour

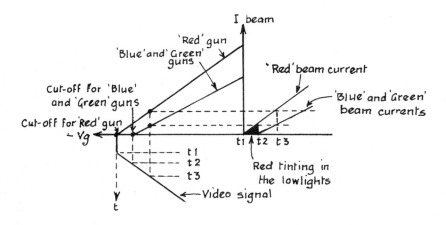

Fig. 13.56 Diagram showing how guns with different cut-offs produce tinting in lowlights.

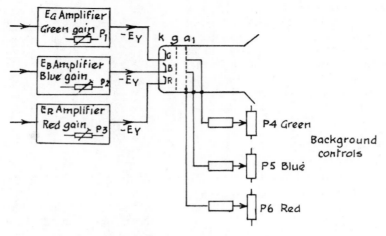

Fig. 13.57 Grey-scale adjustments.

are removed in the lowlights of the picture, and a neutral dark grey shade is obtained. Usually, the second bar from the right of Fig. 13.56 is used for the lowlight adjustment. If there is any colour cast in this low-drive area, the a_1 voltages should be adjusted as follows to remove the colour cast:

Colour Cast	Adjustment
BLUE	Decrease BLUE a_1 voltage
YELLOW	Increase BLUE a_1 voltage
GREEN	Decrease GREEN a_1 voltage
MAGENTA	Increase GREEN a_1 voltage
RED	Decrease RED a_1 voltage
CYAN	Increase RED a_1 voltage

When carrying out the lowlight adjustments there probably will be some change in the colour rendering at the highlight end of the grey scale. Such variations should be ignored; one should concentrate on achieving the correct neutral dark grey at this stage.

An alternative method for carrying out the lowlight adjustments is used with receivers fitted with a 'set white' switch. When operated, this switch collapses the field scan leaving a single horizontal line at reduced brightness on the screen. With only one gun switched on at a time, the appropriate background control is adjusted until the horizontal coloured line just disappears. This method, which is best carried out in near total darkness, sets all three guns to a common cut-off or black level and gives very accurate results.

Highlight adjustment

It now remains to remove any colour tinting at the highlight end of the grey-scale. With the cut-off points of the three guns correctly adjusted, colour tinting in the highlights can occur due to differences in the slope of the characteristics and in the efficiencies of the three phosphors. The effect of variation in slope of the Ib/Vg curves is shown in Fig. 13.58 where the slope of the red gun is less than that of the blue and green guns (which are assumed to be the same). Between instants t_1 and t_2 a good neutral grey-scale will be obtained as the beam currents are identical. Over the period t_2 to t_3, however, there will be some colour tinting (cyan in this case) as the blue and green beam currents are larger than the red beam current. This tinting will increase as the video drive increases in magnitude.

To correct for the dissimilar slopes of the gun characteristics (they may all be somewhat different) it is necessary to adjust the individual video signal drives to the three guns. This requirement is met by including a preset gain control in each of the three drive amplifiers to the guns as shown in Fig. 13.57. The controls $P1$, $P2$ and $P3$ are adjusted to produce the standard white in the highlight areas of the grey scale test pattern. This should be carried out carefully to remove all traces of colour tinting as the resulting white produced has a marked effect on flesh tones in a colour picture. For best results, a visual comparison should be made with an Illuminant D source

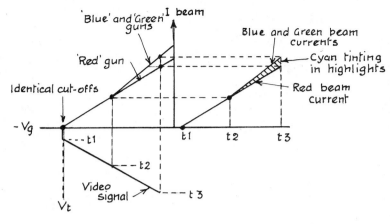

Fig. 13.58 *Lowlights correctly adjusted but tinting in the highlights occurs due to differences in slope of the gun characteristics.*

(special equipment is available for this purpose). The following adjustments should be made to remove any colour cast in the highlights:

Colour Cast	Adjustment
BLUE	Decrease BLUE gain control
YELLOW	Increase BLUE gain control
GREEN	Decrease GREEN gain control
MAGENTA	Increase GREEN gain control
RED	Decrease RED gain control
CYAN	Increase RED gain control

In some receivers, there is no **red** gain control and the full signal is applied to the cathode of the red gun. In this case if a **red** cast is observed, balance may be obtained by increasing both the **blue** and **green** gain controls. On the other hand if a **cyan** cast is observed the **blue** and **green** gain controls should be reduced.

P.I.L. Tube

As the A_1 electrodes of the P.I.L. tube are connected together, individual background controls cannot be used to set the cut-off point of each gun. Thus the lowlights are set by individually adjusting the cathode-to-grid potentials of the guns. One arrangement is shown in Fig. 13.59. Only the blue video output amplifier has been shown as the circuit is repeated for the red and green channels.

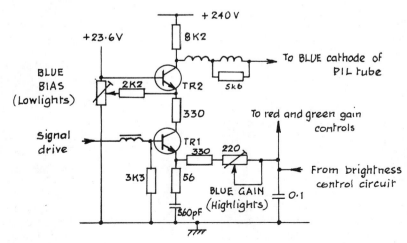

Fig. 13.59 *Video output stage for P.I.L. tube showing grey-scale setting controls.*

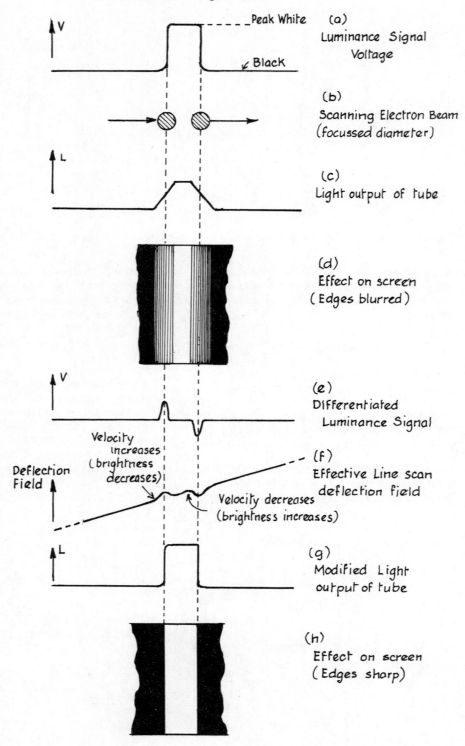

(a)
Luminance Signal
Voltage

(b)
Scanning Electron Beam
(focussed diameter)

(c)
Light output of tube

(d)
Effect on screen
(Edges blurred)

(e)
Differentiated
Luminance Signal

(f)
Effective Line scan
deflection field

(g)
Modified Light
output of tube

(h)
Effect on screen
(Edges sharp)

Fig. 13.60 Scan velocity modulation principle.

The blue bias control sets the forward bias on *TR2* and hence its standing collector potential which is fed to the blue cathode of the tube. During the lowlight adjustments the blue bias preset together with the corresponding presets in the other two channels are adjusted to produce identical cut-off points for the three guns. The blue gain control adjusts the a.c. gain of the amplifier and this preset together with the gain presets in the other two channels are adjusted to give the standard white in the highlights in the normal way.

Brightness control is introduced by feeding a variable d.c. to *TR1* emitter from the brightness circuit. This sets the standing bias on the lower transistor in each output amplifier. Hence when the brightness control is adjusted the d.c. potentials on **all** three cathodes of the tube are varied simultaneously.

SCAN VELOCITY MODULATION

Some receiver manufacturers are now using scan-velocity modulation techniques to improve the sharpness of picture detail on vertical edges. The resolution of picture detail is limited by the size of the focussed electron beam falling on the screen phosphor coating. Although an electron beam may suddenly be cut-on or cut-off by the applied video signal, the effect on the screen is a gradual transition in its intensity over the width of the focussed beam resulting in blurred edges to fast changing video signals. Scan-velocity modulation works by altering the rate of change of the horizontal deflection field during the transitional states of the video signal.

The idea is shown by the diagrams in Fig. 13.60. Fig. 13.60(a) shows a luminance signal pulse that may be expected to produce sharp transitions in the screen image on its leading and lagging edges. In Fig. 13.60(b) the size of the beam in the positions indicated, limits the speed at which intensity transitions can take place. The effect on the light output of the tube is shown in Fig. 13.60(c), where it will be seen that the light transitions are now more gradual resulting in the blurring of the vertical edges of the reproduced image, as shown in Fig. 13.60(d).

To produce an apparent improvement, the luminance signal is differentiated as in Fig. 13.60(e) and then applied to the horizontal deflection field in such a way as to increase the velocity of the deflected beam during black-to-white transitions but to decrease the velocity during white-to-black transitions, as shown in Fig. 13.60(f). The result is that the light output transitions, Fig. 13.60(g), are now more abrupt, effectively restoring the high frequency content lost in Fig. 13.60(c), and a sharpening of the image edges as illustrated in Fig. 13.60(h).

Changes in velocity of the scanning electron beam is carried out by an auxiliary horizontal scan coil incorporated in the main scan coil assembly. The auxiliary coil is supplied from a low output impedance drive amplifier which is fed with the differentiated luminance signal as shown in Fig. 13.61. The direction of the scanning field produced by the auxiliary coil on transitions in the luminance signal is such that it either aids or opposes the scanning field of the normal line scan coils, thereby increasing or decreasing the beam velocity. It is important that any delay introduced by the scan velocity circuitry is matched by the delay in the luminance signal path so that velocity changes of the scanning beam occur at the same instant as transitions in the luminance signal applied to the c.r.t. cathodes.

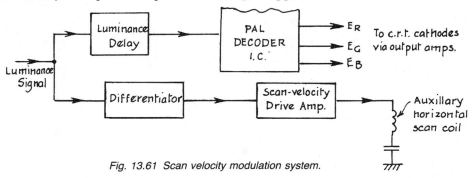

Fig. 13.61 Scan velocity modulation system.

CHAPTER FOURTEEN

SYNCHRONISING PULSE PROCESSING

Objectives

1 To show the basic action of the Sync. Pulse Separator stage and to consider the effects of interference upon its operation.
2 To outline the action of an I.C. Sync. Separator.
3 To explain how the field sync. locking pulse is produced from the composite sync. pulse train and to show how indirect field sync. is produced.
4 To explain the principles and circuits used for Line Flywheel Sync., including i.c. versions.
5 To give reasons for the use of the Sandcastle Waveform.

SYNC. PULSE SEPARATOR STAGE

THE ESSENTIAL PROCESSING of the synchronising pulses is shown in Fig. 14.1.

A sync. separator stage should meet the following requirements.

(1) Remove the picture information from the composite video signal so that only the synchronising pulses are passed on to the timebases.

(2) Process the line and field sync. pulses to make them suitable for synchronisation of the line and field timebases.

(3) As far as possible to be immune from changes in receiver input signal level (a.g.c. is never perfect) so that the output pulses from the stage do not change their form.

(4) Not to be unduly affected by noise pulses.

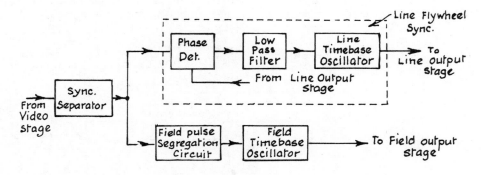

Fig. 14.1 Sync. pulse processing in colour or mono receiver.

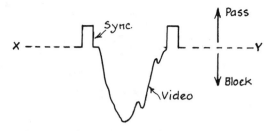

Fig. 14.2 Basic requirement of sync. separator.

The sync. separator stage is designed so that essentially it will pass information above a line such as X–Y in Fig. 14.2 but block or reject information below this line. In this way only the sync. pulse information is passed on to the following stages. The separating function may be carried out by a discrete transistor stage, or an integrated circuit.

Transistor Sync. Separator

Either p-n-p or n-p-n transistors may be used and a basic circuit using a n-p-n transistor is given in Fig. 14.3. The biassing of the transistor must be arranged so that it is conducting during the sync. information but cut-off during the picture content. Also the biassing must be self-adjusting so that the operating point changes with a variation in input signal level.

The composite video signal input is applied

to the base of $TR1$ via $C1$. The action of $C1$, $R1$ and the base-emitter junction of the transistor is to d.c. restore the input waveform so that the tips of the sync. pulses sit just above chassis potential level (waveform B). As a result the transistor only conducts on the tips of the sync. pulses producing across the collector load $R2$ negative-going voltage sync. pulses. The picture content of the input signal drives the base negative so cutting-off the transistor.

To remove any noise present on the sync. pulse tips (which may cause faulty triggering of the timebases) it is necessary to ensure that during the sync. pulse intervals when the transistor conducts, $TR1$ 'bottoms' as illustrated in Fig. 14.4. This may be achieved by suitable choice of $R2$ value allowing bottoming to occur with small base current. In addition, in a number of circuits the transistor is given a small forward bias from a potential divider such as $R3/R4$. This ensures that the sync. pulse tips drive the transistor well into bottoming to give noise-free output pulses. Any reasonable noise on the porches will be excluded as the transistor is reversed biassed.

The presence of stray capacitance across $R2$ produces marked curvature of the output sync. pulses, particularly on the trailing edges. Provided that the pulse leading edges are sharp the trailing edge curvature is not too important.

Chrominance signal information present on

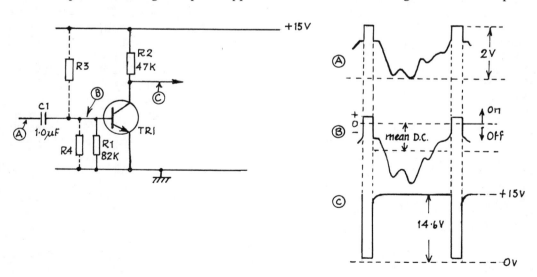

Fig. 14.3 Basic transitor sync. separator stage.

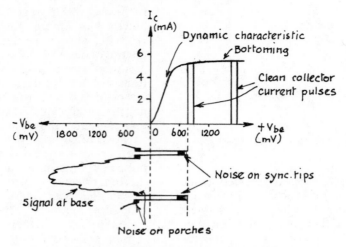

Fig. 14.4 Removing noise on the porches and sync. tips.

the input signal to the sync. separator is either removed or attenuated, since on certain hues the chrominance signal extends into the sync. pulse region and may corrupt the sync. signal. This requirement may be met either by supplying the sync. separator stage with the luminance signal after the chrominance take-out point or by including a low pass *RC* filter at the input to the sync. separator.

Blocking

With the negative modulation system used on 625-line television, large amplitude interference pulses from electrical apparatus, ignition systems and electrical storms can cause problems with timebase synchronisation. This is because during interference the modulated carrier amplitude increases, *i.e.* the interference pulses act in the same direction as the sync. pulses. The effect of such pulses on the operation of the sync. separator may be explained with the aid of Fig. 14.5.

Here line sync. pulses 1 and 2 are d.c. restored by the base-emitter junction of the transistor (assumed to be n-p-n) so that their tips are reproduced at the collector in the normal way. If now large amplitude interference pulses occur as shown they will give rise to a large base current charging the base coupling capacitor. This will cause the reverse bias on the transistor to increase with the result that line pulse 3 is not reproduced at the collector and line pulses 4 and 5 only in part (in this case). The sync. separator is thus said to

'block' and the blocking period is determined by the amplitude and width of the interfering pulses and the time constant of the base circuit *CR*. Thus the effect is to cause the loss of a number of line sync. pulses or possibly several field sync. pulses depending upon the duration and amplitude of the interference. As far as the effect on the line timebase is concerned the effect may not be serious if flywheel sync. is used (which is normally the case). However, during blocking the field timebase may suffer from a momentary loss of field sync. or mistake the interference pulse output of the sync. separator for a field sync. pulse causing erratic triggering. To prevent blocking a **noise-gated sync. separator** may be used.

One arrangement is given in Fig. 14.6. Here the composite video signal is fed to *TR4* together with any interference pulses that are present. *TR4* amplifies and inverts the input which is then applied via an *RC* network to the sync. separator stage *TR3*. This transistor conducts only on the sync. pulses (positive-going at *TR3* base) producing negative-going sync. out from its collector which is fed to the line and field timebases. Without the noise gating, any interference at *TR4* base would be reproduced at *TR3* collector but this is prevented by the action of *TR1* and *TR2* which turn *TR3* OFF during periods of interference.

During interference free reception *TR2* is fully conducting since its base is returned to the positive line via *R3*. Thus the emitter of *TR3* is returned via the conducting *TR2* to

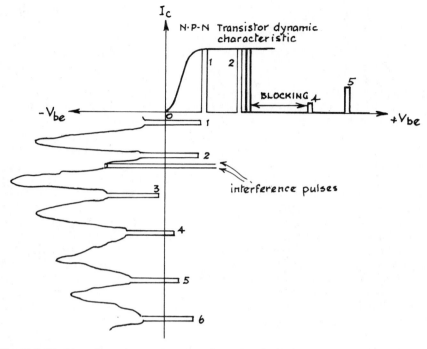

Fig. 14.5 Blocking of sync. separator stage due to interference pulses.

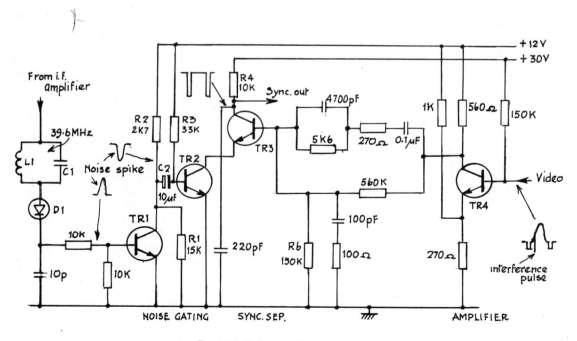

Fig. 14.6 Noise-gated sync. separator.

chassis which has negligible effect on normal sync. separator action. Now, the noise gating section works on the principle that noise pulses have a greater bandwidth than the sync. pulses and are usually of larger amplitude than the sync. or signal frequency components. A signal from the final i.f. amplifier stage is fed to the tuned circuit $L1,C1$ which is tuned to the vision i.f. of 39·5 MHz. Thus $L1,C1$ will reject the carrier and its sidebands corresponding to the low frequencies associated with the sync. pulses. Due to the Q of the tuned circuit the remaining frequencies are passed on to $D1$. This diode rectifies the noise components and its output is fed to $TR1$ base. Thus any large noise pulses present on the input to $L1,C1$ will produce positive-going noise spikes at $TR1$ base and hence negative-going spikes at its collector. These spikes are fed via $C2$ to the base of $TR2$ thus cutting it OFF. This also cuts off $TR3$ and therefore gates out the corresponding interference pulses present at $TR4$ input. Since there is no standing bias on $TR1$ it will not conduct until the noise spike at the base exceeds about 0·7 V. By this means $TR1$ is prevented from conducting on the normal signal component at $L1,C1$ input.

I.C. Sync. Separator

The sync. pulse separator function is well suited to integrated circuit techniques. Conventional circuits may be used to provide class-C operation as for the discrete transistor stage. It would be uneconomic to have just the sync. separator stage in the i.c. thus a number of other low power dissipation functions are included. A typical example is given in Fig. 14.7 which shows a skeleton diagram of the TBA 920 i.c.

In addition to the functions shown, the TBA 920 contains line oscillator, line flywheel sync. circuit and line driver stage which will be dealt with later. With other i.cs. video preamplification and a.g.c. circuits may be incorporated. The TBA 920 may be used in colour or mono receivers.

A composite video signal of typically 3 V in amplitude is applied to pin 8 of the i.c. via an external R–C network. The low pass filter $R1,C1$ removes some of the noise and also reduces the magnitude of the colour burst. $C2,R3$ provide the class-C bias components for the sync. separator stage and standing bias is supplied from $R2$. The automatic bias provided by $C2,R3$ ensures that the sync. separator output is unaffected by variations in input signal level. Noise gating of the sync. separator may be achieved by applying positive-going noise pulses to pin 9. These noise pulses may be derived in a similar way (external to the i.c.) to that described for Fig. 14.16. One output of the sync. separator is fed to pin 7 where sync. pulses only are available at an amplitude of about 10 V. These pulses are fed to the field timebase via an integrating network $R4,C3$ (this network is explained later). The other output is fed to a phase comparator which is concerned with the correct synchronisation of the line oscillator.

An adaptive sync. pulse separator, developed by Philips and used in the TDA 2571,

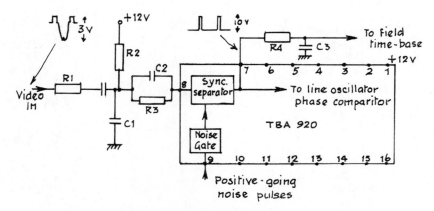

Fig. 14.7 Part TBA 920 I.C.

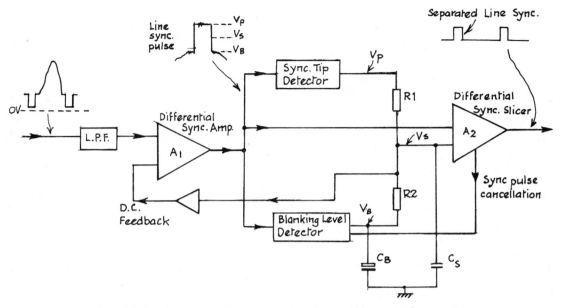

Fig. 14.8 Adaptive sync. pulse separator principle used in some I.C. separators.

TDA 2576A and TDA 2578 i.cs. is shown in schematic form in Fig. 14.8.

This arrangement provides a constant slicing level which does not vary with video signal amplitude or picture content. The slicing level is maintained at half the sync. pulse amplitude and an amplified portion around this level is developed at the output thus eliminating noise on the sync. pulse tips and porches.

The video signal input is applied to a differential amplifier A_1 via a l.p.f. which assists in reducing the effects of multipath reflections and receiver mistuning. The other input to A_1 is the required bias level derived from the voltage stored in C_s. This stage provides linear amplification over the full range of the sync. pulse at all signal levels. The output from A_1 is applied to two detector circuits; one detects the sync. pulse tip level (V_p) and the other the blanking level (V_B) of the sync. waveform. The blanking level is stored in the capacitor C_B. By suitable choice of $R1,R2$ values the required d.c. slicing level (V_S) is obtained. This level is maintained at the centre of the sync. pulse regardless of changes in video signal amplitude and picture content. The differential amplifier A_2 acts as a comparator, comparing the sync. pulse input from A_1 with the slicing level V_S. A_2 rapidly switches as the sync. input varies either side of V_S, producing a clean slice out of the sync. waveform at its output.

SEGREGATION OF VERTICAL AND HORIZONTAL SYNC.

The output of the sync. separator stage contains composite (line and field) synchronising pulses thus it is necessary to segregate these pulses in some way so that appropriate sync. waveforms are fed to the line and field timebase sections of the receiver.

Vertical Sync.

The amplitude of the composite sync. output of the sync. separator stage is constant; the difference between line and field sync. is one of time duration only. It is this time-difference that enables the pulses to be segregated from one another. Essentially, this time difference is converted into an amplitude difference which makes it easy to ensure complete separation.

For extracting the vertical (field) pulses from the sync. pulse train use is commonly made of an integrating circuit, see Fig. 14.9(a). This CR combination has a time

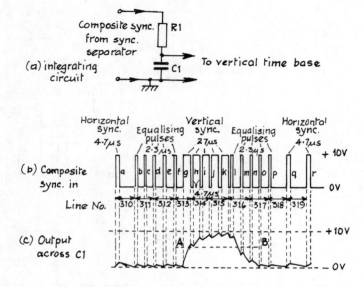

Fig. 14.9 *Showing how an integrator circuit produces an output locking pulse when fed with sync. pulse train (at end of even field).*

constant of about $30\,\mu$s. The value is not critical and variations will be met with in practice.

After the video information has been removed in the sync. separator stage the composite sync. waveform is applied to the integrating circuit $C1,R1$. We will assume that the sync. waveform is positive-going and 10 V in amplitude as in Fig. 14.9(b). Consider the effect on the first line pulse shown, pulse a. During the period of the pulse current will flow in $R1$ charging the capacitor. If the time-constant of the CR is $30\,\mu$s the voltage across the capacitor will only rise a little as the pulse is only $4\cdot7\,\mu$s in duration. Between pulse a and pulse b (a time interval of $59\cdot3\,\mu$s) the capacitor will discharge through $R1$. When pulse b arrives the capacitor will attempt to charge once again but as each equalising pulse is only $2\cdot3\,\mu$s, the charge acquired will be smaller than for a line pulse. Between pulse b and pulse c the capacitor will discharge once more. After a period of five equalising pulses, the voltage across $C1$ tends to settle down to a low voltage of about 1 V (for 10 V sync. pulses) as the time between pulses of $29\cdot7\,\mu$s is approximately thirteen times the equalising pulse width.

When the first field pulse g arrives, $C1$ will charge to a much higher voltage (approximately 6 V) as the pulse width is almost equal to the time-constant of the CR. Between vertical pulses the capacitor will discharge but only by a small amount as the interval is only $4\cdot7\,\mu$s. Subsequent field pulses h, i, j and k will cause the voltage to build up as shown in Fig. 14.9(c). Following the field sync. period, the intervals between the equalising pulses will allow the voltage across $C1$ to fall rapidly as it discharges. Each equalising pulse has the effect of delaying the fall of voltage as $C1$ charges a little during each pulse.

Thus, the effect of the integrating circuit on the composite sync. pulse train is to produce **a large voltage output during the field sync. interval** but only **a small voltage output due to the effects of the line and equalising pulses**. It is a useful exercise for the technician to calculate and hence determine the precise waveshape of the locking pulse out of the integrating circuit. The voltage across the integrating capacitor after the application of each pulse may be found from:

$$V_C = V_1 + V_D\left(1 - e^{\frac{-t_1}{CR}}\right)$$

where:

V_1 = voltage across capacitor prior to start of charge

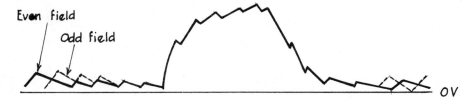

Fig. 14.10 Integrator output on odd and even fields.

V_D = the voltage difference between the pulse amplitude and V_1
t_1 = pulse duration (secs)
CR = integrating circuit time-constant (secs).

Also, by using:

$$V_C = V_2(e^{\frac{-t_2}{CR}})$$

the voltage across the capacitor at the end of the discharge period may be arrived at, where:

V_2 = voltage across capacitor prior to start of charge
t_2 = interval between pulses.

The output from the integrator may be fed to a limiter to remove the effects of the line pulses by clipping off the waveform below a level such as A–B in Fig. 14.9(c) prior to the pulse being applied to the field oscillator. The purpose of the equalising pulses can be seen by reference to Fig. 14.10 which shows the integrator output on odd and even fields. At the start of the equalising pulse period there is discrepance between the two output waveforms due to the half-line difference. After a period corresponding to two and a half lines of equalising pulses the difference disappears and the pulses beome coincident.

The precise instant at which the field oscillator is triggered (thus initiating the field **flyback**) depends upon the setting of the field hold control and the design of the field timebase. It can be arranged that the instant of triggering corresponds to the leading edge of the locking pulse at a level such as A–B in Fig. 14.9(c) to remove the effects of the integrated line and equalising pulses.

A diode (interlace diode) may be used to remove the effects of the integrated line and equalising pulses and an example from a discrete circuit receiver is given in Fig. 14.11.

The composite sync. pulse train (waveform A) from the sync. separator is integrated by R1, C1 but using a longer time-constant than normal (484 μs). This particular time-constant results in integrated line pulses across C1 which are slightly less than the forward voltage drop of D1 (say 1·0 V) and in consequence D1 does not conduct on these pulses. During the field sync. period C1 charges to a more negative value. When the cathode potential of D1 falls about 1 V below that of its anode, D1 conducts allowing C2 to charge to the voltage across C1 via D1. During the rise of voltage across C1 at the end of the field sync. period the diode cuts off and the trailing edge of waveform C is entirely formed by the discharge of C2 via R2 (a long time-constant of 10 ms). Thus the integrated line and equalising

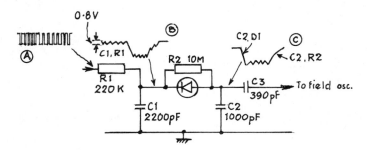

Fig. 14.11 Integrator with interlace diode.

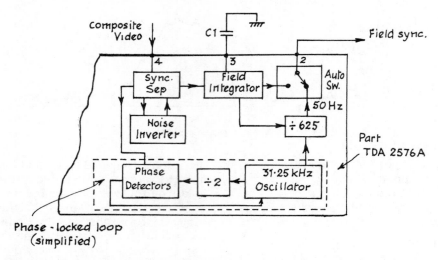

Fig. 14.12 Deriving the field sync. locking pulse by dividing output of oscillator working at twice line frequency.

pulses which are present on waveform B are removed providing a clean locking pulse which is fed to the field oscillator via *C*3.

When an integrated circuit sync. separator is used the integrating network is fitted external to the i.c., such as *R*4, *C*3 in Fig. 14.7. Some improvement in field timebase locking may be achieved by deriving the field sync. indirectly from a divided-down oscillator working at twice line frequency. This idea is used in the TDA 2576A i.c. shown in Fig. 14.12.

During standard television broadcast transmissions, field sync. is obtained by dividing the output of a 31·25 kHz oscillator by 625. This oscillator which after division by two (to provide the line frequency) is maintained very accurately at twice the line frequency by a phase locked loop which compares the output of the divide-by-two stage with the received line sync. pulses. This **indirect** accurately maintained sync. continues to synchronise the field oscillator even when the normal **direct** sync. is lost or mutilated.

During non-standard signals such as from VHS recorders or signal generators, the output reverts automatically to direct field sync. obtained by integrating the field sync. pulse train. This is the purpose of the 'field integrator' block with the integrating time constant controlled by the external *C*1. Non-standard signals are recognised since the ratio

of the 31·25 kHz oscillator to the field frequency is not exactly 625 : 1.

Horizontal Sync.

Direct Sync.

At one time many v.h.f. receivers used direct sync. for the line timebase. Here use was made of a differentiating circuit as in Fig. 14.13(a) having a time-constant of about $0·5-1\,\mu s$. By passing the output from the sync. separator through this circuit, sharp 'spikes' corresponding to the leading edges of the line sync. pulses were generated which were fed to the line timebase to initiate the flyback stroke.

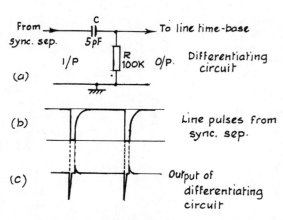

Fig. 14.13 Use of differentiating circuit with 'direct' sync.

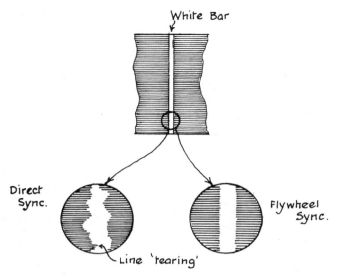

Fig. 14.14 *Comparison of direct and flywheel sync.*

Only the negative-going spikes of Fig. 14.13(c) were used; the positive spikes were lower amplitude and longer duration due to the curvature on the trailing edges of the pulses from the sync. separator and the different time-constant that was effective on the charge and discharge of the capacitor *C*. During the field sync. interval, spikes at twice line frequency were generated but those occurring halfway through a line were of insufficient amplitude to trigger the line timebase.

Flywheel Sync.

The disadvantage with direct sync. is that if a line sync. pulse is missing or mutilated by noise or interference, the synchronism is upset causing 'line tearing' of the picture, see Fig. 14.14. With flywheel sync. the system does not respond to each individual pulse but rather to a succession of pulses. Thus, if a pulse is missing, mutilated by noise or incorrectly timed, the synchronism is unaffected.

This is because the system has momentum like a flywheel and keeps the line timebase synchronised at the correct frequency even if the line sync. pulses are missing for a few lines.

Basic Ideas of Flywheel Sync.

Flywheel sync. systems are based on the **phase lock loop principle** which is shown in block schematic form in Fig. 14.15. In the phase detector, synchronising pulses of fundamental frequency f_s are compared in frequency and phase with a reference signal from the horizontal timebase oscillator (or output stage) of fundamental frequency f_o. If there is a frequency or phase difference between the two inputs, the phase detector generates a correcting signal V_e which is fed to the control stage via a low-pass filter. The filter is an *RC* network with values chosen so that only low frequencies and d.c. are passed on the control stage. The control stage uses the output of the filter to correct the frequency or phase of the

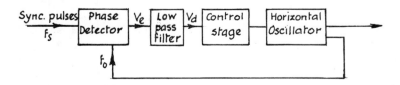

Fig. 14.15 *Principle of phase lock loop.*

line oscillator in such a direction as to reduce the initial error.

With no sync. input to the phase detector, the error voltage V_d is equal to zero and the horizontal oscillator operates at its free-running frequency. When sync. is applied the phase detector compares the frequency and phase of the sync. pulses with that of the horizontal oscillator and generates a correcting signal V_e which is related to the frequency and phase difference of the two signals. V_e is then filtered and the resulting output V_d is applied to the control stage which alters the frequency of the oscillator. The voltage V_d forces the oscillation to vary in a direction to reduce the frequency difference between f_s and f_o. If f_o is close to the input sync. f_s, V_d causes the oscillator to lock with the sync. except for a finite phase difference. This net phase-difference is necessary to generate a correcting voltage V_d to shift the oscillation from its free-running frequency f_o to the sync. frequency f_s.

Lock and Capture

Suppose that f_o is not at the desired frequency f_s when the sync. pulses are applied. The phase detector mixes the two inputs to produce sum-and-difference frequencies. The low-pass filter will remove $f_s + f_o$ and if $f_s - f_o$ falls outside the band edge of the filter it, too, will be removed and no information will be sent to the control stage, *i.e.* the horizontal oscillator will remain at its free-running frequency. As f_o approaches f_s, $f_s - f_o$ decreases and when it falls within the band pass of the filter it will be passed to the control stage. The effect of the beat frequency applied to the control stage will be to cause frequency modulation of the horizontal oscillator.

This produces a small d.c. output from the phase detector which pulls the oscillator into synchronism.

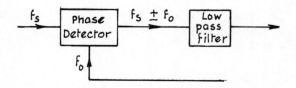

Fig. 14.16 Lock and capture.

Capture (Pull-in) Range

This is the frequency range centred about the oscillator free-running frequency over which the loop can obtain lock with the input sync. It depends primarily upon the band edge of the low-pass filter.

Lock (Hold-in) Range

Once in lock, the oscillator will track f_s. There is now a d.c. output from the phase detector. The lock range is the frequency range over which the oscillator will track f_s centred on the free-running frequency of the oscillator. It is limited by the range of error voltage that can be generated and the corresponding frequency deviation produced in the oscillator. It is essentially a d.c. parameter and is not dependent upon the low-pass filter characteristics. The capture range is never greater than the lock range.

Typically, the capture range may be $\pm 300\,\text{Hz}$ and the lock range $\pm 900\,\text{Hz}$ centred on the nominal line frequency of $15{,}625\,\text{Hz}$.

Phase Detector and Low-Pass Filter

A common discrete transistor circuit arrangement is shown in Fig. 14.17. $TR1$ is a phase-splitter stage fed with positive-going sync. pulses at its base. Forward bias for $TR1$ is provided in the d.c. coupling from the previous stage. Antiphase sync. pulses are produced at the collector and emitter and these are fed to the phase detector diodes $D1$ and $D2$ via $C1$ and $C2$. The pulses cause the diodes to conduct and to charge $C1$ and $C2$ equally with the polarity as shown. Between pulses the capacitors slowly discharge. With equal value resistors $R3$ and $R4$, the resultant voltage at the junction of these resistors will be zero ($R6$ slider set to zero).

Line flyback pulses from the line output stage are used as the reference signal. The d.c. component of these pulses is blocked by $C5$ and the pulses are then integrated by $R7$, $C6$. Thus, at the junction of the two diodes a sawtooth waveform is produced having a positive-going flyback section setting about zero voltage.

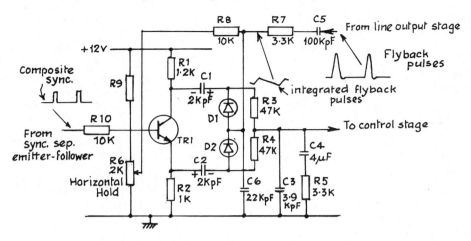

Fig. 14.17 Diode phase detector with phase splitter.

Sync. Pulse and Sawtooth In Phase

When the sync. pulse period occurs as the sawtooth waveform is passing through zero as in Fig. 14.18, the sync. pulse and sawtooth are in phase as regards the circuit operation which is desired. To determine the effect of the sync. pulse and sawtooth voltages applied to each diode one may consider the effective voltage applied to either the cathode or anode of each diode. For example, when the sync. pulse is commencing at $D1$ cathode, the sawtooth voltage is negative at $D1$ anode (instant t_1). This effectively reduces the conduction through $D1$ which is equivalent to reducing the pulse amplitude at $D1$ cathode. As far as $D2$ is concerned at this instant, the negative voltage on its cathode due to the sawtooth increases conduction which is equivalent to increasing the pulse amplitude at $D2$ anode. A little later at instant t_2 the sawtooth is zero and the effective voltage applied to each diode is the same and is that due to the sync. only. At instant t_3, when the sawtooth voltage is positive, the effect at $D1$ anode is to increase conduction whilst at $D2$ cathode it decreses conduction. Accordingly, the effective pulse voltage at $D1$ cathode is increased and that at $D2$ anode is decreased. However, both effec-

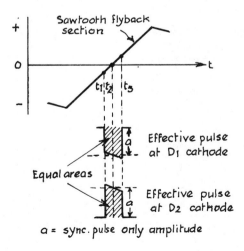

Fig. 14.18 Sync. pulse and sawtooth in-phase.

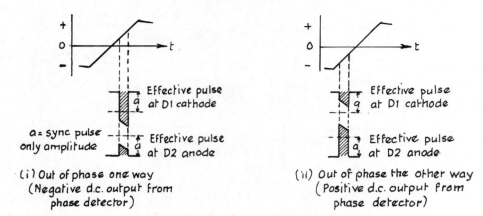

Fig. 14.19 Sync. pulse and sawtooth out of phase.

tive pulses have equal areas so $C1$ and $C2$ will receive equal charges and the resultant voltage at the junction of $R3$, $R4$ will be zero.

Sync. Pulse and Sawtooth Out of Phase

If the sync. pulse period occurs when the sawtooth is going positive as in Fig. 14.19(i), a larger effective pulse is applied to $D1$ than to $D2$. Thus, $D1$ conducts harder than $D2$ and $C1$ receives the greater charge. This causes a net negative d.c. voltage to appear at the junction of $R3$, $R4$. If, on the other hand, the sync. pulse period corresponds to a time when the sawtooth is going negative as in Fig. 14.19(ii), $D2$ conducts harder than $D1$, and $C2$ receives the greater charge. As a result a net positive d.c. voltage is obtained at the junction of $R3$, $R4$.

In both cases where there is an error in phase, an error voltage is obtained at the output which has an amplitude proportional to the initial phase error and a polarity depending on whether the sync. is early or late compared with the zero crossing of the sawtooth.

Although we have been considering phase errors, a small frequency error between the sync. and reference sawtooth results in a similar effect and this is shown in Fig. 14.20. In Fig. 14.20(a) the sawtooth has the same frequency and phase as the sync. which is assumed constant at 15,625 Hz. In Fig. 14.20(b) the sawtooth frequency has been reduced by 300 Hz. Note now that the sync. pulse period corresponds to the negative part of the flyback period on the second and third flyback sections. The effect of increasing the frequency of the sawtooth by 300 Hz is shown in Fig. 14.20(c). Here the period of the sync. pulse corresponds to the positive part of the flyback period on the second and third flyback sections. In Fig. 14.20(d) the sawtooth has the same frequency as the sync. but is slightly out

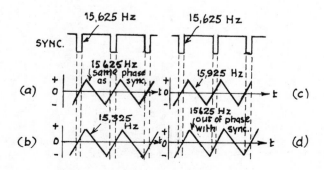

Fig. 14.20 Diagrams showing frequency and phase errors.

of phase, *i.e.* the sync. period lines up with the negative part of the sawtooth flyback section.

Horizontal Hold

In the description of the circuit operation it has been assumed that the slider of the horizontal hold control had been set to zero so that the 'error' voltage was able to swing positive or negative with respect to zero potential. To allow the line oscillator to be set to 15,625 Hz, $R6$ is included. This control feeds a positive potential to the junction of the diodes and hence to the junction of $R3$, $R4$. By varying $R6$ the positive d.c. fed to the control stage alters the frequency of the horizontal oscillator so that it may be set to the nominal line frequency of 15,625 Hz. Thus, with sync. applied to the circuit the 'error' voltage will now swing positive or negative with respect to the potential from the horizontal hold control permitting symmetrical operation about 15,625 Hz.

It will be noted that during adjustment of $R6$ within the lock range of the flywheel circuit, the visible effect on the screen is to cause the picture to shift horizontally to the left and right, *i.e.* it operates like a picture-shift control. It should not be used as such, as one is liable to set $R6$ towards the end of the locking range and the circuit may be unable to cope with subsequent drift.

Low-Pass Filter

$R3$, $R4$ and $C3$ form the low-pass filter. It is this time-constant which gives the arrangement its flywheel effect. The longer the time-constant the more effective is the filter in smoothing out the effect of interference in the sync. waveform. If it is too long however, the capture range is reduced which is important at switch-on. Thus a compromise value must be used. The series network $C4$, $R5$ form a damping circuit to prevent ringing of the control voltage during the field sync. pulse period when the normal sequence of line pulses is broken. The values of the 'anti-hunting' network $C4$, $R5$ are quite critical.

Provision is usually made to **reduce the time constant of the low pass filter** when the receiver is used to replay signals from a **video cassette recorder**. Such machines produce rapid timing variations resulting from the mechanical head-to-tape scanning process. With a long time constant in the phase lock loop, horizontal picture jitter and bent verticals at the top of the picture may result. The shorter time constant required for VCR operation may be switched in automatically when the VCR channel is selected.

I.C. Flywheel Sync.

Many i.c. flywheel sync. phase-locked systems have two operating modes. One is a fast mode to provide a quick pull-in on changing channels and for VCR operation and the other is a slow mode for normal signals after phase lock has been achieved.

An example is shown in Fig. 14.21 for the TDA 2576A sync. processor which employs two phase-locked loops, 'Phase 1' and 'Phase 2'.

The 'Phase 1' loop compares the line sync. pulse phase with the phase of the line oscillator and corrects any errors in the line oscillator frequency. In the i.c. the line oscillator operates at twice the line frequency of 31250 Hz (to enable indirect field sync. to be obtained by division by 625 as explained for Fig. 14.12) but is divided-by-two to provide an input to the phase comparator of the 'Phase 1' loop. This loop has two modes of operation; a fast mode (short time-constant) for pull-in at switch-on and VCR operation and a slow mode (longer time-constant) for holding, once the loop has achieved lock. A coincidence detector automatically determines the time-constant to be used and is supplied with a d.c. voltage on pin 8 which alters in level for normal television reception and VCR operation.

The 'Phase 2' loop compares the phase of the line oscillator with the phase of the line flyback pulses applied via the Sandcastle Generator from pin 14 of the i.c. A correcting voltage is generated on pin 11 and fed back on pin 12 to the 'Phase Correction' block. Superimposed on the correcting voltage is a d.c. voltage from the 'Line Phase' control. This loop compensates for varying delays which can occur between the line drive output on pin 10 and the line output stage of the receiver. Delay variations occur in the line output stage resulting from loading changes

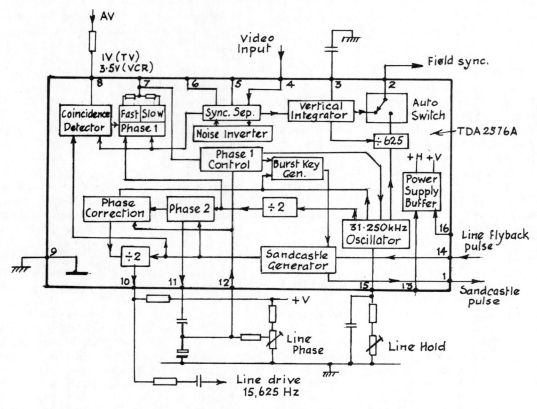

Fig. 14.21 *TDA 2576A sync. processor using two phase-locked loops and incorporating sandcastle pulse generation.*

due to picture content. This effect occurs in most receivers since the e.h.t., which provides the c.r.t. beam current, is derived from the line flyback pulse using an overwind on the line output transformer.

Sandcastle Pulse

There are a number of functions carried out in a modern television receiver that need special timing signals to implement them at the required instant and for the required duration. These functions include: **burst gating**, **burst blanking** and **Ident switching** in the PAL decoder; **line** and **field blanking** of the c.r.t.; **clamping functions** in the video signal stages.

With early colour television receivers these timing signals were generated from time-bases and synchronising circuits but often required special shaping and individual interface circuits. With the widespread use of integrated

circuits it was realised that the important timings needed could be incorporated into a **single waveform** and introduced into the appropriate i.c. via a **single pin**. This timing waveform was given the name 'Sandcastle Pulse' on account of its shape.

A 2-level sandcastle waveform is shown in Fig. 14.22(a). This has one standard level at 3 V corresponding to the line blanking period and another level at 10 V corresponding to the period of the colour burst. These levels may be sensed by detectors inside the controlled i.cs. to extract the required pulse timings. The higher level of 10 V may be used for burst gating and black level clamping whilst the lower level of 3 V is used for line flyback blanking.

The 3-level sandcastle waveform of Fig. 14.22(b) contains the same information as the 2-level waveform (although slightly different standard voltage levels are adopted)

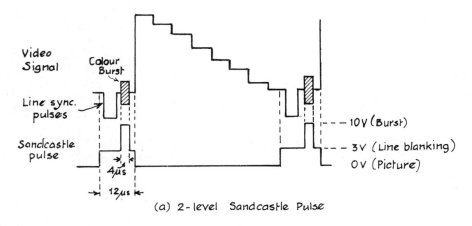

Video
Signal

Colour
Burst

Line sync.
pulses

Sandcastle
pulse

4µs

12µs

- - 10V (Burst)

- - 3V (Line blanking)

0V (Picture)

(a) 2-level Sandcastle Pulse

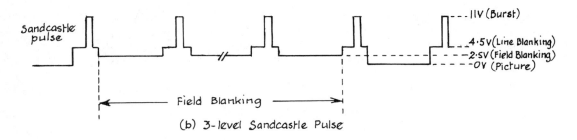

Sandcastle
pulse

- - 11V (Burst)

- 4·5V (Line Blanking)

- - 2·5V (Field Blanking)

- - 0V (Picture)

Field Blanking

(b) 3-level Sandcastle Pulse

Fig. 14.22 Sandcastle pulse.

with an additional level at 2·5 V which is maintained during the field blanking interval (for a standard 21 T.V. lines). The third level which after sensing, may be used for suppressing the field flyback of the c.r.t. and to give timing information corresponding to the reception of teletext signals.

In the TDA 2576A i.c. of Fig. 14.21 a 3-level sandcastle waveform is produced by the 'Sandcastle Generator' block. The higher level of 11 V is obtained from the 'Burst Key Generator' block, the next level of 4·5 V is obtained from the line flyback pulse applied to pin 14 and the lower level of 2·5 V is obtained by counting line pulses (inside the i.c.) to establish the field blanking period.

CHAPTER FIFTEEN

HORIZONTAL SCAN CIRCUITS AND E.H.T.

Objectives

1 To explain the basic operation of discrete transistor and i.c. line generators.
2 To show a basic circuit and give the functions of the line driver stage.
3 To explain the principles of operation of the line output stage.
4 To show the methods used for flyback e.h.t. generation and scan rectification for low voltage supplies.
5 To show the methods used to correct East–West pin cushion distortion for low voltage and high voltage diode modulators.
6 To outline the operation of East–West and North–South correction circuits.

THE HORIZONTAL (LINE) oscillator and its output stage is required to deliver a sawtooth current waveform at 15625 Hz to the line scan coils wound on the tube neck to enable horizontal deflection of the electron beam(s). A typical arrangement used in many modern receivers is shown in Fig. 15.1.

The horizontal scanning rate is determined

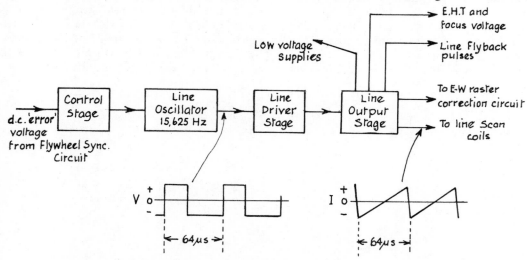

Fig. 15.1 Basic arrangement of the line timebase section used in modern receivers.

by the **free-running line oscillator** stage which is kept in step with the line synchronising pulses by the output of the flywheel sync. circuit via a control stage. The output of the line oscillator is usually in the form of a train of pulses and either the positive or negative pulses are used to switch the line output stage alternatively 'on' and 'off'. The pulses are supplied to the line output stage via the line driver stage which is essentially a pulse amplifier, although some reshaping of the pulses may be carried out in this stage.

The line output stage itself is one of the main 'work horses' of the television receiver. In addition to supplying the sawtooth current waveform to the deflector coils, the stage generates the e.h.t. voltage, focusing potential and other high voltages required by the c.r.t. Other outputs include line flyback pulses to the sandcastle waveform generator, low voltage d.c. supplies and feed to the E–W raster width and correction circuits.

LINE OSCILLATOR STAGE

Discrete Circuit Types

Prior to the widespread use of i.c. line generators, discrete circuit versions found in colour and mono receivers were of three types: Blocking Oscillator; Sinewave Oscillator and to a lesser extent the Astable Multivibrator. These 'free-running oscillators were kept in sync. with the output from the line flywheel sync. circuit via a control stage. For blocking oscillators and multivibrators the control stage (when used) took the form of a d.c. amplifier to amplify the 'error voltage' from the flywheel sync. circuit which was then applied as an 'aiming potential' to correct the frequency of the line oscillator. For L/C sinewave oscillators the 'error voltage' was usually applied via a reactance transistor stage which constituted the control stage or via a vari-cap diode circuit and a capacitance multiplier.

An example of a Blocking Oscillator line generator is given in Fig. 15.2. This circuit uses a flywheel sync. arrangement that does not require a phase splitter (as described for Fig. 14.17). This commonly used circuit although simpler in appearance is more difficult to fully explain. The discriminator circuit comprising $D1$, $D2$, $R2$ and $R3$ compares the phase of integrated line flyback pulses with the phase of the line sync. pulses applied from the sync. separator. Essentially the action is that $D1$ and $D2$ conduct during the period of the

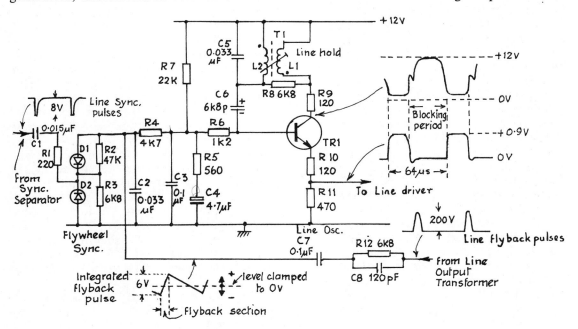

Fig. 15.2 Blocking oscillator.

line sync. pulses and clamp the integrated waveform to zero potential. If the sync. pulses occur at the centre of the flyback section, the centre of the waveform is clamped to zero (the ideal locked position). After smoothing by $R4$, $C3$, zero 'error voltage' will be obtained and the line oscillator will be locked in frequency and phase. If, however, the line sync. pulses occur earlier in the flyback section, the integrated waveform will be clamped to zero nearer to the negative peaks which after smoothing by $R4$, $C3$ will result in a positive d.c. 'error voltage'. Should the line sync. pulses occur later, the integrated waveform will be clamped to zero closer to the positive peaks which after smoothing by $R4$, $C3$ will result in a negative d.c. error voltage. $R4$, $C3$ constitute the low pass filter and $R5$, $C4$ is an 'anti-hunting' network.

Turning now to the line oscillator stage comprising $TR1$ and the 'blocking transformer' $T1$. A blocking oscillator is an LC oscillator designed to produce intermittent operation by using a large amount of positive feedback. The blocking oscillator transformer has high inductance windings $L1$ and $L2$ which are tightly coupled and tuned by $C5$. At switch-on, forward bias supplied via $R7$ turns $TR1$ 'on' and as a result the collector voltage falls. Due to the transformer action and the phase of $L1$, $L2$ windings, the fall in voltage at the collector produces a rise in voltage at the base of $TR1$ which turns the transistor harder 'on'. The increase in current through the transistor results in a further fall in collector voltage and a further rise in base voltage. This accumulative action at switch-on rapidly causes the collector current to saturate and the collector voltage to 'bottom'.

Whilst this action is occurring another effect is taking place at the base of the transistor. Due to the feedback to the base from $L2$, $C6$ is charging with the polarity shown and the effect of the charge on $C6$ is to attempt to reverse bias the transistor. It is prevented from doing so by the positive feedback to the base via $T1$. However, as soon as the collector voltage 'bottoms', transformer action ceases and the base of $TR1$ is taken negative by the charge on $C6$. As a result, collector current ceases and the collector voltage rises towards the line supply voltage.

$C6$ now discharges via $R6$ 'aiming' for the potential at the junction of $R7$, $R4$. However, as soon as the base potential rises just above zero, the transistor commences to conduct and the previous action is repeated. The precise instant that $TR1$ commences to conduct is determined by the 'aiming' potential at the junction of $R7$, $R4$ and this varies with the 'error' voltage from the flywheel sync. circuit.

It will be seen that regular positive-going pulses will be produced across $R11$ having a periodic time equal to the line period of $64\,\mu s$. These pulses are then supplied to the line output stage via the line driver.

With discrete transistor line generators it was more common to use sine wave oscillators which offer the advantage, that even without frequency control, they have a natural tendency to remain stable in frequency.

An example is given in Fig. 15.3(a) along with a reactance control stage. $TR1$ is connected as a Hartley oscillator with $L1$, $L2$ serving as the tapped inductor which is tuned by the capacitive reactance presented between points A and B from the reactance stage $TR2$. These components determine the natural frequency of oscillation. Energy is supplied to the oscillator 'tank' circuit across $L1$ from $TR1$ collector and fed back to the base from across $L2$ via $C1$. Starting bias for $TR1$ is supplied via $R3$ and $D1$. Once oscillations have commenced, automatic bias is provided by $R1$, $C2$ in the emitter circuit.

As is common with this type of oscillator in the line timebase function, the stage is overdriven and does not generate a complete sine wave. It is designed so that the base drive on one half-cycle switches the transistor 'hard-on' until it 'bottoms'; it then remains in this state until the other half-cycle of the base drive switches the transistor 'off'. This results in a near square wave being developed at the collector which is fed to the driver stage via $T1$. To a large extent the mark-to-space ratio of the output waveform is controlled by the value of the base bias resistor $R3$. The v.d.r. $R4$ damps the ringing of $T1$ when the transistor switches 'off'. $D1$ prevents excessive reverse bias voltage being applied to the base–emitter junction of $TR1$.

The frequency of the oscillator may be set to the nominal line frequency of 15625 Hz by adjusting the core of $L1$, $L2$ (line hold). The precise frequency is determined by the output

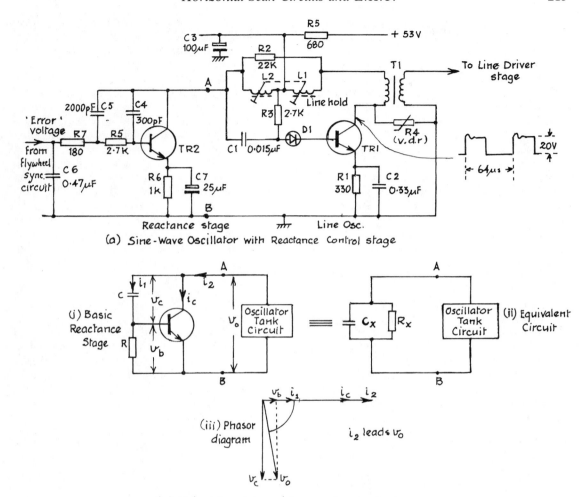

(a) Sine-Wave Oscillator with Reactance Control stage

(b) Principle of transistor reactance stage

Fig. 15.3 Sine-wave oscillator.

of the flywheel sync. circuit which varies the capacitive reactance across A–B from the reactance stage. This capacitance is effectively in parallel with $L2$.

The principle of operation of the reactance stage is illustrated by the diagrams of Fig. 15.3(b). Diagram (i) shows the basic circuit (a.c. operation only) comprising a transistor and a CR network connected across the oscillator tank circuit which is generating a sine wave voltage v_o.

If the reactance of C is large compared with the value of R, the current i_1 flowing in the CR network as a result of the applied voltage v_o will lead v_o by almost 90°. This is shown by the phasors of diagram (iii). The voltage v_b developed across R will be in-phase with i_1 and this is the input voltage to the transistor. The input voltage will give rise to a collector current i_c in-phase with v_b and of magnitude approximately gm v_b. Thus the resultant current i_2 drawn from the oscillator tank circuit leads v_o by almost 90°, *i.e.* the transistor and its CR network is equivalent to a capacitor C_x in parallel with a resistance R_x connected in shunt with the oscillator tank circuit, see diagram (ii). By varying the gm of the transistor, *i.e.* by altering its d.c. base bias, the magnitude of i_c will be altered which varies the effectiveness C_x and the frequency of the oscillator tank circuit. R_x does not affect the oscillator tuning but does cause some slight damping.

In Fig. 15.3(a) the *CR* network is formed by *C5*, *C4*, *R5* and the base–emitter resistance of *TR2*. Values used in this network are such that the base current of *TR2* leads the voltage from the oscillator tank circuit by almost 90°. The collector current will lead the collector voltage to a similar extent. Thus *TR2* output impedance is predominantly capacitive and the value is determined by the forward bias supplied to *TR2* base from the flywheel sync. circuit. Variations in the 'error voltage' from the flywheel sync. circuit will vary the tuning of *L1*, *L2* and thus the frequency and phase of the line oscillator will be adjusted accordingly.

I.C. Line Generator

When in i.c. form, the line generator function is usually only one of many functions included within the i.c. Consequently the i.c. may be referred to as the 'Horizontal Combination' (TBA 920), the 'Line and Field Sync. Processor' (TDA 2576) or the 'Power Processor' (TEA 2029C) *etc*, depending upon the main features that are incorporated.

The line or horizontal oscillator is a voltage controlled oscillator (v.c.o.) whose frequency and phase is controlled by the output of the line flywheel sync. circuit (a.p.c.) and this function is invariably fabricated on the same chip. The actual i.c. oscillator circuit used is generally more complex and may be based on the Miller-Integrator-Oscillator principle followed by pulse shaping circuits to achieve the required output pulse to the line driver stage. Often an external capacitor is fitted which produces a ramp, with the frequency of the oscillator set to the nominal 15625 Hz by a line hold control.

An example is shown in simplified form in Fig. 15.4 for the TBA 920Q Horizontal Combination i.c. featured in early colour television receivers and which could be used with a variety of line output stages.

The horizontal oscillator functions by the charging and discharging of the ramp producing capacitor *C1*. Since this capacitor controls the oscillator frequency it must have good temperature stability and close tolerance. The oscillator is set to the nominal 15625 Hz by applying an adjustable d.c. potential to pin 15 from the 'line hold' control (*P1*).

The flywheel sync. circuit uses essentially

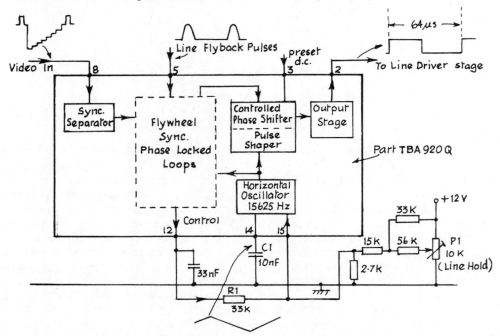

Fig. 15.4 TBA 920 Q Line oscillator.

two feedback loops and during operation if any deviation occurs between the phasing of the line sync. pulses and the line flyback pulses applied at pin 5, a correcting d.c. potential is developed at pin 12 which is fed back to the oscillator control on pin 15 via *R*1.

The output of the horizontal oscillator is applied through a pulse shaper/controlled phase shifter and output stage to provide near square-wave output pulses to the line driver stage. The controlled phase shifter stage compensates for delays occurring in the line output stage. The duration of the positive output pulses from pin 2 may be adjusted from 12–32 μs by a d.c. applied to pin 3 which sets the 'line phase'.

The line timebase 15625 Hz timing waveform may be obtained by frequency division. An example is to be found in the TDA 2576A Sync. Processor which was described in Chapter 14 (Fig. 14.21). Another example is given in Fig. 15.5 for the TEA 2029C Power Processor. The internal functions of this i.c. in addition to line time base generation, include regulation and overload protection of the receiver switched mode power supply, sync. separation and the field time base small signal generation stages.

The core of the i.c. is a phase locked loop and comprises a v.c.o. which oscillates at 500 kHz, the output being divided by 32 to give the line scan frequency of 15625 Hz. One output from the 15625 Hz block is supplied to a phase comparator (phase det 1) where it is compared in frequency and phase with the line sync. pulses from the Sync. Separator block. A control voltage from the phase comparator readjusts the v.c.o. until they are in phase. The *CR* network on pin 22 smoothes the control voltage and the time constant is adjusted by the charge and discharge current controlled by the i.c. An additional phase comparator (not shown) compares the phase of line flyback pulses applied to pin 12 with the synchronised 15625 Hz signal. The frequency of the v.c.o. is determined by the external ceramic filter *CF* connected between pins 18 and 19.

Another output from the synchronised 15625 Hz stage feeds a generator which produces a sawtooth waveform at 15625 Hz. This output together with the signal from the 15625 Hz stage is fed to a comparator amplifier which produces the pulse drive output waveform on pin 10. To prevent overloading of the line output stage during the 'switch-on' phase, the width of the drive pulse on pin 10 is arranged to be slowly increasing. This is achieved by the charging of *C*4 which gradually increases the drive pulse width during start-up. Horizontal picture shift is achieved

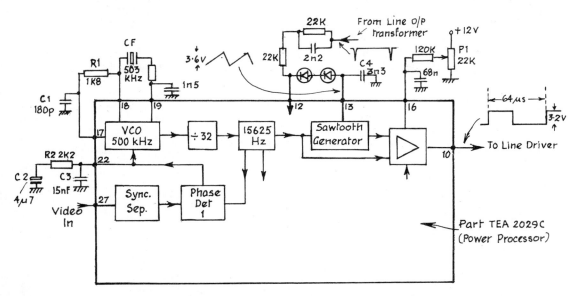

Fig. 15.5 Part TEA 2029C showing line drive waveform generation (simplified).

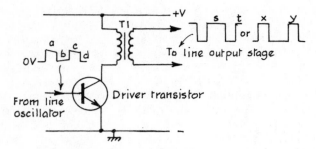

Fig. 15.6 Basic circuit of line driver stage.

by providing a variable d.c. to pin 16 from the shift control $P1$, which via the output on pin 10, causes a small 'off-set' in the line scan current.

LINE DRIVER STAGE

The line driver stage serves two functions: (a) It acts as a buffer stage between the line oscillator and the line output stage. (b) It supplies the high base current required by the line output transistor.

A basic circuit of the line driver stage is given in Fig. 15.6 using an n-p-n transistor but a p-n-p transistor may also be used. The input to the base is the pulse-type waveform supplied from the line oscillator which may be of the discrete transistor type or of integrated circuit form. The driver transistor is switched on by the positive pulses a, c *etc.* and switched off during the intervals b, d *etc.* During the positive pulses the collector current saturates and during the intervals the collector current ceases. This action produces a square wave-

form across $T1$ primary which in turn produces a square waveform across the secondary winding. The waveform developed across the secondary may either be in phase with the base drive or in antiphase with it depending upon the phasing of $T1$ windings. If in phase, the pulses x and y *etc.* will be used to switch the line output transistor ON (assuming an n-p-n transistor) but if in antiphase the pulses s and t *etc.* will be used for this purpose.

When the in phase output is used to switch the line output transistor ON, it will be conducting when the driver transistor is conducting; this is known as **simultaneous operation**. If the antiphase output is used the line output transistor will be conducting when the line driver transistor is OFF. This is **non-simultaneous operation** which is the most common method used in practice.

A circuit example from practice is given in Fig. 15.7 which uses the non-simultaneous mode of operation. Positive-going pulses of suitable duration from $T1$ are fed to $TR1$ base to switch the driver transistor ON causing it to

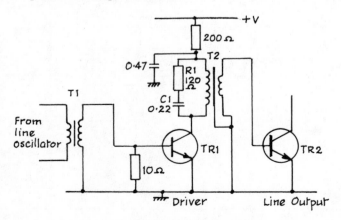

Fig. 15.7 Practical circuit of driver stage.

bottom. During this period when *TR*1 collector current is saturated, energy is put into the driver transformer. When *TR*1 switches OFF, the energy stored in *T*2 supplies the base current for the line output transistor *TR*2 thus switching it ON. *R*1 and *C*1 are placed across *T*2 primary to remove high peak voltages developed during the turn-off of *TR*1 which would otherwise exceed the collector voltage rating of *TR*1. *T*2 provides a step-down ratio to supply the high base current for the line output transistor. With non-simultaneous operation the driver transistor provides the necessary low impedance in the base circuit of *TR*2 when the line output transistor is switched OFF.

LINE OUTPUT STAGE

Basic Circuit

A basic line output stage is shown in Fig. 15.8 and consists of an inductor *L*, a capacitor *C* and two electronic switches *TR*1 (the line output transistor) and *D*1 (the 'efficiency' diode). The inductance of *L* represents the inductance of the deflector coils and the self-inductance of the line output transformer which is used for matching to the deflector coils and for deriving the e.h.t. Capacitor *C* is an external component but also includes the self-capacitance of the deflector coils and line output transformer. As far as a.c. is concerned *C* is effectively in parallel with *L*.

The base drive waveform to *TR*1 base is given in waveform (a). Since the drive waveform is coupled to *TR*1 via *T*1, the waveform will set itself about the mean level of 0 V. At instant t_1 the base voltage is taken positive causing *TR*1 to conduct hard. *TR*1 acts as a switch thus connecting the inductor *L* between the supply line rails. If there is no resistance in circuit, the current (I_L) in the inductor rises in a linear manner as shown in waveform (b) between instants t_1 and t_2 when the base is positive. During this period there is a constant

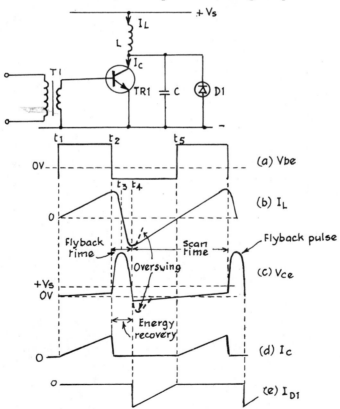

Fig. 15.8 Basic transistor line output stage and waveforms.

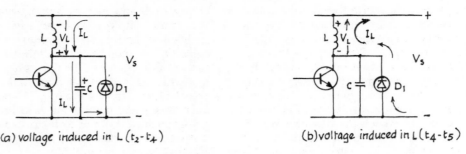

(a) voltage induced in L (t_2–t_4) (b) voltage induced in L (t_4–t_5)

Fig. 15.9 Voltages induced in L.

voltage drop across L, the collector of $TR1$ is bottomed at practically zero voltage and $D1$ is non-conducting.

At instant t_2 the base drive to $TR1$ goes negative thus reverse biasing the transistor and causing I_c to fall to zero. However, the current in L cannot fall to zero immediately. As soon as I_L starts to fall, a voltage is induced in L which tends to maintain the current. The polarity of the induced voltage is shown in Fig. 15.9(a). Now the only path for current to flow is via C. Thus between instants t_2 and t_3 there is an interchange of energy between L and C as the capacitor charges to the induced voltage across L. The actual voltage applied to C is $V_S + V_L$ and this is also present across $TR1$ and the efficiency diode which must both withstand the peak voltage without breakdown occurring.

At instant t_3, I_L has fallen to zero and C is fully charged. Thus, the magnetic field energy initially stored in L has been transferred to C and stored as an electric field. The capacitor now commences to discharge through L and the current reverses direction (t_3–t_4). The voltage across C now decreases and when the voltage across L reaches zero the current is a maximum in the reverse direction. The voltage across C is now equal to V_s.

If nothing else happened the current would decrease as part of a sine curve (shown dotted). However, as soon as I_L starts to fall a voltage is induced in L with polarity shown in Fig. 15.9(b). When this voltage causes the cathode of $D1$ to fall below zero potential, $D1$ conducts and a linearly decreasing current flows in L during the interval t_4–t_5. This assumes that the resistance of $D1$ is small. At instant t_5 the base voltage of $TR1$ goes positive once more and the cycle of events is repeated.

It will thus be seen that during the interval t_1–t_2 when the line output transistor conducts, energy is supplied to the deflector coils and this energy is fully recovered from the deflector coils during the interval t_2–t_4 and then used to produce the other part of the line scan (t_4–t_5). This is the 'efficiency' aspect of the operation and hence the reason for referring to $D1$ as the 'efficiency diode' since the diode provides the current path to produce the other part of the line scan immediately following the recovery period. In practice, of course there will be resistance losses in the deflector coils and the efficiency will be less than 100%. Thus the line output transistor is arranged to switch ON slightly earlier than halfway through the line scan period.

$D1$ is normally used when operating from a low voltage supply, *e.g.* 12 volts. When a high voltage supply is available $D1$ may be dispensed with and the efficiency diode is provided by the collector-base diode of the line output transistor which becomes forward biased at instant t_4 in the same manner as $D1$ became forward biased. Current then flows in the collector-base diode and $T1$ secondary winding. The technique introduces a certain amount of distortion which is only acceptable with high supply line voltages.

The flyback period of the scanning current waveform is a half-cycle of a damped oscillation, the frequency of which is governed by the values of L and C. Now the value of L is determined by the self-inductance of the line output transformer and deflector coils whilst the value of C is settled by the self-capacitance of these components and any added capacitance. Clearly, the flyback time of the scanning current must be within the maximum allowable line flyback time of approximately

11·5 μs. If one aims for a very short flyback time in the design, the peak voltages present across the transistor may be excessive. This is because the energy stored in C is equal to $\frac{1}{2}CV^2$. Thus, for a given energy stored, the effect of reducing C (to reduce the flyback time) will result in an increase in V. Since it is necessary to limit the magnitude of the flyback voltage across the line output transistor, C is made as large as possible within the limits of the maximum allowable flyback time.

Turning off the Line Output Transistor

In ensuring that the line output transistor is adequately bottomed, a base current is supplied which is more than that required for normal operation of a transistor. This base overdrive causes a large number of charge carriers to be stored in the vicinity of the collector-base junction. When the base drive switches the transistor off, considerable time is required to remove the stored carriers and for the collector current to fall to zero. This results in a tail in the collector current waveform as shown in Fig. 15.10(a). The tail can cause excessive collector dissipation since during the fall of current there may be high flyback voltage across the transistor, *e.g.* at instant t_1.

To deal with this problem, the turn-off of the base current may be slowed down as shown in Fig. 15.10(b). This allows the stored carrier numbers to rapidly fall before the base-emitter junction is reverse biased, and in consequence to reduce the collector dissipation of the output transistor (note that at instant t_1 the collector current is zero). A very satisfactory

way of slowing down the base current turn-off is to include an inductor in series with the base and this technique is common in practical circuits.

Use of Auto-Transformer

In practical circuits the line deflection coils are not placed in the collector circuit of the line output transistor because, due to losses, there is a d.c. component of scanning current which would cause the picture on the screen to be off set from centre. Thus it is common to use some form of choke coupling, and if the available h.t. supply is not exactly correct a tapped choke or auto-transformer may be employed to provide currents of suitable amplitude in the deflection coils.

An auto-transformer is invariably used and a practical arrangement is given in Fig. 15.11. Here, connection to the deflection coils is made from a suitable tap on the auto-transformer T_2 via a d.c. blocking capacitor $C2$ which prevents the picture from being off set. The value of this capacitor is suitably chosen to provide some 'S' correction to the scanning current waveform to allow for the 'flat' screen of wide-angle tubes. To protect the transistor against overloads during a c.r.t. flashover an undecoupled resistor ($R1$) is placed in series with the supply feed. Any flashover energy which may find its way to the base circuit via the collector-base capacitance of the transistor is decoupled by $C3$ (value about 1 nF) to protect the base-emitter junction.

The separate efficiency diode shown in Fig. 15.8 is not used as this function is

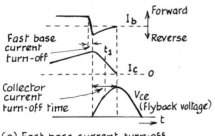

(a) Fast base current turn-off high collector dissipation

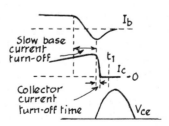

(b) Slow base current turn-off low collector dissipation

Fig. 15.10 Effect of base current turn-off on collector dissipation of line output transistor.

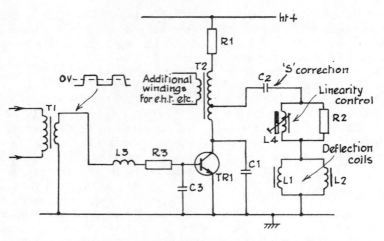

Fig. 15.11 Use of auto-transformer for feeding deflector coils.

provided by the collector-base diode of the transistor which becomes conductive during the period immediately following flyback. C1 is the flyback capacitor, the value of which adjusts the duration of the flyback period (and also the peak voltage present on the collector of the transistor).

The presence of circuit resistance causes unwanted non-linearity in the scanning current which can result in cramping of the picture. This may be dealt with by placing a saturable reactor (L_4) in series with the deflector coils. A saturable reactor consists of a small coil on a ferroxcube core which is biased by a permanent magnet so that the core saturates over part of the line scan. When the core is saturated there is no induced voltage in the coil and no back e.m.f. to oppose the change of scanning current flow. When the core becomes unsaturated, the inductance of the coil is high and a back e.m.f. is produced which is in a direction to oppose a change in current flow. Therefore if the permanent magnet is in the correct direction and of suitable magnitude, the core will remain saturated until the current in the coil produces a flux in the core almost equal and opposite to the flux due to the magnet. When this occurs, an e.m.f. opposing the current change will be induced in the coil. If this is made to correspond to the part of the scan where the rate of change of current is greater than that required, this back e.m.f. will tend to reduce

the rate of change and hence improve linearity. A resistor of suitable value ($R2$) is usually connected across the coil to damp any ringing resulting from the coil inductance and self-capacitance.

To slow down the base current turn-off, and inductor $L3$ is included in series with the base drive. This has a value that adjusts the collector current turn-off to about 7–$10\,\mu s$. When the collector-base junction acts as an efficiency diode, the collector current waveform is as shown in Fig. 15.12. At instant t_1, the collector current of the line output transistor commences to turn-off due to the base voltage going negative and the operation is completed at instant t_2. An induced voltage then appears across the winding of the auto-transformer which lasts until instant t_3 at the end of the flyback period. At instant t_3 the induced voltage in the winding reverses, causing the collector-base junction to conduct and collector current flows once more but in the opposite direction. During the period t_3–t_5 energy is put back into the scanning circuits but before this period has finished, *i.e.* at instant t_5, the base drive forward biases the transistor. If the base voltage goes positive at the centre of the energy recovery period, *i.e.* at instant t_4 the base drive forward biases the transistor base-emitter junction for about $37\,\mu s$ and reverse biases it for $27\,\mu s$.

$R3$ in series with the base voltage feed adjusts the forward voltage drive at the

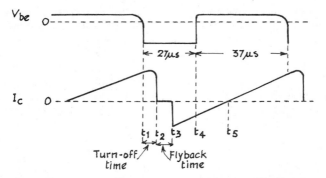

Fig. 15.12 I_C and V_{BE} waveforms simplified for Fig. 15.11.

secondary of the driver transformer $T1$ to suit the V_{be} of the output transistor. This resistor also helps to stabilise base current variations against changes in V_{be}.

Since the line output transistor is kept bottomed when it is in the ON condition, any variations in the h.t. supply will produce variations in picture width. Hence a stabilised supply is required which will normally incorporate a means for setting the h.t. to the required value which will thus set the picture width (and also the e.h.t.).

Although a single transistor is now commonly used for the line output stage, early solid-state receivers employed two transistors in series to share the high peak voltage present during flyback because of the high voltage limitations of transistors at that time. Such an

arrangement is shown in Fig. 15.13 where $TR1$ and $TR2$ form the line output transistors. Each transistor is switched ON and OFF by waveforms derived from separate secondaries of the driver transformer $T1$. It is important that the transistors have the same operating conditions, and a preset control is normally included for this purpose. $L1$ and $L2$ are included to slow down the base current turn-off and $L2$ is made variable to accommodate differences in charge storage time between the two series transistors so that they switch off together.

For safe operation it is essential that during flyback the two transistors have the same peak voltage across them, otherwise premature failure of one or both may occur. This is achieved in this circuit by the potential dividing capacitors $C3$, $C4$ (equal values) and

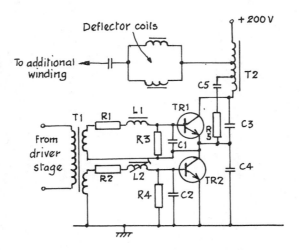

Fig. 15.13 Use of two transistors for voltage sharing.

the series-connected C5 and R5 between the junction of the two transistors and a tap on the auto-transformer T2.

Provision of E.H.T.

We may now consider how the e.h.t. voltage for the c.r.t. is generated. This voltage which may vary from about $+10\,\text{kV}$ for a monochrome portable receiver to $+24\,\text{kV}$ for a large screen colour receiver is invariably generated by the line output transformer. We have seen that during the flyback period a large pulse voltage is developed at the collector of the line output transistor having a magnitude of from about $200\,\text{V}$ to $1\,\text{kV}$ depending upon the maximum V_{ce} of the transistor used. This voltage may be increased to the required e.h.t. voltage by adding a separate winding or extending the main winding of the line output transformer using a suitable turns ratio. If these large voltage pulses are then rectified and smoothed a suitable supply for the c.r.t. final anode may be obtained.

A typical arrangement used in the first generation solid state monochrome portables is shown in Fig. 15.14. Here an extra winding (w_2) is used to step up the flyback pulse voltage present at A (about $200\,\text{V}$) to $10\,\text{kV}$ pulses at point B. Note that pulse voltage at point A is negative-going in this circuit as a p-n-p transistor is used. At point B, $+10\,\text{kV}$ pulses are required but this does not present any problem as the polarity is settled by the winding direction of w_2. The pulses at B are then rectified by the high voltage rectifier unit D4.

After rectification the output of V1 is smoothed using the capacitance present between the final anode and external coating of the c.r.t. This capacitance which varies from about $1000\text{–}2750\,\text{pF}$ is quite sufficient as the frequency of the pulses is high ($15{,}625\,\text{Hz}$) and the current demanded by the c.r.t. is small. With a $2000\,\text{pF}$ smoothing capacitor and a mean beam current of $500\,\mu\text{A}$, the ripple voltage is about $16\,\text{V}$ which represents a voltage variation of only 0.16% on a $10\,\text{kV}$ supply.

With portable receivers operating from a $12\,\text{V}$ supply, there are no voltages available for the focus and first anode electrodes of the c.r.t. These electrodes require positive voltage supplies which are obtained from the additional winding w_4. D3 rectifies the voltage from w_4 which is smoothed at the output by C3. A high voltage supply is also required by the video output amplifier and is obtained from the winding w_3 using the rectifier D2 and smoothing capacitor C2. For these comparitively low voltage supplies it is usual to rectify the

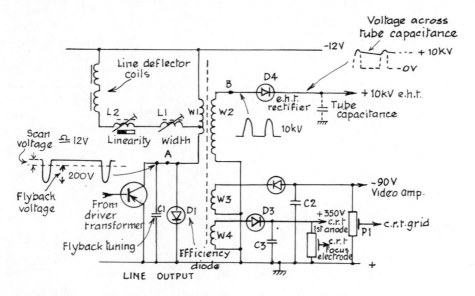

Fig. 15.14 Provision of E.H.T. and other high voltages required in monochrome portable receivers.

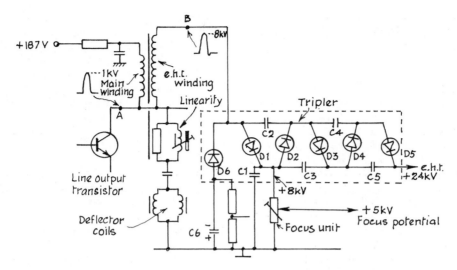

Fig. 15.15 E.H.T. and focus voltage supplies in a mains only colour receiver.

scan side of the waveform (see collector waveform of line output transistor) since a low source impedance and low ripple content is more easily achieved. For e.h.t. and focus variation voltage (in the kV range), the **flyback** part of the waveform is used.

Control over the line linearity is with the aid of a saturable reactor (*L*2) and width control is provided by *L*1. This variable reactance (*L*1) alters the amplitude of the scan current flowing in the deflector coils.

Although it is possible to obtain e.h.t. voltages of the order of 24 kV using a large e.h.t. winding, this method is rarely used nowadays as it is difficult to maintain adequate clearance between winding layers and voltage insulation without increasing the leakage inductance between the main and e.h.t. windings and the stray capacitance of the e.h.t.

winding. It is now common practice to use a moderate e.h.t. winding, stepping up the pulse voltage to about 8 kV and to employ a voltage tripler to produce a final voltage of around 24 kV. Such an arrangement is shown in Fig. 15.15.

The main winding of the line output transformer is extended to produce a turns ratio of 8:1 thereby stepping up the 1 kV pulses present at point A to 8 kV pulses at point B. These pulses are then fed to the tripler rectifying unit which provides + 24 kV at its output to be smoothed by the tube capacitance. The operation of the tripler unit may be understood with the aid of Fig. 15.16. Although the circuit employs five diodes it only acts as a tripler as the input is in the form of pulses and is not sinusoidal. As it is difficult to visualise the operation of the entire circuit

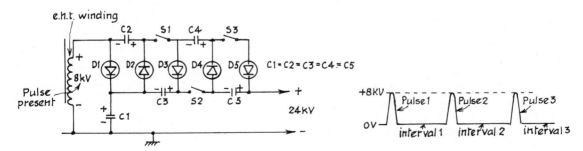

Fig. 15.16 Operation of tripler.

for each pulse applied across the e.h.t. winding, the explanation is simplified by studying the action with the switches *S1–S3* initially open.

Consider therefore the effect in the circuit comprising *D1*, *C1*, *D2*, *C2* and the winding when pulse 1 is applied across the winding. The pulse will cause *D1* to conduct charging *C1* to 8 kV with polarity as shown (*D2* will be non-conducting and therfore *C2* will be uncharged). During interval 1 following the first pulse, *D1* will be non-conducting and the 8 kV across *C1* is applied to the combination of *D2* and *C2*. This will cause *D2* to conduct and for *C2* to charge with polarity as shown to 4 kV, *i.e.* the 8 kV from *C1* divides between *C1* and *C2*. When pulse 2 appears across the winding, *D1* will conduct and *C1* will charge from 4 kV back to 8 kV (*D2* will be non-conducting). During interval 2, *D2* will conduct and the voltages across *C1* and *C2* will equalise at 6 kV, *i.e.* *C2* voltage rises from 4 kV to 6 kV and *C1* voltage falls from 8 kV to 6 kV. On the next pulse (pulse 3), *D1* will conduct causing *C1* to charge from 6 kV back to 8 kV (*D2* will be non-conducting). During interval 3, *D2* conducts once more and the voltages across *C1* and *C2* equalise at 7 kV, *i.e.* *C1* voltage falls from 8 kV to 7 kV and *C2* voltage rises from 6 kV to 7 kV. It will be noted that after each successive pulse the equalised voltages across *C1* and *C2* increase . . . 4 kV . . . 6 kV . . . 7 kV . . . The operation is like a pumping action, the result of which causes, after a number of pulses, the voltage across *C1* and *C2* to rise to 8 kV.

Consider now the circuit with *S1* closed so that *D3* and *C3* are included in the circuit action. Assume that *C1* and *C2* are both charged to 8 kV due to the pumping action previously described. On the next pulse appearing across the winding, *D3* will conduct and *C3* will charge towards 8 kV with polarity as shown; the voltage acting around the circuit *C1*,*C3*,*D3*,*C2* and the winding in a clockwise direction is 16 kV (V_{c2} + winding voltage) but in a counter clockwise direction is 8 kV (V_{c1}). During the following interval period *D3* will be cut off and *D1* is also non-conducting. *D2* will conduct and the voltages across *C1* and *C2* will equalise as described. It has already been shown that *C1* and *C2* will eventually equalise at 8 kV after a number of pulses, thus the

charge on *C3* must increase with each applied pulse until the voltage across it eventually reaches 8 kV.

In a similar manner with *S2* closed adding *C4* and *D4*, *C4* will gradually charge to 8 kV due to the pumping action of the circuit. Finally, with *S3* closed adding *C5* and *D5* to complete the tripler circuit, *C5* likewise gradually charges to 8 kV. As it has already been established that *C1* and *C3* will equalise with 8 kV across each capacitor, the output voltage from the circuit is $V_{c1} + V_{c3} + V_{c5}$, *i.e.* 24 kV as is required. The tube capacitance will charge to the output voltage of the circuit.

Another advantage claimed for the tripler technique is that its internal impedance is lower and thus its voltage regulation is better than when a large e.h.t. overwind is used. In some circuits an additional rectifier (*D6*) is used. This rectifier is reverse biased during the flyback period and cuts off any negative 'rings' at the start of the scan period. When this diode becomes conductive a current flows charging *C6* with the polarity shown. The voltage across *C6* (when of suitable polarity) may be used to provide the a_1 potentials of the colour tube or as an indication of c.r.t. loading for beam current limiting purposes (as in Fig. 15.15).

The focus potential for the c.r.t. is taken from across the first tripler capacitor *C1* and applied to a resistive potential divider contained within a sealed focus unit. A potentiometer is provided in the network to allow the focus potential to be set to the desired value.

Diode-Split L.O.P.T.

In some receivers, instead of employing a conventional voltage trebler, the e.h.t. is obtained from a diode split e.h.t. winding on the line output transformer. The e.h.t. winding consists of four separate identical single layers ($w_1 – w_4$), split by diodes *D1–D3* and an additional diode *D4* as shown in Fig. 15.17(a). The diodes are encapsulated in the line output transformer and eliminate the need for a separate voltage multiplier.

The principle of operation is shown in Fig. 15.17(b) where the distributed inter-layer capacitances C_a, C_b and C_c are used as reservoir capacitors. Across each of the winding layers is developed 6–7 kV of peak flyback voltage. Assuming that there is 6 kV across

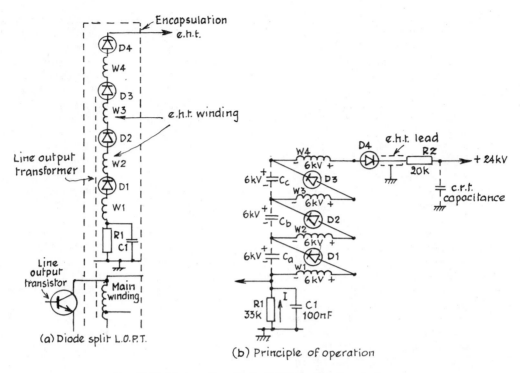

(a) Diode split L.O.P.T.

(b) Principle of operation

Fig. 15.17 Diode-split method of E.H.T. generation.

each layer, the three distributed reservoir capacitors will charge via D1, D2 and D3 during the period of the pulse producing + 18 kV with respect to the earthy end of w_1 at the left-hand side of w_4. This voltage, together with the 6 kV across w_4, is applied to D4 which will conduct producing 24 kV across the capacitance of the screened e.h.t. lead which acts as reservoir capacitor for D4. Resistor R2 and the tube capacitance are used for smoothing the e.h.t. supply. In the event of an e.h.t. flashover, R2 limits the current flow to protect the line output transistor. The screened e.h.t. lead together with the filter formed by R2 and the tube capacitance prevents unwanted line radiation. The current I drawn from the e.h.t. supply by the tube will produce a negative d.c. voltage across R1, C1 and this can be used for beam current limiting purposes.

Harmonic Tuning

The design of the line output stage is very complex. The increase in scanning angle, e.h.t. voltage and beam current of modern

tubes and the extra loading of the convergence circuits of colour receivers has led to a much greater power demand on the line output stage. Line output transistors must pass peak collector currents of 2–3 amperes and withstand peak voltage up to 1·5 kV at the collector. The efficiency of the stage has been improved by the use of better core materials in the line output transformer and deflector coils and by the use of deflector coils with improved shaped windings.

Additionally, the efficiency of the output stage has been improved by the use of harmonic tuning, a technique whereby energy that would normally be lost as heat is recovered from the line output transformer. This loss of energy arises from the leakage inductance of the transformer and occurs principally between the main and e.h.t. winding. The idea of leakage inductance is shown in Fig. 15.18 where some of the flux of the main winding does not link with all of the turns of the e.h.t. overwind. This leakage flux may be represented in an equivalent circuit as a series inductance to the main winding. An approxi-

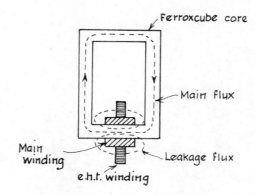

Fig. 15.18 *Leakage flux in line output transformer.*

mate equivalent circuit of the line output transformer is shown in Fig. 15.19. Here $L1$ represents the inductance of the main winding and scanning coils and $C1$ is the self-capacitance of the winding and any added capacitance. The e.h.t. winding is represented by $L2$ and $L3$ is the leakage inductance. Associated with $L3$ is some stray capacitance $C3$. $C2$ represents the capacitance of the e.h.t. rectifier connected to the high voltage end of the e.h.t. winding. The switch S represents the output transistor which is fed from the supply V_S.

During the scan when S is closed, current builds up in $L1$. At the commencement of flyback when S opens, large voltages are induced in $L1$ and $L2$ as previously explained and the direction of these voltages are as indicated by the arrows. No voltage is induced in $L3$, of course, as the flux from $L1$ does not link with $L3$. The sudden rise in voltage across $L1$ and $L2$ which is applied to $L3$ causes a damped oscillation at a frequency determined by $L3,C3$. If the magnitude of the oscillation is high, it extends into the scan causing striations on the left-hand side of the picture as the oscillatory voltage across $L3$ is applied back to

across $L1$ (main winding and scan coils). Apart from the effect on the picture, the energy in $L3,C3$ is a loss as it is not recovered by the efficiency diode circuit. However, use can be made of the oscillation by tuning $L3,C3$ to approximately three times the frequency of $L1,C1$ (which determines the flyback).

The oscillatory voltage across $L3,C3$ is applied partly across C–D and partly across A–B but is applied between these points in opposite directions. The effect is shown in Fig. 15.20(a) and (b). It will be seen that by tuning the leakage inductance to about three times the flyback frequency, the voltage is applied to the e.h.t. rectifier, Fig. 15.20(a), in such a direction as to increase the e.h.t. voltage. On the other hand, the voltage across $L3,C3$ applied to the collector of the output

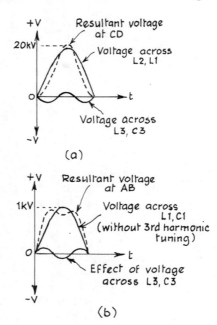

Fig. 15.20 *Third harmonic tuning.*

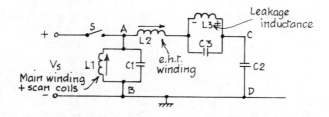

Fig. 15.19 *Approximate equivalent circuit of line output transformer.*

transistor, Fig. 15.20(b), has the effect of reducing the peak voltage across the output transistor which is clearly desirable. Also, since the voltage across $L3, C3$ is zero at the end of flyback there is less chance of striations appearing on the picture.

A common method of tuning the leakage inductance is by adding a single or two extra windings: the latter arrangement is shown in Fig. 15.21. Here windings w_3 and w_4 increase the coupling between the main and e.h.t. windings thereby reducing the leakage inductance. By varying the turns of these two windings, the leakage inductance may be tuned to about three times the flyback frequency (third harmonic tuning).

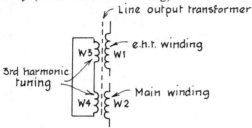

Fig. 15.21 Method of tuning the leakage inductance.

In some receivers the leakage inductance is tuned to **five times the flyback frequency** (see Fig. 15.22). This technique provides a relatively flat-topped pulse for the e.h.t. rectifier

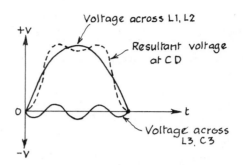

Fig. 15.22 Fifth harmonic tuning.

and improves the e.h.t. regulation. Often a variable inductor is fitted between the main and e.h.t. windings for factory tuning.

RASTER SHAPE CORRECTION

In a monochrome receiver **pin-cushion distortion** of the raster is corrected by small permanent magnets fitted on the deflection coil assembly. This method of correction cannot be used in a colour receiver as the fields of the magnets would upset purity and convergence. If correction is carried out at the deflection centre (that is via the deflection coils) then purity and convergence will be unaffected. An idea of the nature of the correction required is given in Fig. 15.23(b) and (c).

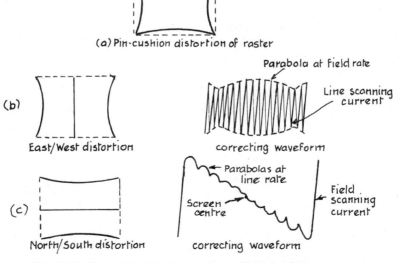

Fig. 15.23 Pin-cushion distortion and correcting waveforms.

The **east/west component** of distortion is corrected by modulating the line scan current with a parabola at field rate. This has the effect of reducing the line scan amplitude at top and bottom of the picture compared to the centre thus straightening out the vertical edges of the raster. To correct the **north/south component** of distortion the field scan current is modulated with parabolas at line rate. This has the effect of slowing down the rate of downward movement of the beams halfway through each line scan over the first part of the field scan and to increase the rate of downward movement at the centre of each line scan over the second part of the field scan.

Pin-Cushion Correction (90° tubes)

In receivers fitted with 90° delta gun tubes the most common method of correcting pin-cushion raster distortion is to employ a transductor connected between the line and field scan coils so as to introduce some cross-modulation.

The essential circuit is shown in Fig. 15.24(a), where I_F and I_L are the field and line scanning currents respectively. The transductor consists of an E core made of ferroxcube with windings on all three limbs.

East-West Correction

For east-west correction the windings $L3$ and $L4$ act as a shunt load on the line scan coils thereby by-passing some of the deflection current. The amount of current that by-passes the line scan coil is made proportional to the field scan current.

$L3$ and $L4$ (the load windings) are wound so that the line current in them produces fluxes through $L1/L2$ in opposite directions. Thus there is no transformer action between $L3,L4$ and $L1,L2$. During the middle of the field scan when the current in $L1,L2$ is small, the limbs of the transductor are unsaturated and the inductive reactance of $L3$ and $L4$ is high. As a result $L3,L4$ shunt little of the line scan current. Suppose that the field scan current of

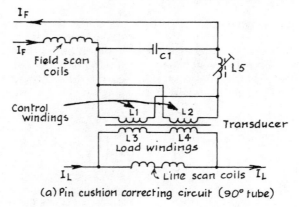

(a) Pin cushion correcting circuit (90° tube)

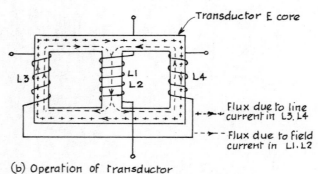

(b) Operation of transductor

Fig. 15.24 Pin-cushion transductor.

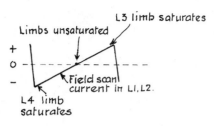

Fig. 15.25 Effect of field scan current on saturation of left and right hand limbs of transductor.

Fig. 15.25 is increasing in the positive direction and that the flux produced in the core of the transductor due to current in $L1,L2$ is in the direction shown in Fig. 15.24(b). Note that in the right-hand limb the fluxes due to $L1,L2$ and $L4$ act in opposite directions, but in the left-hand limb they are in the same direction. This causes the magnetic saturation of the left-hand limb to progressively increase as the field scan current amplitude increases. In consequence, the inductive reactance of $L3$ decreases causing the load windings to shunt more of the line scan current. Similarly, when the field scan current increases in the negative direction the magnetic saturation of $L4$ limb increases, reducing the inductive reactance of $L4$ which again causes the load windings to shunt more current from the line scan coils. Due to the magnetic properties of the core material the change in magnetic saturation causes a parabolic modulation of the line deflection current.

North-South Correction

We have seen that during east-west correction one of the two outer limbs saturates. When this occurs the fluxes due to the line currents in $L3$ and $L4$ no longer cancel in the centre limb. As a result there is then transformer action between $L3,L4$ and $L1,L2$, *i.e.* an e.m.f. will be induced in $L1,L2$. This e.m.f. takes the form of pulses at line frequency since during saturation of each limb the line currents flowing in $L3,L4$ will alternately increase and decrease the saturation of the limbs during each half of the line scan. The pulses induced into $L1,L2$ will change polarity according to which limb becomes saturated during the field scan. $L5,C1$ integrate the pulses from $L1,L2$ to produce an approximate parabolic voltage

across $C1$. This voltage causes a parabolic correcting current to flow in the field scan coils. Control over the adjustment in the north-south direction is provided by $L5$.

Pin-Cushion Correction (110° tubes)

Greater pin-cushion distortion errors occur with 110° than with 90° tubes and it is no longer possible to obtain adequate correction with the transductor just described.

In 110° receivers, **individual N-S and E-W correction circuits** are included in the **field and line timebase sections** of the receiver.

East-West Correction

For east-west correction a **diode modulator** connected in the line output stage is normally employed. There are two types of diode modulator used; the low voltage and high voltage type. In the **low voltage type** the diodes operate at the normal **scan–rectifying voltages** whereas **one of the diodes** in the **high voltage type** operates as an energy recovery diode at the **same voltage as the line output transistor**.

A basic circuit for a low voltage diode modulator is given in Fig. 15.26(a). In effect the line current is modulated by including in series with the line scan coils a 'variable loss' inductor $L1$. When the losses of $L1$ are large, maximum current flows in the line scan coils producing maximum width. Conversely, when $L1$ is exhibiting small losses, minimum current flows in the line scan coils causing minimum picture width. By varying the losses of $L1$ in a **parabolic manner at field rate** the desired correction may be achieved.

The turns ratio between the main winding w_1 of the line output transformer and an additional winding w_2 is about 5:1. During the line **scan** a voltage (V_1) of about 28 V is induced in w_2 with the polarity shown. The ratio of $L2$ to $L1$ is about 4:1 and since (neglecting $C3$) these are effectively across w_1 as far as a.c. is concerned, the voltage across $L1$ (V_2) is also 28 V during the scan. During the line scan $D1$ and $D2$ conduct to provide l.t. supplies of 28 V. $D1$ rectifies the voltage across w_2 with $C1$ acting as reservoir capacitor to provide a 28 V supply for the transistor stages of the receiver. $D2$ rectifies the voltage across $L1$ with $C3$ acting as a reservoir capacitor to

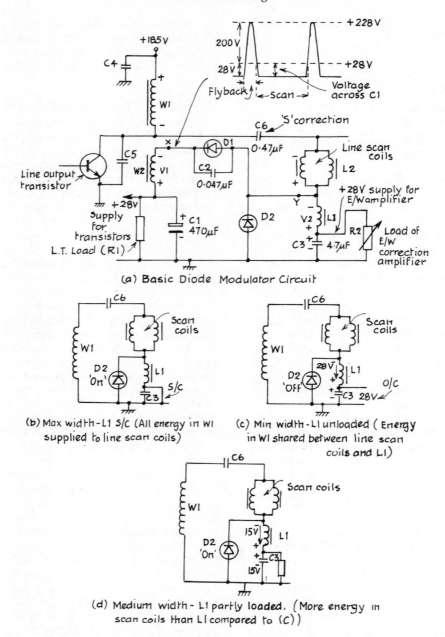

(a) Basic Diode Modulator Circuit

(b) Max width - L1 S/c (All energy in W1 supplied to line scan coils)

(c) Min width - L1 unloaded (Energy in W1 shared between line scan coils and L1)

(d) Medium width - L1 partly loaded. (More energy in scan coils than L1 compared to (c))

Fig. 15.26 E-W raster correction (110° tubes) using Low Voltage Diode Modulator.

provide a 28 V supply for the E-W amplifier which provides a variable load across C3, represented by the variable resistor R2. The waveform shown at point X gives the reference levels when C1 has charged to 28 V. As the load (R1) draws current from C1 its voltage will fall causing the scan voltage to fall below zero. This will cause D1 to conduct to replenish the charge lost by C1. Since during the scan, the waveform at point Y is of the same magnitude, the same d.c. reference levels apply due to the 28 V across C3. As the loading across C3 is increased, D2 conducts harder to replenish the charge lost by C3.

If the variable load across $C3$ is a s/c as in Fig. 15.26(b), $L1$ is effectively shorted out since point Y is connected to chassis by the conducting $D2$. Under this condition all of the scanning energy from w_1 is supplied to the line scan coils resulting in maximum picture width. When the variable load across $C3$ is o/c as in Fig. 15.26(c), $D2$ is off (as long as $C3$ holds its charge) and the scanning energy is shared between the scan coils and $L1$, resulting in minimum width. With an intermediate load across $C3$ as in Fig. 15.26(d), $C3$ is only partly damped by the E-W amplifier and the voltage across $L1$ will reach, say, 15 V during the scan. Under this condition, $L1$ appears more lossy than in situation (c) and a greater amount of scan energy is fed to the line coils than in (c) resulting in medium picture width.

During the flyback $D1$ and $D2$ are reversed biased and the only connection between points X and Y is $C2$. This capacitor is necessary to maintain constant tuning of the line output transformer since the inductance of $L2$ and $L1$ in series varies with the modulation from the E-W amplifier. The flyback voltage at X is constant but that at Y varies with the loading of $C3$, thus the charge held by $C2$ varies with the loading during E-W correction. This is equivalant to connecting $C2$ between the upper end of w_2 and points partly way down

the winding. The reflected capacitance due to $C2$ across the fifth harmonic tuning capacitor $C5$ compensates for variations in inductance loading. In this way, the tuning of the transformer and e.h.t. is kept constant.

Width control may also be affected by the diode modulator circuit by varying the steady loading across $C3$. The diode modulator for east-west correction is used in both delta gun and in-line 110° c.r.ts.

A basic circuit for a high voltage diode modulator is shown in Fig. 15.27. It has the advantage of not requiring a matched secondary winding (such as w_2 in Fig. 15.26) on the line output transformer or a d.c. load circuit.

The circuit consists of two series connected flyback capacitors ($C1$ and $C2$) in parallel with the modulating diodes $D1$ and $D2$ connected across the line scan coils $L1$ and the modulating inductor $L2$. $C3$ is the 'S' correction capacitor. The modulator is called 'high voltage' since $D1$ is connected to the collector of the line output transistor $TR1$.

The width of the picture is determined by the scan voltage across $L1$. If this voltage is altered the width of the picture is changed. During the first part of the line scan when $TR1$ conducts, current flows in $L1$, $L2$ and $TR1$ whilst during the second part of the line scan energy is recovered from $L1$ by $D1$ and from

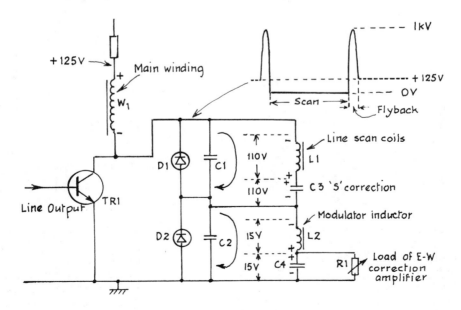

Fig. 15.27 Basic circuit of high voltage diode modulator.

L2 by *D2*. With a 125 V supply, there will be 125 V induced into w_1 during the scan period and this voltage is shared between *L1* and *L2*. If the average voltage induced into *L2* is about 15 V there will be 110 V induced into *L1*.

If *C4* is short-circuited by the load of the east-west correction circuit, the lower end of *L1* is effectively connected to chassis as regards a.c. via the conducting *D2* and 125 V will be induced into *L1* during the first part of the line scan. With a larger voltage across *L1* the picture width will be increased. On the other hand if the load presented across *C4* is open circuit there will be a greater voltage induced into *L2* and the voltage across *L1* will be less than 110 V, hence the picture width is reduced.

During flyback, the energy stored in *L1* flows into *C1* and that in *L2* flows into *C2*. If the values of *C1* and *C2* are chosen so that $L1C1 = L2C2$ then both circuit loops will have the same flyback time.

It is now necessary to consider the circuit for producing the variable loading. One example is given in Fig. 15.28 which drives a diode modulator in a receiver employing a 110° 20AX in-line tube.

The input to the circuit is a field sawtooth voltage developed across sensing resistors *R1* and *R2* which carry the field scanning current. This voltage waveform is applied to *TR1* base via a clipping circuit consisting of *R3,D1,D2* and *R5* which rounds the top and bottom of the waveform. *R5* adjusts the amount of rounding to provide correction in the four corners of the raster. *TR1* stage is connected as a Miller integrator with feedback from collector to base via *C1* and *C2*. Thus a basic parabolic waveform is obtained at the collector which is modified by the feedback network *R9*, *C3* and *R8*, also *R7* in the collector to base feedback path. The amplitude of the output parabola is adjusted by *R10*, the lower end of which is taken to a suitable d.c. bias via *R12* to avoid interaction with the width control. *R10* adjusts the amount of pin-cushion correction along the centre horizontal axis of the raster.

TR2, *TR3* and *TR4* form a Darlington trio driver stage providing a high current gain and low output impedance. The emitter voltage for *TR4* is supplied from the diode modulator and *R17* provides negative voltage feedback for the Darlington circuit. At *TR2* base a small amount of sawtooth voltage is added to the parabola input to provide some tilt. When the input to *TR2* base is most negative, *i.e.* at the centre of the field scan, *TR2* is driven hard which in turn drives *TR3* and *TR4* hard. Thus

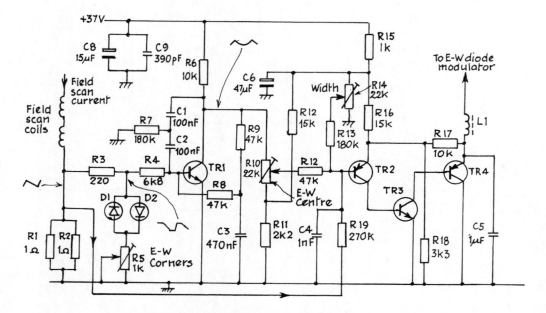

Fig. 15.28 E-W raster shape correction circuit (Dynatron).

the resistance of *TR*4 is low and the loaded capacitor (*C*3 of Fig. 15.26) is heavily loaded which increases the picture width. Towards the commencement and end of the field scan when the input to *TR*2 is less negative, the Darlington trio is driven less hard and the resistance of *TR*4 is increased which tends to reduce the picture width. *R*14 adjusts the d.c. level of the parabola applied to *TR*2 and the control thus acts as picture width. The choke *L*1 ensures that the E-W drive circuit presents a high impedance to the diode modulator at line frequency; at field frquency *L*1 is ineffective. Also, together with *C*5, the choke prevents line frequency currents from entering *TR*4 stage.

Similar circuits may be used for 30AX tubes but the amount of correction required depends upon such factors as tube type, gun structure and deflection coil assembly. East-West correction circuits may be fabricated in i.c. form such as the TDA 4950 used in the Ferguson ICC5 (IMC) Series colour televisions.

North-South Correction

North-south pin-cushion distortion is generally less severe than east-west distortion and in some receivers is not used. However, with the larger screen 110° receivers where its effect is more noticeable coupled with the trend to produce picture geometry of higher quality, north-south correction circuits will be incorporated. An interesting arrangement used by TCE is shown in Fig. 15.29.

Here pin-cushion correction is obtained by introducing a sine wave correction current at line frequency into the field scan current. The operation of the circuit is as follows.

*D*1 and *D*2 form a diode modulator bridge in conjunction with resistors *R*3, *R*4 and *R*5 and is supplied with waveforms at line and field frequency. Equal but opposite phase line frequency waveforms are a.c. coupled to the diodes and these waveforms become balanced about the steady + 25 V fed to *D*1 anode and *D*2 cathode as shown. The common junction of the diodes is also at + 25 V. During the flyback period of the pulses *D*1 and *D*2

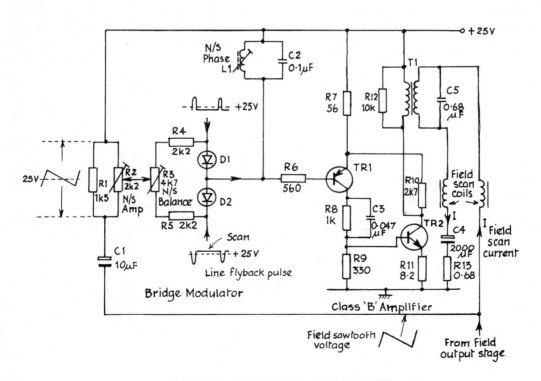

Fig. 15.29 N-S raster shape correction (TCE).

conduct but during the scan period the diodes are OFF. When the diodes conduct (with only the line waveforms applied), the diode bridge is balanced since the line pulses cancel at the junction of the diodes.

A field sawtooth voltage, a.c. coupled via $C1$, is developed across $R1$ and $R2$. This waveform becomes balanced about $+25$ V as shown. A portion of the waveform is applied from $R2$ to the two diodes via $R3$, $R4$ and $R5$ which unbalances the bridge. For the positive half of the field scan waveform, $D1$ conducts harder than $D2$ causing the voltage at the junction of the diodes to rise above $+25$ V when the diodes are ON and return to $+25$ V when the diodes are OFF. The reverse action takes place during the negative half of the field scan when $D2$ conducts harder than $D1$. The voltage at the junction of the diodes thus takes the form shown in Fig. 15.30(a) (neglecting the effect of $L1$, $C2$). Due to the presence of $L1$, $C2$ however, the pulse output at the diode junction causes $L1$, $C2$ to ring at line frequency as shown in Fig. 15.30(b). Note that when the polarity of the pulses in (a) change, the sine wave ringing changes phase by $180°$.

Waveform (b) is now applied to the base of $TR1$ which, together with $TR2$, forms a class-B amplifier. $TR1$ and $TR2$ will thus only conduct on the negative half-cycles of the input to $TR1$

base. The resulting half-sine current pulses in $TR2$ are fed to the primary of $T1$, the secondary of which is tuned to line frequency by $C5$. The pulses cause the secondary to ring and modulate the field scan current passing through $T1$ secondary as shown in Fig. 15.30(c).

Although sine wave correction is used for convenience (it should be parabolic) the correction is not exactly right, but is adequate in practice. Because sine wave correction is used and the phase of the sine wave ringing introduced by $L1$, $C2$ may not coincide with the phase of the locked line timebase, $L1$ is made adjustable so that the correction is applied in the centre of each line scan as is required. $R1$ adjusts the amplitude of field sawtooth applied to the diode bridge and thus sets the amplitude of the sine wave correction. $R3$ allows one diode to have more field sawtooth than the other diode thereby permitting a greater amount of correction to be applied at the top or bottom of the screen.

In both north-south and east-west correction circuits, some **sawtooth component** is often added to the basic parabolic correction to compensate for **keystone (trapezium) distortion** of the raster. Some typical raster distortions and their correction are given in Fig. 15.31.

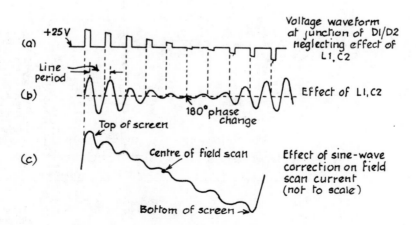

Fig. 15.30 Waveform associated with circuit of Fig. 15.29.

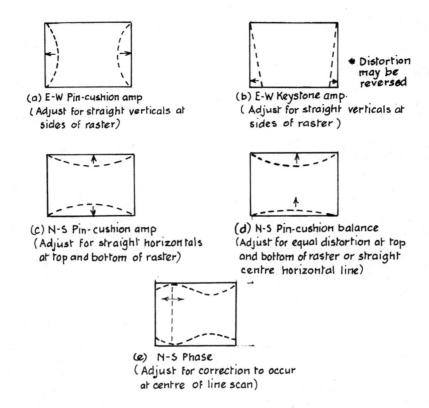

(a) E-W Pin-cushion amp
(Adjust for straight verticals at
  sides of raster)

(b) E-W Keystone amp.
(Adjust for straight verticals at
  sides of raster)

✳ Distortion
  may be
  reversed

(c) N-S Pin-cushion amp
(Adjust for straight horizontals
 at top and bottom of raster)

(d) N-S Pin-cushion balance
(Adjust for equal distortion at top
 and bottom of raster or straight
 centre horizontal line)

(e) N-S Phase
(Adjust for correction to occur
  at centre of line scan)

Fig. 15.31 *Raster shape errors and their corrections in receivers using RCA 110° precision-in-line tube.*

CHAPTER SIXTEEN

VERTICAL SCAN CIRCUITS

Objectives

1 To show the basic principle of sawtooth forming for the field timebase.
2 To consider the operation of discrete and i.c. field oscillator and output stages.
3 To study the basic action of the flyback booster and to show its application in i.cs.
4 To outline the operation of a switched-mode field output stage.
5 To trace the signal path for a class 'B' fully integrated field i.c. for use with the 30AX system.

THE BASIC FUNCTION of this section of the receiver is to deliver a linear sawtooth current at 50 Hz to the field scan coils to produce vertical deflection of the electron beam(s) of the c.r.t. A practical arrangement used in solid state receivers is given in Fig. 16.1.

The master timing for field deflection is provided by an approximate sawtooth voltage output from the free-running field oscillator. This stage is kept in sync. by the locking pulse output of the field integrator. As power transistors capable of delivering up to several amperes peak are used in the output stage, the base current input must be comparitively high, say, 20–50 mA. Thus to avoid placing too great a load on the field oscillator stage, a driver amplifier is used to provide the base current drive to the output stage. An emitter-follower amplifier is often chosen for the driver stage function as this configuration provides a good match between the high output impedance of the field oscillator and the low input impedance of the output stage. Also, the isolation from the output stage given by the driver

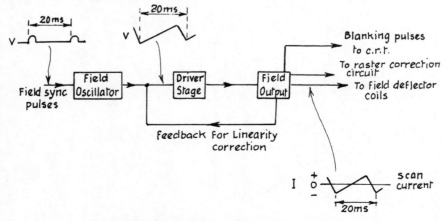

Fig. 16.1 Basic arrangement of field timebase.

permits a more stable operation of the field oscillator.

Unlike its line output counterpart, the field output stage operates as an **amplifier** and not as a switch (except for switched-mode field deflection). Its function is to raise the current drive at its input to about 1·0–2·0 A peak-to-peak for full vertical scan of the display tube and with good linearity. Some form of negative feedback may be used to correct for non-linear operation of the transistors and often positive feedback is employed via a suitable circuit to correct for the shape of the exponential output from the sawtooth oscillator.

The field output stage will also provide flyback suppression pulses for the c.r.t. and an output to the east-west raster correction circuit. North-south raster correction (see Chapter 15) may also be applied to the field deflection coil circuit.

FIELD OSCILLATOR AND OUTPUT

Discrete Circuit Versions

Field Oscillator

The basic principle used in the field time-base is shown in Fig. 16.2. To produce an approximate sawtooth voltage a *CR* network and a switch are used. When *S* is opened (instant t_o) *C* charges towards the supply rail via *R* causing the voltage across *C* to rise exponentially. At instant t_1, *S* is closed which allows *C* to rapidly discharge via the low resistance of the switch, and for the voltage across *C* to rapidly fall. If the switch is now opened once more at instant t_2, the capacitor will commence to recharge exponentially again via *R*. Thus if the switch is opened and closed regularly at the correct instants a repetitive voltage waveform of approximate sawtooth shape will be developed across *C*. In practice, the switch is formed by the field oscillator which due to its free-running action allows *C* to alternately charge and discharge at regular intervals. The linearity of the scan period of the waveform depends upon the time-constant of *CR* in relation to the time interval that the switch is opened. Employing a time constant which is long compared with the period that the switch is opened reduces the non-linearity as only a small section of the charging curve is used.

A popular field oscillator in portable monochrome receivers and some early colour receivers was the blocking oscillator and the basic circuit of one arrangement is shown in Fig. 16.3. *T1* is the blocking transformer and *C1*, *R1* and *R2* form the frequency-determining components with values chosen to provide a free-running frequency of approximately 50 Hz. The field-hold control *R2* allows the frequency of operation to be set below that of the incoming sync. pulses so that correct synchronism is achieved. Negative-going field sync. from the field pulse integrator is applied to *TR1* collector via *C4* and *R6*. These pulses appear as positive-going pulses at *TR1* base (due to reversal by *T1*) and initiate the commencement of field flyback when *TR1* comes hard ON. During the field scan when *TR1* is OFF, *C1* discharges via *R1* and *R2*. *D1* damps the overswing at *T1* secondary when

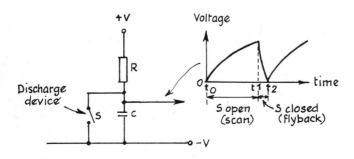

Fig. 16.2 Principle of forming the field sawtooth voltage waveform.

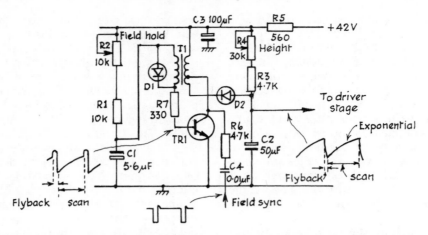

Fig. 16.3 Basic circuit of blocking oscillator field oscillator stage with sawtooth forming CR.

*TR*1 switches OFF to prevent the 'ring' from upsetting the circuit operation.

The sawtooth forming network is formed by *C*2 charging up towards the positive supply rail via *R*3 and *R*4. This latter resistor is made variable to serve as the picture height control. During the field scan when *TR*1 is OFF, *C*2 is charging, the voltage across *C*2 rises exponentially. When *TR*1 comes hard ON at the commencement of flyback, *C*2 rapidly discharges via the low resistance path of *D*2, a section of *T*1 primary and *TR*1. *D*2 isolates the sawtooth forming network from *TR*1 collector voltage during the scan period when the diode is reverse biased.

A method frequently used in commercial circuits for linearising the waveform fed to the driver stage is by applying positive feedback

from the field output stage as shown in Fig. 16.4. The sawtooth forming capacitance is now split into two parts *C*2 and *C*5. Both capacitors charge up via *R*3 and *R*4 during the scan and discharge via *D*2 and *TR*1 during flyback. Thus there will be exponential sawtooth waveform V_{e1} and V_{e2} across the capacitors of magnitudes depending upon *C*2,*C*5 relative values. In order to linearise the waveform across the capacitor combination, a feedback voltage taken from the output stage is integrated by *R*7, *R*8 and *C*5 to produce across *C*5, a parabolic type waveform V_p. The actual waveform fed to the driver stage is the sum of three components V_{e1}, V_{e2} and V_p. Control over the amount of correction required is provided by the preset resistor *R*7 and *R*9, and addition of the three components

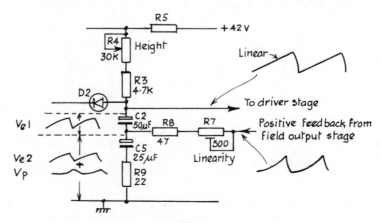

Fig. 16.4 Use of positive feedback and integrating network to linearise sawtooth voltage waveform fed to driver.

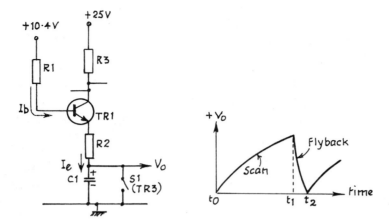

Fig. 16.5 Basic principle of sawtooth forming in Fig. 16.6.

results in a linear sawtooth waveform to the driver stage.

In a number of receivers, a regenerative type switch employing p-n-p and n-p-n transitors is used for the field oscillator. One example is given in Fig. 16.6 and Fig. 16.5 shows the basic principle of operation.

In Fig. 16.5 at switch-on (instant t_0), S1 is open and base current is flowing in *TR1*. The resulting emitter current I_e causes C1 to charge and the voltage across the capacitor rises exponentially (this corresponds to the field scan). At the instant t_1, the switch S is closed and C1 rapidly discharges producing the field flyback. This process is then repeated

when at instant t_2 S1 is opened allowing C1 to be recharged by *TR1* emitter current.

In reality S1 is replaced by *TR3* (see Fig. 16.6) which is controlled by the transistor *TR2*. At switch-on when base current flows in *TR1*, the emitter current of *TR1* is initially large and *TR1* collector voltage is lower than *TR2* base voltage. In consequence, *TR2* is non-conducting and therefore, *TR3* is also non-conducting. This allows C1 to charge and for the voltage across the capacitor to rise exponentially. As the charging of C1 proceeds, the charging current I_e decreases causing *TR1* collector current to also decrease. Thus during the charging of C1 the collector

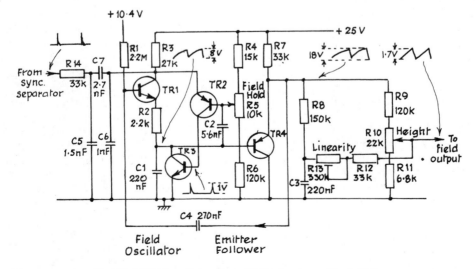

Fig. 16.6 Field oscillator stage (Philips) regenerative switch.

voltage of $TR1$ will be rising and at some particular instant the voltage will be higher than that at $TR2$ base. As a result $TR2$ will become conductive making $TR3$ conductive as well. As soon as $TR3$ becomes conductive a negative-going voltage step occurs at its collector which is passed to the base of $TR2$ via $C2$. This voltage step makes $TR2$, and therefore, also $TR3$, highly conductive. $C1$ is now discharged very rapidly via the conducting transistor $TR3$. When $C1$ ia almost fully discharged, the discharge current through $TR3$ becomes so small that $TR3$ becomes blocked. As a result a positive-going voltage step occurs at $TR3$ collector which is supplied to $TR2$ base via $C2$. This positive-going step cuts off $TR2$ and therefore $TR3$ also cuts off. $C1$ is now recharged by the emitter current of $TR1$ and the voltage across $C1$ rises until $TR2$ becomes conductive when the process is repeated.

The sawtooth voltage across $C1$ is applied to the base of the emitter-follower stage $TR4$. The linearity of this waveform is, however, poor and to improve it the waveform from $TR4$ emitter is fed back to $TR1$ base via $C4$. This feedback is a form of bootstrapping and in addition to linearising the voltage across $C1$ it increases its amplitude. Note that $TR1$ base is supplied from a $10 \cdot 4$ V line, thus without bootstrapping the voltage across $C1$ could not rise above the base line potential.

With no feedback, the effect of the exponential rising voltage across $C1$ is to gradually reduce the base current of $TR1$ and in consequence the emitter charging current. When feedback, is applied as in Fig. 16.7, the rising base voltage compensates for the rising voltage across $C1$ allowing $TR1$ base current to remain more constant. Thus $TR1$ emitter charging current will be more constant and the rise of voltage across $C1$ is made more linear.

The free-running frequency of the oscillator can be adjusted by $R5$ which sets $TR2$ base voltage and hence the instant at which it becomes conductive. To synchronise the oscillator, positive-going field sync. pulses are applied to $TR2$ emitter via the integrating network $R14$, $C5$, $C7$ and $C6$. These pulses determine the precise instant that $TR2$ and $TR3$ become conductive and hence set the instant of the commencement of field flyback.

To provide a linear voltage feed to the field

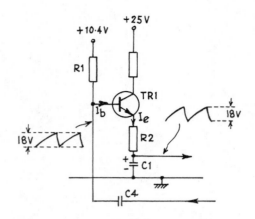

Fig. 16.7 *Use of feedback to improve linearity of voltage across C1.*

output stage, the emitter waveform of $TR4$ is integrated by $R8$, $C3$. The resulting parabolic voltage across $C3$ is then added to the output waveform from the slider of the height control $R10$. The linearity of the current in the field scanning coils is influenced by the voltage across $C3$, and $R13$ (field linearity control) provides some adjustment over the amount of parabolic voltage that is added to the output.

Field Output

The vertical output amplifier may operate in class A, class B or class AB and an example of a class A output stage for use in a small portable receiver is given in Fig. 16.8.

This circuit uses direct coupling between the driver $TR1$ and the output transistor $TR2$. $C1$, $C2$, $R1$ and $R2$ constitute the sawtooth forming network. During the field scan $C1$ and $C2$ charge towards the -12 V supply line and during the field flyback, when $S1$ closes by the action of the field oscillator, the capacitors rapidly discharge via $D1$ and the switch. $TR1$ is the driver stage, connected as an emitter-follower. Its high input impedance reduces the loading on $C1$, $C2$ and its low output impedance allows sufficient base current drive to the output transistor $TR2$. The field deflection coils are fed from the output transistor via choke-capacitance coupling, $L1$ and $C3$.

At the end of flyback when $S1$ is just about to open, $TR1$ base is at chassis potential thus $TR1$ is non-conducting. Therefore $TR2$ is also

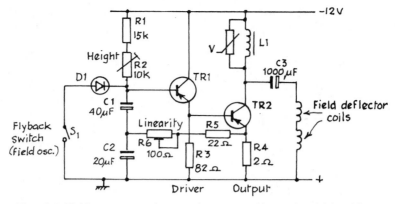

Fig. 16.8 Field output stage in monochrome portable receiver (class 'A').

non-conducting. After S1 has opened and C1, C2 commence to charge, TR1 turns on which causes TR2 also to turn on. Thus an increasing current flows in TR1 and TR2 during the scan period. When flyback occurs and S1 closes, the falling voltage across C1, C2 reduces the current in TR1 and TR2 until at the end of flyback, the collector voltage of TR2 rises above the line supply rail. To prevent damage to TR2, a v.d.r. is connected across L1 to arrest the voltage overswing. Sometimes a diode is used in place of the v.d.r.

The advantage of this circuit arrangement is that the output transistor is conducting throughout the whole of the scan period (class-A operation) thus its mean dissipation is high and efficiency low. Also the choke is bulky and expensive. It should be noted, however, that the choke and capacitor C3 allows the current in the deflector coils to fully reverse during flyback when the energy stored in the choke (during the scan) causes a reversal in the voltage induced in it at the commencement of the flyback period.

Where greater deflection power is required, *i.e.* in receivers employing large screen sizes and deflection angles, a more efficient output stage is needed. Push-pull output stages are the most common and these may feature complementary transistors operating in class B or class AB. An example is given in Fig. 16.9 and is taken from the same receiver

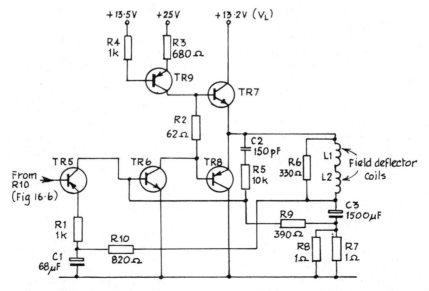

Fig. 16.9 Complimentary output stage (class 'B') associated with field oscillator of Fig. 16.6.

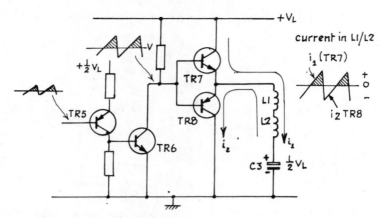

Fig. 16.10 Simplified circuit of Fig. 16.9 showing principle of operation.

as the oscillator stage of Fig. 16.6. The circuit is entirely d.c. coupled and the d.c. conditions are stabilised by d.c. feedback via $R10$. Capacitor $C1$ eliminates any a.c. feedback along this path. A.C. feedback for linearity correction takes place from $R7$, $R8$ via $R9$ to $TR6$ base.

The principle of operation of the output stage may be explained using Fig. 16.10, where the circuit has been simplified and rearranged to show clearly the biasing of $TR6$ ($TR5$ receives its bias from the previous stage shown in Fig. 16.6). At switch-on $C3$ charges to half the line supply voltage. *i.e.* $\frac{1}{2}V_L$, which is the voltage at the commoned emitter connection of $TR7$ and $TR8$. Because of its large value $C3$ performs the same function as a battery of voltage $\frac{1}{2}V_L$. The sawtooth voltage applied to $TR5$ base is amplified by $TR5$ and $TR6$ to produce the drive waveform for the output pair at $TR6$ collector. During the positive periods (shown hatched) at $TR6$ collector, $TR7$ (n-p-n) conducts and $TR8$ (p-n-p) cuts off. Current (i_1) then flows through the deflector coils in the direction shown. During the negative periods at $TR6$ collector, $TR8$ conducts and $TR7$ cuts off. Current (i_2) then flows in the reverse direction through the deflector coils with the d.c. voltage from $C3$ supplying the current in $TR8$.

If the transistors were operated in true class-B, then during the crossover from one transistor to the other, there would be no current in the deflector coils because $TR7$ and $TR8$ require at least $0.7\,\text{V}$ between base and emitter to make them conduct. The effect of

this on the screen would be a bright horizontal line in the middle of the picture corresponding to the crossover halfway through the field scan. To prevent this, $TR9$ and $R2$ are added in the practical circuit of Fig. 16.9. The value of $R2$ is selected to give a small forward bias to $TR7$ and $TR8$ so that there is a small standing current in the output pair. The collector current for $TR6$ and the base current for $TR7$ and $TR8$ are supplied from the current source circuit $TR9$. Resistor $R6$ limits voltage peaks across the deflector coils during flyback and $C2$, $R5$ prevent undesired decays.

Integrated Circuit Versions

I.C. field stages are now the most common. In some receiver designs the field oscillator and driver are fabricated in i.c. form but couple to a discrete transistor output stage. In other designs the complete field timebase function is in i.c. form but the field oscillator and driver are often included in one i.c. device which may also feature sync. pulse separation, line oscillator and flywheel sync. functions with the output stage in a separate i.c. device attached to a suitable heat sink.

Flyback Booster

The supply line voltage fed to the field output stage must be of sufficient voltage to embrace the voltage across the field scan coils for both the scan and flyback periods. The amplitude of the flyback voltage may be reduced by damping the flyback with the aid of

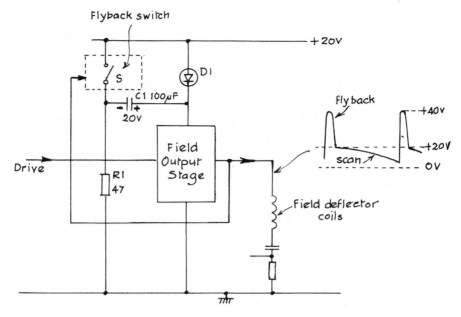

Fig. 16.11 Principle of flyback booster.

a capacitor, resistor or v.d.r. thus reducing the level required of the supply voltage rail.

In many receivers, however, special attention is given to the voltage requirements of the flyback period to enable full reversal of the current in the scan coils to be achieved. This is commonly implemented by using a **flyback booster generator** to increase the supply to the field output stage during the period of the field flyback. This technique saves increasing the steady supply voltage to the output stage producing a power saving of about 50% and a corresponding lowering of heat dissipation.

The principle of the flyback booster is shown in Fig. 16.11. During the scan period the 20 V d.c. supply is applied to the field output stage via the conducting $D1$ and the electronic switch S is open. $C1$ then charges up to the d.c. supply via $R1$ and $D1$. At the commencement of field flyback, S closes (being operated by the flyback pulse) and the voltage across $C1$ is effectively added to the supply rail voltage. This provides a boost in supply voltage to the output stage allowing the current in the scan coils to fully reverse. When S closes, $D1$ cuts-off and $C1$ rapidly loses its charge during the flyback section, thus the boosted supply of 40 V only lasts for a short period.

The field flyback booster principle is commonly adopted and is featured in i.cs. such as the TDA 1044, TDA 1170S and TDA 3651. An example is given in Fig. 16.12 for the TDA 1044 i.c. which uses a discrete transistor output stage.

The i.c. incorporates the field oscillator (Linear Sawtooth Generator block) which is synchronised by field locking pulses applied to pin 8. This stage is supplied with 12 V at pin 12 and has a frequency determined by the value of $C1$ connected to pin 10 and the setting of the field hold control which adjusts the d.c. on pin 11. Feedback from the field output stage via $P1$ adjusts the linearity of the generator sawtooth.

The sawtooth waveform is fed to the 'S' correction block with the amount of 'S' correction set by the value of the components connected to pin 1. Whilst 'S' correction is invariably applied to the line scan (see Chapter 13, Figs 13.16 and 13.17) it is not always applied to the field scan. However, since large screen sizes and large deflection angles exaggerate scan non-linearity in both the horizontal and vertical directions, 'S' correction may be applied to the field scan as in this receiver.

The differential output amplifier of the i.c.

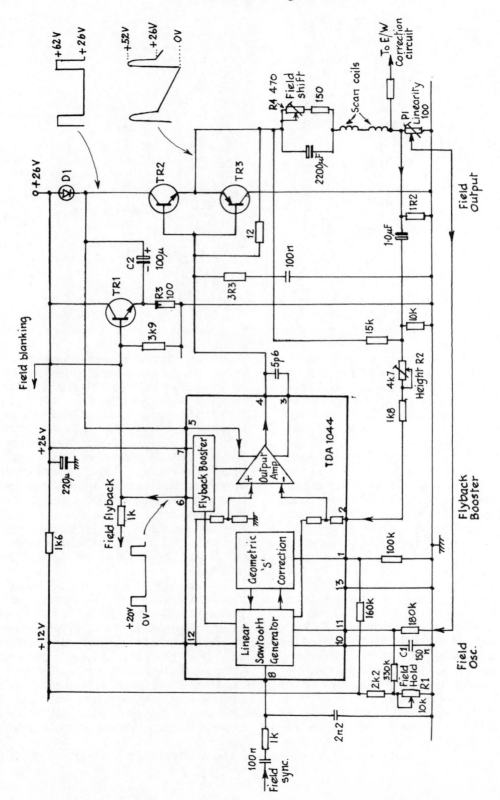

Fig. 16.12 I.C. Field Oscillator with Flyback Booster and Discrete Class 'B' Field Output Stage (TCE).

is an inverting type and is fed on one input with a d.c. from an internal potential divider. The other input is fed with the 'S' corrected sawtooth and also a sawtooth from the field scan coils via the negative feedback which enters on pin 2 by way of the height control $R2$. By varying the amount of feedback, the gain and hence the picture height is controlled. The output on pin 4 goes to a complementary symmetry output stage operating in class 'B' push-pull and comprising the discrete transistors $TR2$ and $TR3$.

Turning now to the flyback booster section when during the field scan the output stage receives $+26$ V, supplied via the conducting $D1$. During this period $C2$ is charged via $R3$ to 26 V. At flyback a positive-going pulse from the flyback booster emerges at pin 6 and causes the emitter follower stage $TR1$ to conduct. This results in the left-hand plate of $C2$ rising to $+26$ V thus causing the right-hand plate to rise to $+52$ V as $D1$ becomes reversed biassed. This voltage is fed to the i.c. output stage at pin 5 and also to the output transistors $TR2$ and $TR3$ thus permitting the scan coil current to reverse as is necessary.

$R4$ (vertical shift) adjusts the amount of d.c. flowing in the field scan coils and thus acts as the field shift control.

Switched-Mode Field Output Stage

All of the small signal functions of the modern television receiver are now fabricated in integrated circuit form. It is mainly in the high voltage and high power areas where discrete transistors are to be found. Field output stages using class 'B' operation in 110° receivers dissipate about 12 W and this power has in the past precluded the use of a fully integrated field timebase and output stage. By using a switched-mode output stage (class 'D') instead of the conventional class 'B', the power dissipation may be reduced to 5 W which enables the output stage to be included in the i.c. Switched-mode field deflection was first developed for use with 110° 20AX in-line colour tubes.

The basic principle of switched-mode field deflection is shown in Fig. 16.13. If a train of pulses with a constant and equal mark-to-space ratio are fed to a low-pass filter as shown in Fig. 16.13(a), the output voltage of the filter will be equal to half the peak amplitude of the pulses, *i.e.* the mean value of the pulses.

Consider now the output of the filter if it is fed with a train of pulses of increasing width as in Fig. 16.13(b). Since the LC filter will give the average value of the pulses at every instant, the output will be low at the start of the pulse train and near to the peak value of the pulses at the end. Thus the output of the filter will be a rising ramp voltage as shown.

In practice the pulse width modulated train is fed to the field output stage as shown Fig. 16.13(c). The pulses switch the i.c. output transistors ON and OFF and their resultant pulsed output is supplied to the deflector coils

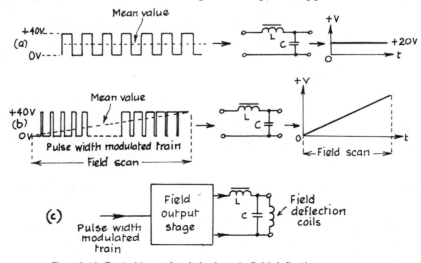

Fig. 16.13 Basic ideas of switched-mode field deflection.

via the *LC* filter which ensures that a linear rising current flows in the coils. Since with switched-mode operation the output transistors are either fully ON or fully OFF, *i.e.* act as switches, the power dissipation in them is quite small. Thus the efficiency of the arrangement is improved when compared with conventional class-B field output stages.

The pulse-width modulated train is produced using analogue-to-digital conversion and the basic principle is shown in Fig. 16.14. A 50 Hz sawtooth and a 150 kHz triangular waveform (both generated within the i.c.) are fed to separate inputs of a differential amplifier (1) as in Fig. 16.14(a). When the amplitude of the triangular input is greater than that of the sawtooth input, the output from the differential amplifier switches ON the common-emitter amplifier (2); the output is then at a low voltage state. During the periods when the amplitude of the triangular input is less than the sawtooth, amplifier (2) is OFF and the output is at a high voltage state. In Fig. 16.14(b) the shaded area represents the conduction of amplifier (2). At the start of the scan period the shaded area is wide and amplifier (2) is ON for long periods. Halfway through the scan, amplifier (2) is ON and OFF for equal periods whilst at the end of the scan where the shaded area is narrow the amplifier is ON for short periods. For the field flyback

period, once this has been initiated by the sawtooth input, the output of amplifier (2) remains at a low voltage state as the result of the action of a feedback loop (not shown in this diagram). Thus, for a period of approximately 1 ms in every 20 ms, the system is not switched at high frequency.

A block diagram of the TDA 2600 switched-mode field deflection i.c. is given in Fig. 16.15 together with the essential external circuitry.

The 50 Hz sawtooth waveform is generated in block (2) with the timing controlled by the external timing resistor $R2$ and the split capacitors $C1$, $C2$. Negative-going sync. is applied from $R1$ to pin 11 of the i.c. A sync. inverter [block (1)] is provided to accommodate positive-going sync. signals. The sawtooth output is available at pin 10 and a portion is integrated by $R3$, $C2$ and applied to the junction of $C1$ and $C2$. This modifies the linearity of the waveform at pin 12. Resistor $R5$ provides some control of the final linearity. The sawtooth output is also fed forward from the potentiometer $R4$ (which serves as the height control) to the input of the preamplifier [block (5)] on pin 7. Also a.c. coupled to pin 7 is a feedback signal from the deflection current sensing resistor $R6$. This feedback signal is responsible for locking the output of the common emitter stage of Fig. 16.14(a) in one state during the field flyback period.

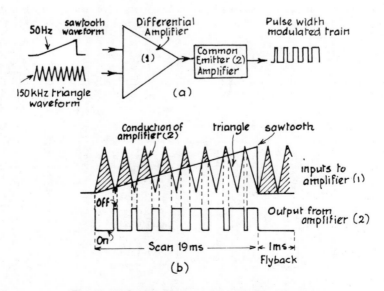

Fig. 16.14 Generating the pulse-width modulated train.

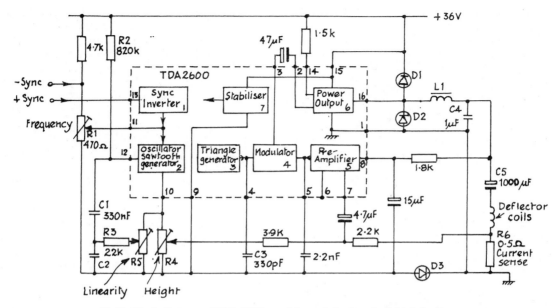

16.15 Block diagram of TDA 2600 used for switched-mode field deflection.

The sawtooth output of block (5) together with the mixed feedback signal is fed to one input of the modulator [block (4)] which contains the differential amplifier discussed in connection with Fig. 16.14. The other input to the modulator comes from the 150 kHz triangle waveform generator [block (3)]. The timing of the triangle output waveform from this block is controlled by the external capacitor C3. The modulator thus produces a pulse width modulated train as previously described and this is fed to the field output stage [block (6)].

Two Darlington pairs are used for the field output stage arranged as an 'upper' and a 'lower' pair. The modulator output switches the upper and lower pairs alternately ON and OFF at the switching rate of 150 kHz. To reconstitute the 50 Hz sawtooth drive to the deflector coils the output from block (6) is fed via the low-pass filter L1, C4. This filter removes the switching ripple and supplies a sawtooth current to the field scanning coils via C5. D1 and D2, connected external to the i.c., are energy-recovery diodes and return the stored energy in the inductor L1 to the supply rails.

In practice L1 is replaced by a tapped choke to avoid a bright-up across the centre horizon-tal region of the raster which is caused by dissimilarities in the clamping levels of the i.c. output transistors and their associated diodes.

Fully Integrated Field Stages

An example is shown in Fig. 16.16 for the TDA 2653A. This i.c. incorporates the field oscillator, sawtooth generator, buffer stage and output stage together with flyback booster.

This i.c. is intended for use in large screen receivers adopting the 30AX or PIL-S4 systems. The lower power requirements of the 30AX scan coils permits a class 'B' output stage to be used. Typically the 30AX field coils have a resistance of 6·2 ohms, an inductance of 10 mH and require about 2·1 A peak-to-peak scanning current. With a class 'B' output stage, the maximum power dissipation for the i.c. is only about 4·8 W with some 2·9 W dissipated in the scan coil load. In this case the class 'B' stage compares favourably with the switched-mode output stage and has the advantage of a relatively simpler circuit arrangement.

The frequency of the field oscillator is determined by the value of C1 connected to pin 13 and the variable resistor R1 (field hold)

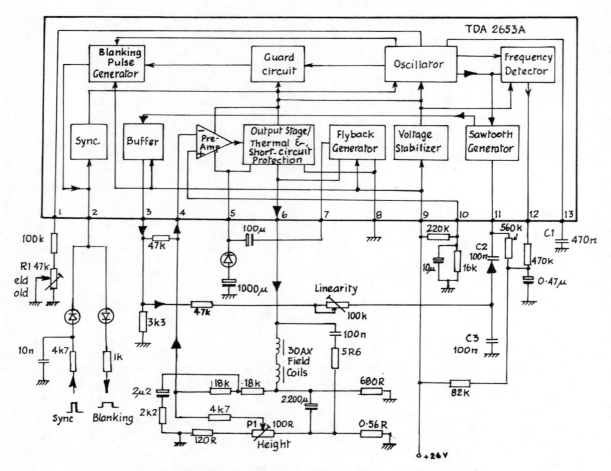

Fig. 16.16 *Fully integrated field stages with class 'B' output using TDA 2653A I.C.*

connected to pin 1. The oscillator is synchronised by positive-going field sync. at 1–12 V in amplitude applied to pin 2. An output from the oscillator is supplied to a sawtooth generator with the sawtooth forming capacitor comprising C2 and C3 connected to pin 11. The output from the sawtooth generator is fed to a buffer stage whose output is supplied from pin 3 to pin 4, the pre-amplifier input. The sawtooth output is also supplied from pin 3 via a shaping network which includes R2 (field linearity) to pin 11.

The pre-amplifier has two inputs applied to the inverting input; one input is the buffered

sawtooth arriving on pin 4 and the other is an a.c. feedback signal from the scan coils adjusted by P1. This control sets the gain of the pre-amplifier and hence the picture height. The output of the pre-amp drives the class 'B' output stage which supplies a linear sawtooth current to the field scan coils connected to pin 6. The output stage is protected against a short-circuited load and a thermal cut-out is included that switches off the circuit if the temperature inside the i.c. exceeds about 175°C. A flyback generator is included to boost the voltage to the output stage during the period of the field flyback.

CHAPTER SEVENTEEN

POWER SUPPLIES

Objectives
1 To outline the features of a high current regulated supply.
2 To explain the basic operating principles of forward and flyback switched-mode stabilisers.
3 To show examples of practical circuits for switched-mode power supplies including synchronised types.

STABILISATION

A NUMBER OF different stabilised d.c. supplies are required in a modern colour television receiver, *e.g.* 5 V, 12 V, 25 V, 95 V and 190 V as well as the high voltage supplies for the c.r.t.; 400 V (A_1): 5 kV (focus anode): 22 kV (final anode).

Stabilised supplies are needed to avoid changes in picture height, width and focus as well as variation in vision or sound signal processing due to changes in the mains supply voltage or current demand of the various circuits, particularly the high current ones such as the line output stage. Relatively simple stabilising circuits may be used for supply lines feeding low current circuits, but more complex arrangements are employed for high current circuits such as the field or line output stage.

Some of the desirable features of a high current regulated power supply, illustrated by Figure 17.1 are:

(a) V_{out} remains substantially constant in spite of any increases or decreases in V_{in} to the regulator from the mains rectifier.

(b) V_{out} remains substantially constant in spite of any normal increase or decrease in the load current I_L.

(c) Protection should be offered to the load circuit if V_{out} rises above a set level (excessive voltage protection).

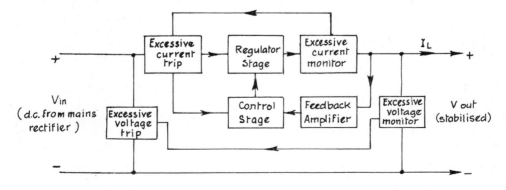

Fig. 17.1 Basic elements of high current regulated supply in colour receiver.

(d) Protection should be offered to the power supply itself in the event of excess-current being drawn by the load due to a fault condition (excessive current protection).

In addition, some form of 'slow start-up' should be used to limit switch-on surges.

Regulator Stage

This stage forms the heart of the stabilised power supply. A series transistor may be used whose effective resistance may be varied in order to obtain a constant output voltage. The disadvantage of this form of stabilising element is that energy dissipated in the device is lost causing a lowering of efficiency particularly at high currents, also the heat generated raises the temperature inside the receiver cabinet.

In early solid state receivers, an SCR employing phase control was used as the stabilising element to provide a high voltage-high current supply to the line driver and line output stage. All other d.c. supplies including the c.r.t. heater supply were obtained by scan rectification of voltages induced into additional windings of the line output transformer. The main disadvantage of thyristor controlled supplies is that unless a mains transformer is used, the chassis of the receiver is live no matter which way round the mains input is connected.

The most common form of regulator used in the majority of current receivers is a 'switch' element which forms part of a 'switched-mode' power supply. This series switch element is alternatively fully 'on' and fully 'off'. When fully 'on' there is no power dissipated when passing current since ideally there is no voltage drop (in practice due to its small resistance there will be a small voltage drop and some small power dissipation). When the device is fully 'off' there is no current flow so there is no power dissipation. By varying the 'closed' to 'open' time of the switch element, the mean power to the load can be varied. This is the essential principle of switching-mode stabilisers.

SWITCHING-MODE STABILISERS

Basic Circuits

(a) Forward Converter

If the 'regulator' or 'stabiliser' is a switch which is alternatively closed and opened, when opened no energy will be fed to the load. Since continuous energy is required by the load it is necessary to use some form of energy storing device and an inductor is used for this purpose. The basic arrangement of a switched-mode (forward converter) stabiliser is given in Fig. 17.2.

The d.c. input to the circuit is obtained by rectifying the a.c. mains with $C1$ acting as reservoir capacitor. When the switch S is closed, current flows round the circuit and through the load in the direction shown in Fig. 17.2(a). The current flowing in $L1$ causes a magnetic field to be set up and energy is stored in this field. If the switch is now opened as in Fig. 17.2(b) the magnetic field around $L1$ collapses inducing a voltage V_L into the inductor. This voltage causes $D1$ to conduct which maintains the current in the load in the same direction as previously. Thus, when the switch is opened, the load uses the energy stored in the inductor with $D1$ acting as an 'efficiency' diode. $C2$ is a smoothing capacitor.

The output voltage will depend upon how much current flows when the switch is closed.

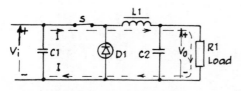

(a) Current flow when switch is closed

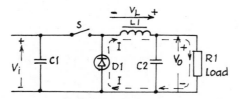

(b) Current flow when switch is open

Fig. 17.2 Basic circuit of switching mode stabiliser (Forward converter).

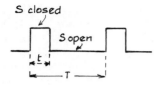

Fig. 17.3 Switching waveform.

If the time that the switch is closed can be varied, the output voltage may be varied. In practice, *S* is an electronic switch fed with a switching waveform like that shown in Fig. 17.3. The ratio of the time *t* that the switch is closed to the periodic time *T* is known as the 'duty cycle', and the magnitude of the output voltage is given by:

$$V_\mathrm{o} = V_\mathrm{i}\frac{t}{T}.$$

The circuit may be used as a stabiliser by detecting any changes in the output voltage V_o and correcting it by altering the ratio of t/T.

The basic arrangement of the switching-mode or 'chopper' supply used in T.C.E. 3000 receivers is given in Fig. 17.4. This circuit provides a constant voltage of 65 V at 2 A for the line, field and sound output stages.

In place of the switch in Fig. 17.2 we now have a transistor *TR*1 (the chopper). This is fed

with 240 V d.c. on its collector from a half-wave rectifier *D*1 connected to a suitable point on the mains input auto-transformer *T*2. *C*1 acts as a reservoir capacitor. *TR*1 is switched ON and OFF at line rate with pulses applied between its base and emitter from the secondary of *T*1. When *TR*1 is ON current flows in the load, taking the path shown by the broken line and causing energy to be stored in the inductor *L*1. During the interval that *TR*1 is OFF the voltage induced into *L*1 maintains the current in the load which now takes the path indicated by the arrows via the conducting *D*2. *C*2 smoothes out the switching ripple (15,625 Hz).

*TR*1 must have a very fast 'turn-on' and 'turn-off' capability at several amperes. The energy fed into *L*1 is in bursts of about 18 μs duration. The source impedance of the power supply is extremely low (about 1 ohm) and the circuit efficiency is around 80% thereby reducing the power dissipation from 260 W to 180 W for a typical colour receiver. The high frequency used for the operation of the chopper enables large reductions to be made in size and weight of wound components such as *L*1 and *T*1, hence they are cheaper.

Switching pulses for the chopper transistor are generated by a monostable oscillator triggered by line frequency pulses. To stabilise

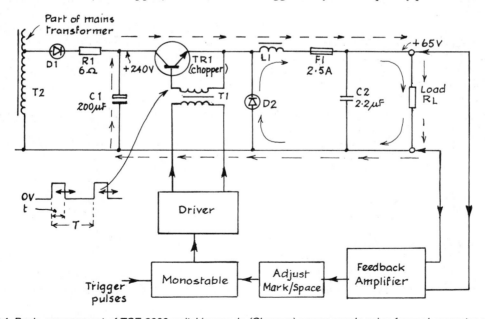

Fig. 17.4 Basic arrangement of TCE 3000 switching mode (Chopper) power supply using forward converter principle.

the output voltage (65 V) of the chopper supply against supply voltage and load current variations, it is necessary to alter the mark-to-space ratio of the switching pulses to $TR1$. This is the purpose of the 'feedback amplifier' stage which samples the 65 V rail voltage and produces a control voltage to adjust the mark-to-space ratio of the monostable oscillator. If the 65 V rail voltage decreases, the 'on' time of $TR1$ is increased by lengthening the pulse duration t. Conversely if the 65 V rail voltage increases, the pulse duration is decreased.

To prevent the chopper transistor overworking at switch-on, it is arranged for the monostable oscillator to provide a minimum mark-to-space ratio. Gradually the mark period widens as the 65 V rail voltage increases thereby ensuring a 'slow start'.

(b) Flyback Converter

In the basic switched mode circuit of Fig. 17.2 energy is passed to the inductor and load when the switch is closed and energy is supplied to the load from the inductor when the switch is open. This type of switch-mode power supply is sometimes referred to as a 'forward' converter. An alternative arrangement is given in Fig. 17.5(a) where the energy storing inductor $L1$ is placed in shunt with the input.

When the switch S is closed, the supply is connected across the inductor but the diode $D1$ is reverse biased. Current thus increases in the inductor causing energy to be stored in it. When the switch is opened, an induced voltage

(the reverse of that previously applied) is developed in the inductor which biases ON $D1$. Current then flows into $C1$ and the load. This arrangement is sometimes called a 'flyback' converter. One disadvantage is that since current flows into the load only during the OFF time of the switch (or transistor); the output ripple of $C1$ is greater than with the forward converter. However, since all of the energy to be transferred to $C1$ and the load is first stored in $L1$), it is possible to easily achieve isolated regulated supplies by adding windings to $L1$. The idea is shown in Fig.17.5(b) where the inductor is replaced by a transformer $T1$. When the switch is closed energy is stored in the transformer (no current passes to the load as $D1$ and $D2$ are reverse biased). On opening the switch, voltages are induced into the secondaries which forward bias $D1$ and $D2$, allowing current to be fed to the loads and output capacitors. V_o is the stabilised output voltage of the main supply and V_a the stabilised output of an auxiliary supply. The mean level of these output voltages are stabilised by controlling the ON time of the switch at a given switching frequency.

A switched-mode power supply based on the flyback converter principle is shown in Fig. 17.6 for the advanced technical features of the Ferguson TX85 chassis used with small screen 90° in-line c.r.ts. This power supply provides stabilised d.c. outputs of 97·5 V, 12 V and 13 V from the secondary windings w_3, w_4 and w_5 of the chopper transformer $T1$.

$TR1$ is the chopper transistor which is switched 'on' and 'off' at a frequency of

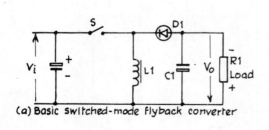

(a) Basic switched-mode flyback converter

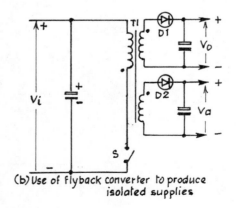

(b) Use of flyback converter to produce isolated supplies

Fig. 17.5 Alternative form of switched mode power supply.

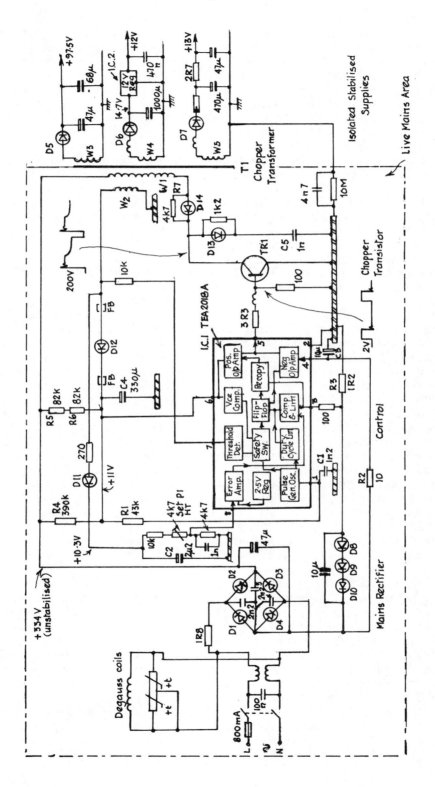

Fig. 17.6 Switched-mode power supply (Ferguson TX85) using flyback converter principle.

30 kHz. The d.c. supply for the chopper stage is provided by the unregulated 334 V output of a full wave rectifier comprising $D1$–$D4$. When $TR1$ is switched 'on' current flows in the primary of $T1$ and energy is stored in this winding (w_1). When $TR1$ is switched 'off' voltages are induced into the secondary windings w_3–w_5 and recified by their respective diodes $D5$–$D7$. The d.c. output of $D6$ is fed to an additional i.c. regulator which provides a stabilised 12 V supply. Smoothing circuits are included in each of the rectified outputs.

Control over the switching of $TR1$ is provided by $IC1$ (TEA 2018A). The frequency of the switching pulses to $TR1$ is set by $R1$ and $C1$ connected to pin 1 of the i.c. Voltage regulation is achieved by a feedback winding w_2 on the chopper transformer. The voltage from this winding is rectified by $D11$, smoothed by $C2$ and fed to pin 8 of the i.c. via the 'Set HT' potentiometer $P1$ to adjust the mark-to-space ratio of the drive pulses to $TR1$ from pin 5. To ensure that $TR1$ is efficiently turned 'off' a negative voltage must be applied to $TR1$ base. This negative voltage is derived by the inclusion of the diodes $D8$–$D10$ in $TR1$ emitter circuit. The negative voltage is smoothed by $R2$ and $C3$ at pin 4 and fed out of the i.c. on pin 5.

Two forms of overload protection exist in the system. Firstly, a facsimile of the chopper transformer current is provided by the feedback winding w_2 which feeds current into pin 7 of the control i.c. If $T1$ should become saturated due to an adverse increase in load current, the drive from pin 5 will be inhibited until such a time as $T1$ recovers from the overload condition. The second measure is a peak current monitoring circuit. Here a sawtooth voltage is developed across $R3$ that is proportional to the collector current of $TR1$. If this voltage (applied to pin 3) should become excessive, $IC1$ will turn off $TR1$. Both of these modes of protection are temporary and $IC1$ will try to recover on the next cycle.

During the 'start-up' phase $C4$ is charged via $R4$, $R5$ and $R6$ and once the voltage on pin 6 exceeds 5·8 V the i.c. will start to generate drive pulses to $TR1$ until the current in $T1$ primary is sufficient to energise the secondaries. The voltage from w_2 is then rectified by $D12$ and supplied to pin 6 of the i.c.

During the 'off' period of $TR1$ the rate of rise of the collector voltage is limited by $C5$, charged via $D13$. $R7$ and $D14$ control the back e.m.f. induced in $T1$ primary and reduce the ringing effect.

The maximum power consumption of the receiver is 65 W at maximum beam current and maximum sound. The 97·5 V rail is used in the field output and line output stages, the 13 V rail in the audio and line driver stages and the 12 V rail for the tuner, luminance/chrominance processing and i.f. stages *etc*.

A conventional mains voltage degaussing circuit using a dual positive temperature coefficient thermistor operates each time the receiver is switched 'on'.

Synchronised Switched-Mode Power Supply

When the switching of the chopper stage is synchronised to the frequency of the line timebase it is possible to re-arrange the system in several ways. For example, it may be arranged so that some of the basic functions normally carried out by the line output stage are performed by the power supply section. Also it is possible to use a waveform from the chopper transformer to provide the drive for the line output stage, thereby eliminating the need for a line driver stage. An additional benefit of a synchronised power supply is that there is no beat frequency produced between the switched-mode power supply and the line output stage scan current in the voltage supply rail, as there would be with an asynchronous switched-mode power supply.

An outline of such a system used in the TCE TX10 series receivers is given in Fig. 17.7.

Mains input fed to the bridge rectifier produces a 360 V unstabilised supply to the chopper transistor $TR1$. Full-wave rectifiers $D1$ and $D2$ fed from $T2$ secondary produce a 24 V unstabilised supply to the chopper driver $TR2$ via $D14$, and after reduction to 12 V by a series regulator a supply to the start oscillator circuits in $IC2$.

The chopper $TR1$ is switched 'on' and 'off' at line rate by pulses applied to $T4$ from the driver stage $TR2$. The pulses are produced inside $IC2$ and are synchronised to the line frequency of 15,625 Hz by the output of $IC1$.

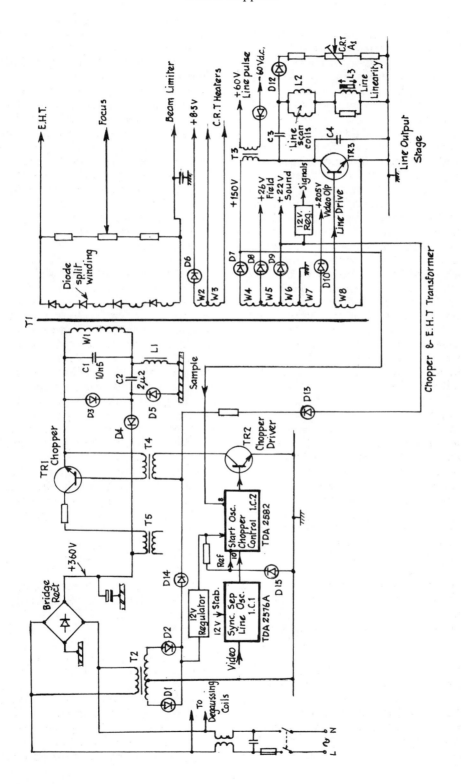

Fig. 17.7 Outline of synchronous switched-mode power supply.

Chopper Operation

The basic circuit of the chopper is given in Fig. 17.8 which acts partly as a forward converter and partly as a relaxation pulse generator. When $TR1$ is switched 'on' by its base drive, the input voltage V_u is applied across w_1 and $L1$ with polarity as shown causing a linear rising current to flow in the two inductors. The amount of energy stored in $L1$ is a function of $TR1$ 'on' time.

When $TR1$ switches 'off' the voltages across $L1$ and w_1 reverse. The voltage across $L1$ causes $D5$ to conduct and the energy stored in $L1$ is transferred to $C2$ via $D5$. At the same time the energy stored in w_1 is transferred to $C1$ which tunes w_1. Energy is then transferred back to w_1 as part of an oscillation which produces a 'flyback pulse' across w_1. Diode $D3$ is reversed biassed during this flyback period as its cathode is clamped to $0\,V$ by the conducting $D5$ and its anode is at a negative potential defined by V_{L1} and the flyback pulse across w_1.

At the end of the flyback period, $D3$ begins to conduct and $C2$ is placed across w_1 which clamps V_{w_1} to V_{c_2}. Because $C2$ is a large value it absorbs the energy in a linear manner. $TR1$ now switches 'on' again and $D3/D5$ switch 'off'. Current now builds up in w_1 and $L1$ as energy is once again stored in these inductors.

Any surplus energy in $C2$ is transferred back into the supply via $D4$ which improves the circuit efficiency.

Chopper Transformer Supplies

The flyback pulse voltage ($V_{flyback}$) is stepped-up and rectified by the diode split winding on the secondary of $T1$ to provide an e.h.t. of approximately $+25\,kV$ and also a variable voltage for the focus anode of the c.r.t. A $205\,V$ line for the video output stage is also obtained by rectifying the flyback pulse across w_7 by $D10$.

All other supplies which includes the $+150\,V$, $+26\,V$ and $+22\,V$ lines are derived by rectifying the scan part (V_{scan}) of the voltages induced into w_4–w_6 by the diodes $D7$–$D9$. The scan part of the waveform provides a longer conduction time for the rectifiers and a lower internal impedance.

Mark/Space Control

To control the mark/space ratio of $TR1$ switching, a sample of the $+150\,V$ rail feed to the line output stage is supplied to pin 8 of $IC2$. This voltage is compared with a reference voltage of $6\cdot2\,V$ produced by the zener diode $D15$ connected to pin 10. A correcting voltage produced by an internal error amplifier is fed to a mark/space control stage in the i.c., the output of which regulates the 'on' time of $TR1$ via the driver stage $TR2$.

If the mains voltage should fall or there is an increase in brightness causing the $+150\,V$ rail to fall, the 'on' time of $TR1$ is increased to compensate.

The system operation ensures a 'slow start' at switch-on by components (not shown) connected to pin 5 of $IC2$. At switch-on the slow start circuitry provides drive pulses so that the chopper transistor only passes short duration current pulses. The mark period then gradually widens until the normal regulatory action comes into operation. Over-voltage

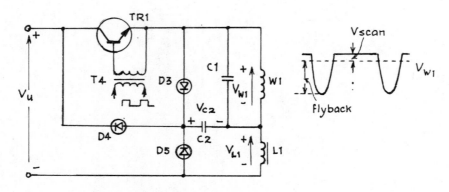

Fig. 17.8 Chopper operation.

and over-current protection are also included (chopper current is sampled by $T5$).

Line Output Stage

Drive for the line output transistor $TR3$ is obtained from the waveform developed in w_8 using the scan part of the waveform. The circuit is conventional with flyback tuning provided by $C4$, 'S' correction by $C3$ with the efficiency diode formed by the collector-base junction of $TR3$. The line scan coils $L2$ have a saturated line linearity coil $L3$ in series.

Line flyback pulses developed at $TR3$ collector are rectified by $D12$ to provide an A_1 supply for the c.r.t. This ensures that should the line output stage fail the screen will immediately be blanked out. The secondary of $T3$ provides a $+60$ V line pulse which is used for sandcastle pulse generation and line sync. reference.

APPENDIX

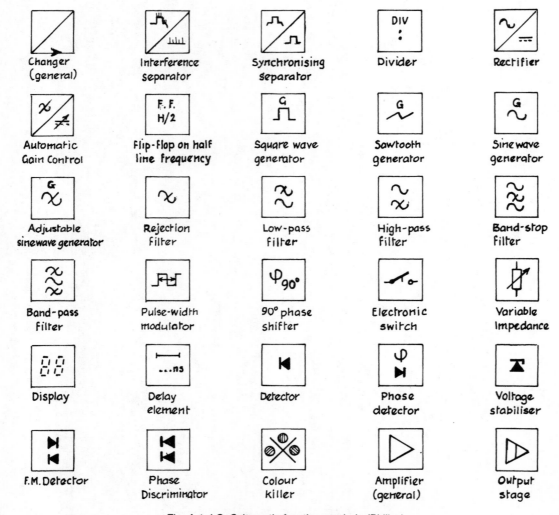

Fig. A.1 I.C. Schematic function symbols (Philips).

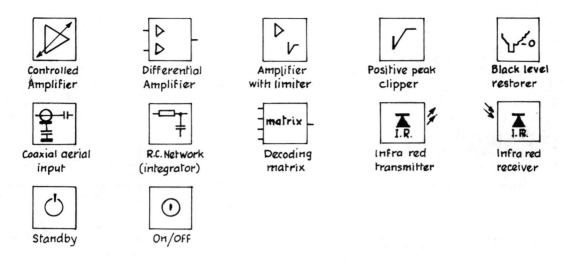

Fig. A.1 I.C. Schematic function symbols (Philips).

INDEX